Master Planning
in **Manufacturing**
using
Microsoft Dynamics 365
for Operations

2017 Edition

Other Books by Scott Hamilton

Supply Chain Management Using Microsoft Dynamics AX: 2016 Edition,
Visions, Inc. (2016)

Process Manufacturing Using Microsoft Dynamics AS: 2016 Edition,
Visions, Inc. (2016)

Warehouse Management Using Microsoft Dynamics AX: 2016 Edition,
Visions, Inc. (2016)

Discrete Manufacturing Using Microsoft Dynamics AX 2012,
Visions Inc. (2012)

Food Products Manufacturing Using Microsoft Dynamics AX 2012,
Visions Inc. (2012)

Managing Process Manufacturing Using Microsoft Dynamics AX 2009,
Visions Inc. (2010)

Managing Wholesale Distribution Using Microsoft Dynamics AX 2009,
privately published (2010)

Managing Lean Manufacturing Using Microsoft Dynamics AX 2009,
Visions Inc. (2010)

Managing Your Supply Chain Using Microsoft Dynamics AX 2009,
Printing Arts (2009)

Managing Your Supply Chain Using Microsoft Dynamics AX 4.0,
Printing Arts (2007)

Managing Your Supply Chain Using Microsoft Axapta 3.0, McGraw-Hill (2004)

Managing Your Supply Chain Using Microsoft Navision, McGraw-Hill (2004)

Maximizing Your ERP System, McGraw-Hill (2003)

*Managing Information: How Information Systems Impact Organizational
Strategy* (with Gordon B. Davis), Business One Irwin (1993)

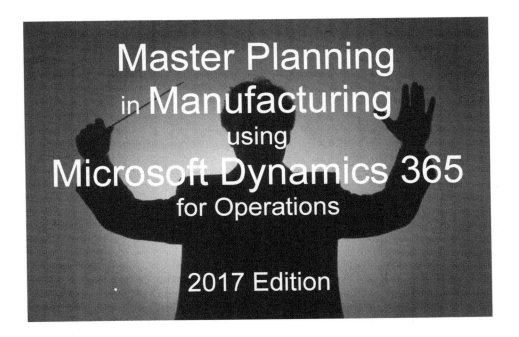

Master Planning
in Manufacturing
using
Microsoft Dynamics 365
for Operations

2017 Edition

Scott Hamilton, Ph.D.

Print ISBN 978-0-9973071-7-7
eBook ISBN 978-0-9973071-8-4

Contents

Preface

This book focuses on how Microsoft Dynamics 365 for Operations supports master planning to coordinate supply chain management (SCM) in manufacturing businesses. It covers the essential capabilities of master planning as well as additional considerations for different functional areas and manufacturing scenarios. The targeted reader consists of SCM professionals that need to learn the master planning capabilities for running a manufacturing business, and want to employ standard functionality as much as possible. With few exceptions, the book contents also apply to the previous version of Dynamics AX 2012 R3.

The book contents draw on the master planning topics covered in the 2016 Editions of my books about SCM in discrete manufacturing and process manufacturing. The evolving scope of master planning capabilities has been tracked in previous books. Previous books about discrete manufacturing included the 2004 Edition (for AX 3.0), the 2007 Edition (for AX 4.0), the 2009 Edition (for AX 2009), and the 2012 edition (for AX 2012). Previous books about process manufacturing included the 2009 Edition (for AX 2009) and the 2012 Edition (for AX 2012).

A trail guide and topographic maps provide essential information when exploring any unfamiliar territory. They identify the most important features of the landscape and provide insights about key considerations and trail variations. Similar essentials apply to those exploring the use of an ERP system to run their business. This essential guide identifies the most important features of the embedded conceptual models and business processes related to master planning, and provides insights about key considerations and variations.

Many people have provided useful insights about the master planning capabilities within the software. This includes the many Microsoft people involved in developing the software capabilities and the related user documentation. This also includes the many co-workers, field consultants and users that have been helpful in shaping my understanding of the software and its usage. In addition, many people contributed feedback to this current book as well as previous books which acted as source material. They are too numerous to mention by name, but I am forever thankful for their contributions.

This book would not have been possible without the facilitative help from Envista corporation, especially the supportive leadership by John Stitz and the technical assistance by Derek Sigurdson.

The book reflects my interpretation of how to use Microsoft Dynamics 365 for Operations. Errors of omission and commission, and any misunderstandings, are hopefully minimized.[1] Corrections and suggestions are welcome, and they can be sent to **ScottHamiltonPhD@Outlook.com**.

Each day of writing was started with the following prayer:

> Creator of all things, give me a sharp sense of understanding, a retentive memory, and the ability to grasp things correctly and fundamentally. Grant me the talent of being exact in my explanations, and the ability to express myself with thoroughness and charm. Point out the beginning, direct the progress, and help in the completion. Through Christ our Lord.

---

[1] The book is for information purposes only. The author, publisher and Microsoft make no warranties, expressed or implied, in the presentation of information.

Chapter 1

Introduction

The planning calculations in an ERP system for manufacturing can provide significant benefits by coordinating supply chain activities driven by S&OP (sales and operations planning) game plans. They help orchestrate success across the organization. However, these calculations often represent one of the more complex and misunderstood aspects of system usage, which limits the ability to achieve the benefits. This book focuses on how to effectively use the planning calculations to run a manufacturing business. The book contents apply to those businesses using Microsoft Dynamics 365 for Operations; they also apply to those using the previous version of Microsoft Dynamics AX 2012 R3.[1] They are termed master planning calculations within the Microsoft software, although many people refer to them with different names such as MRP.

The targeted reader consists of SCM professionals that need to learn the master planning capabilities for running day-to-day operations in a manufacturing business. This chapter starts with suggestions for the targeted reader and describes the organization of the book chapters as well as the scope of book topics. It also covers several aspects of terminology and highlights the use of example screens to illustrate key points. These considerations are reflected in the following sections within the chapter.

1. Suggestions for the Targeted Reader
2. Organization of the Book Chapters
3. Scope of Book Topics and Prior Research
4. Terminology used in the Book
5. Example Screens used in the Book
6. Summary of Case Studies

---

[1] Dynamics 365 for Operations and Dynamics AX are registered trademarks of Microsoft.

1.1 Suggestions for the Targeted Reader

The targeted reader consists of SCM professionals that need to learn the master planning capabilities for running day-to-day operations in a manufacturing business. In many cases, they represent those responsible for maintaining the S&OP game plans within a company, where the role has traditionally been called a master scheduler. In other cases, they represent members of the project team responsible for system implementation. In some cases, they may need to learn master planning because of a change in positions or job responsibilities. In addition, many people with some experience may want to confirm and extend their knowledge via selective learning of master planning topics.

The broad range of master planning capabilities can be segmented into three groups consisting of core topics, additional considerations, and variations of scenarios. These three groups are reflected in the learning objectives shown in Figure 1.1, and in the organization of book chapters shown in Figure 1.2.

Figure 1.1 Suggestions for the Targeted Reader

Learning Objective	Estimated Pages	
	Applicable	Total
Learn Core Topics for Master Planning	90	124
Learn Additional Considerations for Master Planning	50	86
Incremental Learning for Different Scenarios		
- Master Planning in Multicompany Scenarios		8
- Master Planning in Process Manufacturing Scenarios		32
- Master Planning in Project Manufacturing Scenarios		8
- Master Planning in Lean Manufacturing Scenarios		8
Total =	140	266
Selective Learning of Master Planning Topics		
- Topics for the Master Scheduler role	90	
- Topics for the Production Planner role	50	
- Topics for the Purchasing Agent role	25	
- Topics for the DRP Coordinator role	20	

Learn Core Topics The core topics start with common S&OP scenarios and several basics of master planning. The basics include one-time setup considerations about master plan policies and the master planning parameters, and the day-to-day considerations about performing master planning and net change explosions. The master planning logic generates different outputs for analyzing and coordinating supply chain activities. The analysis tools include information about net requirements and capacity requirements, and the coordination tools include planned orders, action messages, calculated delay messages, and suggested production schedules.

The core topics include decisions about modeling inventory locations, the use of coverage planning data to model SCM decision making, the use of demand forecasts, and several sales order considerations such as delivery promises, reservations, and the analysis of delivery alternatives.

Learn Additional Considerations Many additional considerations apply to master planning logic, since it builds on the foundation of information about items, bills of material, routings, production orders, purchase orders, transfer orders, quality management, and batch number tracking. The inventory batches for a batch-controlled item may have shelf life dates, batch attributes, and/or batch disposition codes.

Learn Major Variations of Scenarios One or more major variations of master planning scenarios may apply to a given manufacturing enterprise. A common variation involves coordination of a multicompany supply chain. Other variations apply to process manufacturing scenarios and the unique aspects of using formulas and batch orders. Additional variations apply to project manufacturing scenarios and the unique aspects of project sales orders, item forecasts, and item requirements. Master planning calculations can also apply to lean manufacturing scenarios, such as generating planned kanbans that can be firmed to create scheduled kanbans, and providing the basis for calculating the number of fixed kanbans.

Selective Learning of Topics Selective learning often applies to different roles, such as the roles of a master scheduler, production planner, purchasing agent and DRP coordinator. Selective learning can also apply to specialized topics.

Quantify the Amount of Learning A page count analysis provides a rough metric for quantifying the amount of learning, as illustrated in the right side of Figure 1.1. The total number of book pages provide one metric, and the applicable pages for a given company or role provide a second metric.

1.2 Organization of the Book Chapters

The book chapters can be segmented into three groups consisting of core topics, additional considerations, and variations of scenarios, as described in the previous section. Figure 1.2 summarizes these three groups and the chapter titles.

Figure 1.2 Organization of Book Chapters

Core Topics for Master Planning

Chapter

2	Common S&OP Scenarios
3	Basics of Master Planning
4	Analyze Results of Master Planning
5	Modeling Inventory Locations
6	Coverage Planning Data to Model SCM Decision Making
7	Using Demand Forecasts
8	Sales Order Considerations

Additional Considerations

Chapter

Item Master Considerations	9
Bill of Material Information	10
Routing Information	11
Production Order Considerations	12
Purchase Order Considerations	13
Transfer Order Considerations	14
Considerations about Batch-Controlled Items	15
Quality Management Considerations	16

Major Variations of Master Planning Scenarios

17	Master Planning in a Multicompany Supply Chain
18	Master Planning in Process Manufacturing Scenarios
19	Master Planning in Project Manufacturing Scenarios
20	Master Planning in Lean Manufacturing Scenarios

The explanation of core topics provides a linear sequence for learning the master planning capabilities. A linear sequence also applies to the additional considerations impacting master planning logic. Some of these additional considerations -- such as bills of material, routings, and production orders – include extended explanations that may be too detailed for some readers, and they can be skimmed. The explanation of each major variation covers just the incremental differences in master planning logic. An extended explanation is provided for process manufacturing scenarios because they involve key differences in the use of formulas and batch orders, and a wide variety of production processes and types of products.

1.3 Scope of Book Topics and Prior Research

This book focuses on the master planning capabilities for running a manufacturing business, and this focus guided the selection of book topics and prior research. It draws on the prior research documented in the 2016 Editions of my previous books about <u>supply chain management in discrete manufacturing</u> and <u>process manufacturing</u> which covered master planning as part of the broader scope of SCM capabilities.

My prior research about the master planning capabilities have extended across every software version since AX 3.0, and additional research and hands-on testing were conducted for the latest version of Dynamics 365 for Operations (version 1611). A comparison of master planning capabilities between this latest version and the previous version of AX 2012 R3 indicates that almost every capability described here applies to both versions, and the few exceptions are identified in Appendix B. For that matter, a very high percentage of book content also applies to the previous version of AX 2012, and a slightly lower percentage applies to AX 2009 with multisite capabilities enabled.

Given the book's focus, it does not cover the related SCM topics that build on the same information. Examples include the product costing capabilities and calculated sales prices. It does not cover master planning considerations for retail-oriented operations, or the many technical and administrative aspects of master planning.

More comprehensive explanations about the scope of book topics and prior research are provided in Appendix A.

1.4 Terminology Used in the Book

The terminology associated with many aspects of supply chain management can vary widely between companies and ERP systems. It is often difficult to clearly understand the meaning of a term -- such as inventory status, order status, reservations, make-to-order products, and planning data for an item -- without a lengthy discussion about its significance.

As much as possible, this book consistently uses the same terminology to describe the functionality and underlying conceptual models within the latest software version, which was also used to create the example screens. As already noted in the previous section, the book contents also apply to the previous version of AX 2012 R3, although the terminology (and example screens) would differ slightly when compared to the latest software version of Dynamics 365 for Operations.

Several aspects of terminology are especially relevant to the master planning capabilities. The master planning task generates a set of master plan data based on its master plan policies, and these two aspects are simply termed a master plan. Multiple master plans may be used for different purposes, but this book focuses on the master plan for managing day-to-day operations. The master planning logic calculates net requirements for items and capacity requirements for resources, including those related to planned orders. Deleting a master plan simply deletes the planned orders and the related planned capacity requirements within the set of master plan data.

The master planning task calculates the explosion information for manufactured items based on bills of material. A separate calculation – termed an Explosion – can also be performed for a selected order line, where you typically delete the existing explosion information as part of the calculation. This is sometimes termed a net change explosion, and this book employs both terms interchangeably.

1.5 Example Screens in the Book

This book focuses on the embedded conceptual models and business processes within the standard software. Figures containing example screens illustrate key points. The example screens have been highly personalized to identify just the key fields for a given topic, and artistic license was sometimes employed to fit things into a single figure. The book includes more than 40 example screens.

The user experience and navigational details are difficult to convey with example screens, but the embedded conceptual models and business processes still apply whether accessing the software from customized pages, workspaces, web-based applications, or hand-held devices.

1.6 Summary of Case Studies

Case studies illustrate how the software functionality applies to many different scenarios in manufacturing. Each chapter includes case studies applicable to the topic, and a complete list of case studies is provided at the end of the book.

Chapter 2

Common S&OP Scenarios for Master Planning

One of the cornerstones of effective supply chain management consist of sales and operation planning (S&OP) game plans, and master planning calculations help coordinate activities that meet the game plans. They help run the company from the top and orchestrate success. The nature of an S&OP game plan depends on several factors, such as the need to anticipate demand for an item, the item's primary source of supply, and the need for linkage between a sales order and the item's supply order. Demand forecasts are often used to anticipate demand.

This chapter reviews common S&OP scenarios in manufacturing, and covers key elements of the game plans for each scenario. The chapter starts with a baseline model of operations that represents common software usage and dominate business practices, and provides a foundation for explaining variations. These considerations are reflected in the following sections within the chapter.

1. Baseline Model of Operations
2. Common S&OP Scenarios in Discrete Manufacturing
3. Common S&OP Scenarios requiring Linkage to Sales Orders
4. Other Variations of S&OP Scenarios
5. Guidelines concerning S&OP Game Plans
6. Additional Case Studies

2.1 Baseline Model of Operations

A baseline model of operations represents the common use of Dynamics 365 for Operations and dominant business practices within many manufacturing businesses. It provides a foundation for simplified explanations about how to use the software to manage the business, and for explaining variations to the baseline

7

model. In summary, the baseline model focuses on a single company with one or more sites (and their related warehouses), and with standard products identified by an item number. Each item's inventory is tracked by site, warehouse and bin location, with inventory replenishment logic at the site/warehouse level. Each manufactured item requires bill of material information, with optional definition of routing data. The following points provide more detailed explanations about the baseline model of operations.

Single Company and Instance   The baseline model consists of a single company using a single instance. Some scenarios involve multiple companies within one instance and possible partitioning of these companies within the database. A multicompany supply chain is treated as a variation to the baseline model.

Multiple Inventory Locations Identified by Site and Warehouse   Each physical location is typically identified by a site and an associated value for a "site" financial dimension. The site-specific financial dimension supports financial reports by site. Each site has one or more warehouses. Each warehouse has one or more bin locations, although use of bin locations is not mandatory. The definition and use of warehouse locations differ significantly between the basic and advanced approach to warehouse management.

Material Items Identified by Item Number   Material items are identified by an item number. In some cases, an item may be identified by an item number and one or more additional fields termed variant codes. In other cases, a product configurator can result in the creation of a configuration ID for a configurable item, so that the identifier consists of an item number and configuration ID. These are treated as variations to the baseline model of operations.

Bill of Material and Routing for a Manufactured Item   A bill of material defines the product structure for a manufactured item, and the related production orders help coordinate activities. The alternative approach of using formulas (and the related batch orders) is treated as a variation to the baseline model, and covered in a separate chapter. With either approach, most scenarios will also define production resources and routings for manufactured items, but this information is optional.

Standard or Actual Costing for Material Items   Each material item must be assigned an inventory valuation method reflecting a standard cost or actual cost method. With standard costing, a costing version must be defined for standard costs, and each material item must have an item cost record for each site with inventory.

Replenishment Logic applies to the Site/Warehouse Level Replenishment logic is defined by an item's coverage planning data, and applies to the site/warehouse level. In some cases, the logic may only apply to the site.

Batch and/or Serial Numbers for a Material Item The use of batch and/or serial numbers is treated as a variation to the baseline model. A separate chapter covers the master planning considerations for batch-controlled items.

2.2 Common S&OP Scenarios

The nature of an S&OP game plan depends on several factors, such as the need to anticipate demand for an item, the item's primary source of supply, and the need for linkage between a sales order and the item's supply order. When demand needs to be anticipated, for example, demand forecasts often provide a key element of S&OP game plans for stocked end-items or stocked components. The item's primary source of supply may reflect production orders in a manufacturing operation as well as purchase orders and transfer orders in a distribution operation. The need for linkage becomes important for make-to-order and buy-to-order products to provide visibility of the sales order demand and for tracking actual costs of goods sold. A given company typically has several major scenarios where each scenario employs different key elements in the S&OP game plans.

The common S&OP scenarios can be broadly grouped in different ways. For explanatory purposes, we'll consider two different groups reflecting the need for linkage between a sales order and an item's supply order. This section covers the first group of S&OP scenarios that do not require linkage. The second group requiring linkage is covered in the next section. A third grouping consists of other variations of S&OP scenarios, but these still build on the options regarding "linkage" versus "no linkage" to sales orders.

Several common S&OP scenarios are summarized in Figure 2.1 and described below. For each scenario, the figure identifies the key elements of the S&OP game plan and several additional considerations, including the typical basis of sales order delivery promises. Demand forecasts often represent a key element, and a subsequent chapter describes a typical process to maintain the S&OP game plans using demand forecasts for make-to-stock products (Section 7.1), for stocked components of make-to-order products (Section 7.9), and for stocked products in a distribution network (Section 7.10).

Figure 2.1 Common S&OP Scenarios

Scenario		Key Elements of S&OP Game Plan	Additional Considerations	Basis of Delivery Promises
No Link to Sales Order	Make-to-Stock End-Item or Stocked Product in a Distribution Operation	Min-Max Quantities	Coverage Code = Min-Max Calculation of minimum quantity	ATP
		Demand Forecast	Coverage Code = Period Forecast consumption by sales orders Using an inventory plan (safety stock)	
		Manual Master Schedule	Coverage Code = Manual or Period	
	Completely Make-to-Order	Sales Order	Coverage Code = Period or Requirement	CTP or Perform Explosion
	Make-to-Order End-Item with Stocked Components	Sales Order for End-Item	Coverage Code = Period or Requirement	
		Demand Forecast for stocked components or	Coverage Code = Period Forecast consumption by all demands Using an inventory plan (safety stock)	
		Min-Max Quantities for stocked components	Coverage Code = Min-Max Calculation of minimum quantity	

Stocked End-Item based on Min-Max Quantities   The simplest S&OP approach employs min-max logic to carry inventory in anticipation of actual demand, where an item's coverage planning policies define the minimum and maximum quantities by site/warehouse. The minimum quantity represents an implied demand forecast, where the quantity typically reflects the daily usage rate multiplied by the number of days for the item's lead time. With min-max logic, when an item's projected inventory falls below its minimum quantity, master planning logic will generate a planned order that achieves the item's maximum quantity (subject to an order quantity multiple). The values for an item's minimum and maximum quantities can be fixed, or specified as a pattern (termed the minimum key and maximum key). You can automatically calculate the minimum quantity based on historical average usage over the item's lead time, as described in a subsequent chapter about calculating safety stock requirements (Section 7.7). Sales order delivery promises can be based on available-to-promise (ATP) logic.

Stocked End-Item based on a Demand Forecast   The combination of demand forecasts and actual sales orders drives inventory replenishment using period lot-sizing logic. This involves forecast consumption logic to avoid doubled-up requirements. The number of days for period lot-sizing purposes reflect the desired frequency of delivery for an item, with more frequent delivery of A items (such as daily or weekly periods) compared to B and C items (such as monthly periods).

In addition to the demand forecasts, an inventory plan (expressed as safety stock requirements) can be used to anticipate higher-than-expected actual demand, and meet customer service objectives regarding stock outs, partial shipments and delivery lead times. You can automatically calculate the safety stock requirement based on variations in historical usage and the desired customer service level, as described in a subsequent chapter about calculating safety stock requirements (Section 7.7).

The planned orders are typically firmed (or approved before firming) in the near term to reflect the desired production schedule and to account for material and capacity constraints. The combination of planned orders and actual production orders represents the item's master schedule, and provides the basis for making delivery promises using ATP logic. Case 2.1 illustrates demand forecasts for make-to-stock items.

Stocked End-Item based on a Manual Master Schedule   The master schedule starts with manually-created planned orders with an approved status, and firming these planned orders results in actual production orders. The item's coverage code can be manual (which does not support net requirement inquiries) or period (where you suppress the action messages). Demand forecasts are not typically entered. This approach avoids the complexities associated with forecast consumption logic, and provides the basis for making delivery promises using ATP logic. Case 2.2 illustrates the use of a manual master schedule.

Completely Make-to-Order End-Item   The S&OP game plan consists of actual sales orders for a completely make-to-order product, where performing an explosions or CTP logic provides the basis for making delivery promises. Alternatively, delivery promises can reflect a quoted lead time that often represents the item's cumulative manufacturing time. The master planning calculations generate planned supply orders to meet the sales order demand, where the planned orders reflect the item's planning data (such as coverage codes of period or requirement) as well as the BOM and route versions for manufactured items. This scenario generally implies a pipeline of sales orders with future delivery dates that exceed the item's cumulative lead time.

Make-to-Order End-Item with Stocked Components   The use of stocked components can shorten the delivery lead time for make-to-order products, and provide the basis for delivery promises based on CTP logic. Demand forecasts or min-max quantities can drive replenishment of these stocked components, as illustrated by the two options in Figure 2.1.

The use of demand forecasts for stocked components involves forecast consumption by any demand, such as dependent demands stemming from production orders for the make-to-order product. An inventory plan may also apply to stocked components.

Another key element of the S&OP game plan consists of sales orders for the make-to-order product. Master planning calculations will generate planned supply orders to meet the sales order demand, where the planned orders reflect the item's planning data (such as a coverage code of period or requirement) as well as the BOM and route versions for the item. Case 2.3 illustrates make-to-order products built from stocked components.

2.3 Common S&OP Scenarios requiring Linkage to Sales Orders

Some S&OP scenarios involve make-to-order or buy-to-order products that require linkage between a sales order and the item's supply order. An additional type of linkage applies to make-to-order components. These scenarios are summarized in Figure 2.2 and described below. For each scenario, the figure identifies the key elements of the S&OP game plan and several additional considerations. These considerations include creation of the supply order, the suggested coverage code, automatic marking, and the typical basis of sales order delivery promises.

Figure 2.2 Common S&OP Scenarios Requiring Linkage to Sales Orders

Scenario		Key Elements of S&OP Game Plan	Additional Considerations	Automatic Marking	Basis of Delivery Promises
With Link to Sales Order	Make-to-Order or Configure-to-Order Product with Stocked Components with Make-to-Order Components	Sales Order for the product	Create production order from the sales order line	Yes	CTP or Perform Explosion
			Firm the planned production order stemming from sales demand Coverage Code = Requirement	Marking Policy = Yes	
		Demand Forecast or Min-Max Quantities for stocked components	Coverage Code = Period or Min-Max Calculation of minimum quantity	Marking Policy = No	
		Reference Orders for pegged supply components	Auto-create the production order Coverage Code = Period or Req	Yes	
	Buy-to-Order Item Special Order or Direct Delivery Order	Sales Order & Purchase Order for the Item	Create PO from the SO or Create PO by linking to a SO	Yes	
			Create PO from the SO Create PO on Direct Delivery page		

Make-to-Order Product requiring Linkage between the Sales Order and Production Order A make-to-order production strategy often involves linking a production order to the sales order line, thereby providing visibility of the sales order demand in production. The reference fields for each order display this link.   The basis for establishing this linkage builds on the software functionality for marking.   The marking functionality simply provides visibility of the linkage for standard cost items. With actual cost items, marking supports additional functionality to override the suggested matching of a receipt (such as the production order) to an issue (such as the sales order).

Two basic approaches can be used to create this linkage. As shown in Figure 2.2, the first approach involves creating the production order from the sales order line, which results in automatic marking.   The second approach involves firming the planned production order that stems from the sales order demand, which requires the "update marking" policy as part of the firming dialogue. Case 2.4 illustrates a make-to-order product requiring linkage to the sales order demand.

The linkage between a sales order and production order can be considered a soft link, since changes to the sales order quantity or date do not automatically update the production order. When attempting to delete the sales line, a message displays a warning about the linked production order, and a separate step must be taken to delete the production order. Conversely, deleting the production order removes the linkage and does not impact the sales line. If applicable, a new production order can be created for the sales line.

Make-to-Order Product with Stocked Components The use of stocked components can shorten the delivery lead time for make-to-order products, as described in the previous section.

Make-to-Order Components with Linkage between Production Orders A make-to-order component may be employed in a make-to-order product, where the production order for the component is tightly linked to the parent item's production order. You designate the make-to-order component with a line type of *Pegged Supply* in the BOM or formula for the parent item.   Scheduling the production order for the parent item automatically generates a linked order (termed a reference order) for each make-to-order component. The linkage is identified by the reference fields for each production order and by marking information. This linkage is slightly different then the linkage between a sales order and production order, and reflects much tighter linkage between the production orders.

2.4 Other Variations of S&OP Scenarios

The variations of S&OP scenarios have been explained so far in terms of two groupings reflecting differences about the need for linkage between a sales order and its supply order. Additional master planning considerations apply to other variations of S&OP scenarios. Several other variations are listed below and covered in separate chapters.

- ◆ Multicompany supply chain
- ◆ Process manufacturing scenarios
- ◆ Project manufacturing scenarios
- ◆ Lean manufacturing scenarios

These other variations of S&OP scenarios still build on the options regarding "linkage" versus "no linkage" to sales orders.

2.5 Guidelines Concerning S&OP Game Plans

Effective S&OP game plans lead to improved firm performance. Metrics include reductions in stock-outs, delivery lead time, missed shipments, partial shipments, and expediting efforts. Metrics also include improvements in customer service. The lack of effective game plans is typically cited as a leading cause of poor ERP system implementations. The following guidelines provide suggestions for improving the effectiveness of S&OP game plans.

Minimum Planning Horizon for Each Game Plan A saleable item's cumulative lead time represents the minimum horizon for a game plan, and additional months provide visibility for purchasing and capacity planning purposes. This minimum planning horizon should be reflected in the item's time fences, such as the coverage and forecast time fences.

Reviewing and Updating Game Plans The process for reviewing and updating each game plan should be embedded into the firm's regularly scheduled management meetings focusing on demands and supply chain activities. An agreed-upon game plan reflects a balance of conflicting objectives related to sales, engineering, manufacturing, inventory, purchasing and accounting. Periodic revisions to game plans should be reflected in updated forecasts and promised delivery dates.

Primary Responsibility for Maintaining Game Plans The person(s) acting as a master scheduler typically maintains the game plans and obtains management agreement. This role requires an in-depth understanding of sales and supply chain capabilities, as well as the political power to achieve agreed-upon game plans. The responsibility for providing information about demand forecasts and inventory plans typically belongs to the sales function, with a hand-off to the master scheduler. However, this responsibility is sometimes assigned to the master scheduler. The master scheduler's responsibility for an item's game plans can be identified by the buyer group or production pool assigned to the item.

Formulating Realistic Game Plans Realistic game plans require identification of capacity and material exceptions that would constrain the plans, and then eliminating the constraints or changing the plan. Identification of material-related exceptions typically starts with suggested actions, while capacity exceptions are identified using load analysis of key resources. In many cases, a realistic game plan must anticipate demands and demand variations via forecasts and inventory plans for stocked material. Finite capacity planning can also contribute to a realistic game plan.

Enforcing Near-Term Schedule Stability Near-term schedule stability provides one solution for resolving many conflicting objectives, such as improving competitive efficiencies in purchasing and production and reducing exceptions requiring expediting. It provides a stable target for coordinating supply chain activities and removes most alibis for missed schedules. Near-term schedule stability can benefit from inventory plans and realistic order promises about shipment dates. It involves a basic trade-off with objectives requiring fast response time and frequent schedule changes. The critical issue is that management recognizes the trade-offs to minimize near-term changes. An item's freeze time fence represents one approach to support near-term schedule stability, since master planning logic will not suggest planned orders during the frozen period. Case 2.5 illustrates improvements in near-term schedule stability.

Making and Maintaining Realistic Sales Order Promises Realistic delivery promises represent the key link between sales commitments and supply chain activities. You can calculate a realistic promised delivery date during order entry, and also through calculated delay messages indicating a projected delay in delivery. A key aspect of promised delivery dates is to reduce and isolate the number of exceptions requiring expediting. When available inventory only partially satisfies the sales order requirement, one solution approach involves splitting delivery across two sales order line items (or delivery lines) with different shipment dates.

Executing Supply Chain Activities to Plan Master planning logic makes an underlying assumption that everyone works to plan, and provides coordination tools to communicate needed action. For example, it is assumed that procurement will ensure timely delivery of purchased material so that manufacturing can meet production schedules. It is assumed that distribution will make on-time shipments, and that valid delivery promises were made by sales. An unmanageable number of exceptions will impact this underlying assumption and the usefulness of coordination tools.

Reducing Exceptions that Require Expediting The intent of near-term schedule stability, valid delivery promises and shipment dates, realistic game plans, and executing to plan is to reduce the number of exceptions to a manageable level. This improves the usefulness of coordination tools to meet the S&OP game plans.

2.6 Additional Case Studies

Case 2.1: Demand Forecasts for Office Furniture An office furniture manufacturer produced and stocked different end-items based on demand forecasts, and sales order delivery promises were based on ATP logic. Entries of the demand forecasts reflected weekly increments (with start-of-week due dates) over a rolling three month time horizon (which reflected the cumulative manufacturing lead time), and monthly increments for the next nine months. The master scheduler translated the monthly forecasts into the weekly increments and relevant due dates over the rolling three month time horizon. The translation considered months containing 4 versus 5 weeks, and also weeks with less than 5 working days. Forecast consumption logic was based on fixed monthly periods defined by a single reduction key assigned to all items. Sales orders with ship dates in a given month consumed the demand forecasts within the month. As time moved forward, the weekly increments of unconsumed forecast became past-due and were ignored by master planning logic.

Case 2.2: Manual Master Schedule for Medical Devices A medical device company produced a line of medical devices that required a manually maintained master schedule to reflect the planner's decision-making logic about production constraints. The medical devices required an expensive outside operation for sterilization, where multiple end-items could be sterilized at the same time. The scheduling considerations included a cost-benefit analysis about amortizing the fixed fee for sterilization over the largest possible number of end-items subject to a weight maximum, while still building the product mix for customer demands and avoiding excess inventory. A manually maintained master schedule proved most effective for this case.

Case 2.3: Electric Motors built from Stocked Components A manufacturer of standard electric motors produced end-items based on a pipeline of sales orders, where sales order delivery dates were initially assigned based on CTP logic. The motors were built from stocked components to shorten delivery lead times, especially those components with long lead-times. Demand forecasts were entered for these stocked components. In this scenario, the demand forecasts were defined for an item allocation key, which identified the stocked components and a mix percentage of their typical usage. The demand forecasts were entered in weekly increments over a 3-month rolling time horizon and monthly increments thereafter.

Case 2.4: Make-to-Order Products requiring Linkage with the Sales Order One product line at a manufacturing company represented make-to-order products, where visibility of the related sales order was critical for production. Each production order was linked to a sales order line item. In most cases, this linkage was established by firming a planned production order with marking, where master planning logic generated the planned order that reflected the sales order demand and a coverage code of requirement. In some cases, the linkage was established by creating the production order from the sales order line.

Case 2.5: Improve Near-Term Stability in the Master Schedule A manufacturing company wanted to enforce near-term stability in the master schedule, thereby gaining production efficiencies and reducing exceptions requiring expediting. They tracked the requested changes to this near-term schedule, and the reasons for each request, and the master scheduler (plus a team of other key people) formally approved or rejected each requested change. An analysis of the requested changes and their reasons provided the basis for improving the near-term stability and the associated benefits.

2.7 Executive Summary

The ability to run the company from the top requires a sales and operations planning process that formulates an S&OP game plan for each saleable product. The nature of an S&OP game plan depends on several factors, such as the need to anticipate demand for the item, the item's primary source of supply, and the need for linkage between a sales order and the supply order. This chapter summarized the common S&OP scenarios and provided guidelines for improving the game plans. Case studies highlighted variations in the use of S&OP game plans.

Chapter 3

Basics of Master Planning

The primary engine for coordinating supply chain activities is termed the Master Planning task. Based on several master plan policies, it considers demands and supplies to generate a set of master plan data along with several key outputs that support detailed analysis of the calculations and act as coordination tools. These elements comprise the basics of master planning.

This chapter focuses on the basics of master planning for managing day-to-day operations. The starting point involves an understanding of master plan policies and the companywide parameters for master planning, where these represent one-time setup considerations. For on-going purposes, the basics include performing the master planning calculations. Additional facets include the significance of calendars, the different types of demands and supplies, master planning by site versus site/warehouse, and the rationale for using different sets of master plan data. These considerations are reflected in the following sections within the chapter.

One-time Setup Considerations
1. Master Plan Policies for Managing Day-to-Day Operations
2. Scenarios Requiring a Static and Dynamic Master Plan
3. Master Planning Parameters

Ongoing Considerations
4. Perform Master Planning Calculations
5. Perform an Explosion
6. Master Planning with Finite Capacity and Material
7. Significance of Calendars
8. Summary of Demands and Supplies
9. Master Planning by Site versus Site/Warehouse
10. Rationale for using Different Sets of Master Plan Data

3.1 Master Plan Policies for Managing Day-to-Day Operations

Most scenarios can employ a single set of master plan data to support a company's daily working operations. A typical user-assigned identifier for this master plan could be *DailyPlan, CurrentPlan or WorkingPlan*. The next section covers scenarios requiring two sets of data (termed the static and dynamic master plans) to support a company's daily working operations.

This single set of master plan data is generated by the Master Plan task, which uses information about demands and supplies and several master plan policies. This section introduces some of the key policies. It does not attempt to cover all policies because they apply to specific scenarios, and subsequent sections about relevant scenarios describe the additional policies.

Key Master Plan Policies Several master plan policies are critical, as illustrated by the example data shown in Figure 3.1 where the identifier of the master plan is "WorkingPlan."

Figure 3.1 Example Screen of Key Master Plan Policies

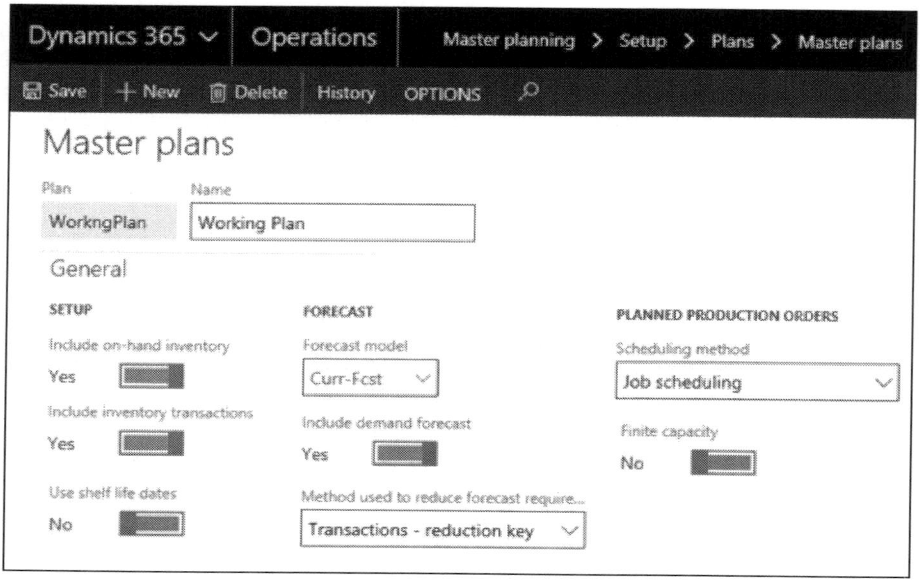

Based on the example data in the figure, the master planning calculations will include on-hand inventory and expected inventory transactions about receipts and issues. They will not include logic about shelf life dates. This logic would apply in some scenarios described in a subsequent chapter (Section 15.2), and illustrated in the case study about food products (Case 3.3). The calculations will also include the current demand forecasts associated with the forecast identifier of "Curr-Fcst" and forecast consumption logic will reflect time buckets defined by a reduction key. A subsequent chapter provides further explanation of demand forecasts (Section 7.2), and forecast consumption logic using a reduction key (Section 7.3).

Several policies apply to the planned production orders generated by master planning calculations, including the scheduling method and consideration of finite capacity. A subsequent chapter about routing information provides further explanation of the two scheduling methods (Section 11.10), and a subsequent section within this chapter summarizes master planning with finite capacity.

Additional Master Plan Policies The additional policies apply to different contexts, and are best described in subsequent sections about each context. This includes master plan policies about optional sources of demands and supplies (Section 3.8), action messages (Section 6.11), calculated delay messages (Section 6.12), safety margins (Section 6.15), time fences (Section 6.16), intercompany planning (Section 17.1), and production sequencing for planned batch orders (Section 18.8).

3.2 Scenarios Requiring a Static and Dynamic Master Plan

Some scenarios require two sets of master plan data -- termed the static and dynamic master plans -- to support a company's daily working operations. Typical user-assigned identifiers include *StaticPlan* and *DynamicPlan*. The previous explanation of master plan policies also applies when using two sets of master plan data. The same policies would be assigned to both master plans.

When using this approach, the Master Planning task is performed for the static master plan, and the set of data is automatically copied to the dynamic master plan. The static plan remains unchanged until the next time that you run the master planning task, and provides a stable basis for analysis and actions. The dynamic plan will be updated by subsequent transactions, which can result in constant changes to planned orders.

The constant changes often stem from performing an explosion for a selected order (or CTP logic) to calculate delivery promises about make-to-order products. These calculations generate planned orders when there are insufficient supplies for the salable end-item or its components. The planned orders immediately communicate the need for replenishment. However, some scenarios perform multiple explosions when checking delivery promises for an order, or a sales order may be deleted (after performing an explosion) because the customer is only asking about delivery promises or finds them unacceptable. The situation results in constant changes to planned orders, and possible confusion for buyers and planners.

The arguments about using one versus two sets of master plan data have been covered in the literature.[1] It is my experience that very few situations require two master plans for managing day-to-day operations, and the exception often represents make-to-order scenarios using net change explosions or CTP logic to calculate sales order delivery dates.

3.3 Master Planning Parameters

Several parameters represent companywide policies governing the use of master plans and the master planning calculations. These are defined on the Master Planning Parameters page.

Key Master Planning Parameters The key parameters determine whether master planning logic employs one versus two master plans. Other key parameters determine the basis for the rescheduling assumption, the assumed date when running the master planning task on weekends, and the assumed start time when performing an explosion. These parameters are illustrated in the example screen shown in Figure 3.2, and described below. They represent a subset of all master planning parameters.

◆ *Use of one versus two master plans.* Most scenarios can employ a single set of master plan data, as illustrated in Figure 3.3 by the same identifier of *WorkingPlan* for both the current static master plan and the current dynamic master plan. Some scenarios employ two sets of data (as described in the previous section), and use the related policy "Copy the complete and updated static master plan to the dynamic master plan."

◆ *Use dynamic negative days.* This parameter reflects a key aspect of the rescheduling assumption in master planning logic, which determines when to use a scheduled receipt to fulfill a requirement rather than generating a new planned order. A subsequent chapter about coverage planning data describes the rescheduling assumption (Section 6.13).

[1] An excellent analysis about using one versus two master plans was provided in a previous article by Evert Bos.

Figure 3.2 Example Screen of Master Planning Parameters

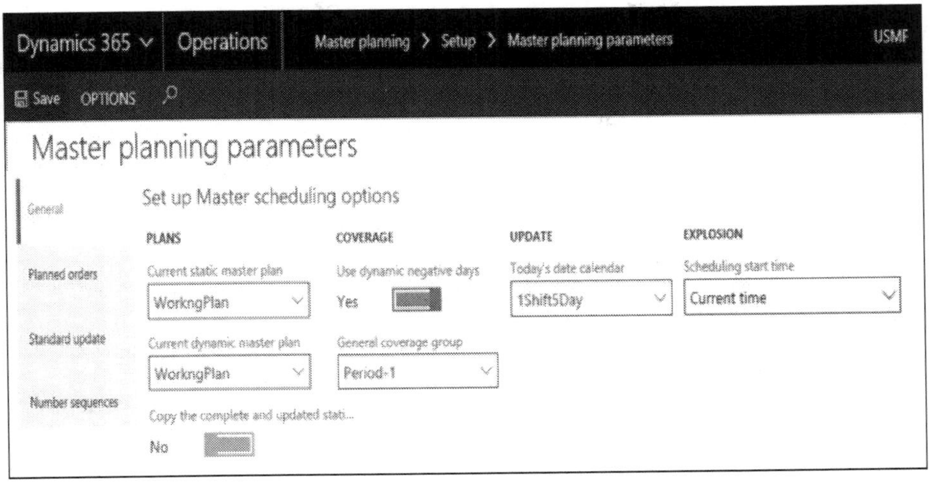

- *General coverage group.* This coverage group will act as the default value when it has not been specified for an item. A subsequent chapter describes the significance of coverage groups (Section 6.1).

- *Basis of the run date when performing the master planning task on weekends.* The applicable run date should reflect the next working day defined by the specified calendar for "Today's date calendar". If this field is blank, the run date will reflect the current system date.

- *Assumption about the scheduling start time (for Explosions).* In most scenarios, a net change explosion should assume a start time of the current system time. An alternative assumption consists of the beginning of the work day for today's date – as defined by the "Today's date calendar" mentioned in the previous point.

Additional Master Planning Parameters The additional parameters apply to different contexts, and are best described in subsequent sections about each context. This includes the start time for calculating delays, the expected receipt time for planned orders, and default dialogue values when firming planned orders.

3.4 Perform Master Planning Calculations

The master planning task represents the primary engine for coordinating supply chain activities. It generates several key outputs that support detailed analysis of the calculations and act as coordination tools. You run the master planning task daily in most scenarios, but it can be run more often. The master planning calculations can also be performed for a selected item, as an explosion for a selected order, or as part of CTP logic for a sales line. These options are summarized in Figure 3.3 and explained below. The figure also illustrates the dialogue for performing three of the options.

Figure 3.3 Options to Perform Master Planning Calculations

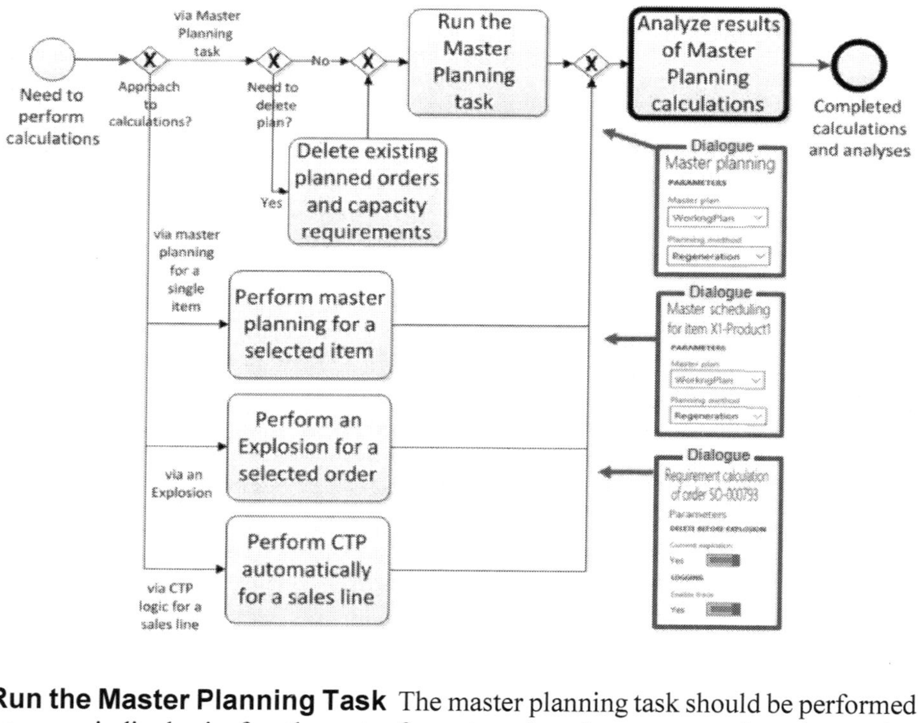

Run the Master Planning Task The master planning task should be performed on a periodic basis for the set of master plan data representing day-to-day operations. The task generates a set of master plan data based on several master plan policies and parameters. These were explained in previous sections. The resulting set of master plan data provides the basis for further analysis.

Several options apply to running the master planning task. It can be run with a Regeneration or Net Change approach, either for all items or selected items.

◆ *Regeneration approach.* The Regeneration approach for all items will automatically delete planned orders (and related planned capacity requirements) within the selected set of master plan data, and then generate new planned orders. When using two sets of master plan data, you run the master planning task for a selected master plan that represents the static plan, and the resulting set of master plan data will be automatically copied to the master plan that represents the dynamic plan.

In contrast, the Regeneration approach for selected items will not automatically delete planned orders; they must be deleted beforehand by running the Delete Plan task. In addition, it will not automatically copy the set of master plan data.

◆ *Net Change approach.* The Net Change approach only applies when running the master planning task for just the dynamic master plan (which must be identified as such in the Master Planning Parameters). It will generate planned orders that cover only those requirements that were created or changed since the master planning task was last run, and the action dates and delayed dates will be updated for all requirements.

◆ *Net Change Minimized approach.* This represents a slight variation to the Net Change approach, where action dates and delayed dates will only be updated for new or changed requirements.

The run date reflects the current date and time, although a master planning parameter can identify the run date as the next working day when it is performed over a weekend.

Run Master Planning for a Selected Item The master planning task can be performed for a selected item by initiating it from certain pages – including the Net Requirements and Supply Schedule for the item, and the Requirements Profile for an order for the item. The related dialogue enables you to select the desired master plan and planning method (such as regeneration), as illustrated in Figure 3.3. The run date reflects the current date and time.

Perform an Explosion for a Selected Order Performing an explosion (also termed in a net change explosion) reflects the same calculations as the master planning task, and you can analyze the resulting explosion information such as planned orders. You can optionally firm the planned orders. When using two sets of master plan data, it only updates the set of data identified as the dynamic plan. It can be performed from multiple starting points such as a sales order line, and Figure 3.3 illustrates the related dialogue. The explosion typically reflects the current date and time. The next section provides further explanation about performing an explosion.

Perform CTP Automatically for a Sales Order Line Capable-to-promise (CTP) logic employs the same calculations as an explosion, although one exception may apply. They are automatically performed after entering a sales order line with a delivery date control option of CTP. Just like performing an explosion, it only updates the set of data identified as the dynamic plan when using two sets of master plan data. A subsequent chapter on sales orders explains the delivery date control options (Section 8.4) and the exception concerning an assumption about on-hand inventory (Section 8.6).

Delete the Existing Planned Orders and Capacity Requirements The figure includes this optional step, where the Delete Plan task results in the deletion of existing planned orders and capacity requirements. This step provides a clean starting point for the calculations, and it is normally performed automatically by running the Master Planning task for all items.

3.5 Perform an Explosion

Performing an explosion -- also termed a Net Change Explosion within this book – employs the same calculations as the Master Planning task, such as netting logic and the generation of planned orders. When using two sets of master plan data, the net change explosion only updates the set of master plan data identified as the dynamic plan. It is often employed when calculating a promised ship date for a sales order line for a make-to-order product. After entering the sales line, you initiate the explosion to access a "Requirement Calculation" dialogue and then perform the calculations. The resulting calculations (displayed on the Explosion page) identify all levels of requirements and the applicable planned orders and messages. You can optionally firm these planned orders. In addition, when the explosion has been performed for a sales order line, you can optionally transfer the calculated date to the confirmed ship date. The next chapter provides example screens of the explosion information (Section 4.2).

An explosion can be viewed and performed from other pages, including those for planned orders, production orders, transfer orders, action messages and calculated delay messages.

As an additional capability, performing an explosion can provide an explanation of master planning logic. You specify the calculation of this "trace" information as part of the *Requirement Calculation* dialogue for performing the explosion, and then view the results on the *Explanation* tab of the Explosion page. The explanation applies to the multi-level product structure for the item. It provides a detailed breakdown of the coverage planning calculations, and the generation of action messages and calculated delay messages.

3.6 Master Planning with Finite Capacity and Finite Material

The master planning calculations can optionally consider finite capacity or finite material or both in generating planned orders. This is sometimes termed a constrained plan when both are used, and it ensures that resources are not overbooked and manufacturing doesn't start before materials are available. Use of a constrained plan typically applies to a near-term horizon, and the relevant horizon depends on the scenario. It also represents an advanced topic rather than one of the basics for master planning, so it will be summarized here with references to relevant sections in subsequent chapters. Case 3.5 illustrates use of master planning with a constrained plan.

Master planning with finite capacity involves several concerns. The primary concern involves the consideration of finite capacity (for designated resources) for planned production orders. A subsequent chapter about routing information provides an extended explanation about resource capacity (Section 11.2) and the relevant master plan policies (Section 11.3).

Master planning with finite material also involves several concerns. The primary concern involves the use of calculated delay messages to designate items representing the finite material. A subsequent chapter about coverage planning data provides an extended explanation about calculated delay messages and suggested guidelines for effective usage (Section 6.12).

Slightly different considerations apply when scheduling existing production orders. As part of the scheduling dialogue, you can selectively include consideration of finite capacity or finite material or both. A subsequent chapter provides an extended explanation about scheduling production orders (Sections 12.4 and 12.5).

3.7 Significance of Calendars

The use of calendars provides critical information for master planning calculations. A calendar defines the working days (aka open dates) for shipping and receiving purposes, and the working hours for production resources. The key assignments of a calendar are summarized in Figure 3.4 and described below. The figure also highlights several exceptions which support optional use of working days.

Figure 3.4 Calendars and the optional use of Working Days

Assignment of a Calendar

Define working days (aka open dates)	Vendor
	Customer
	Mode of Delivery
	Warehouse
	Item *

Define working hours within working days	Production Resource
	- Represents a machine
	- Represents an employee
	- Represents a type of production worker

Special Cases

Optional Use of Working Days

Coverage Planning Data for an Item	Lead time for a purchased item
	Lead time for a manufactured item
	Lead time for transfers
	Safety margins

Delivery Date Control	Delivery dates for sales orders
	Delivery dates for transfer orders

Legend: * = Calendars for items are not typically used

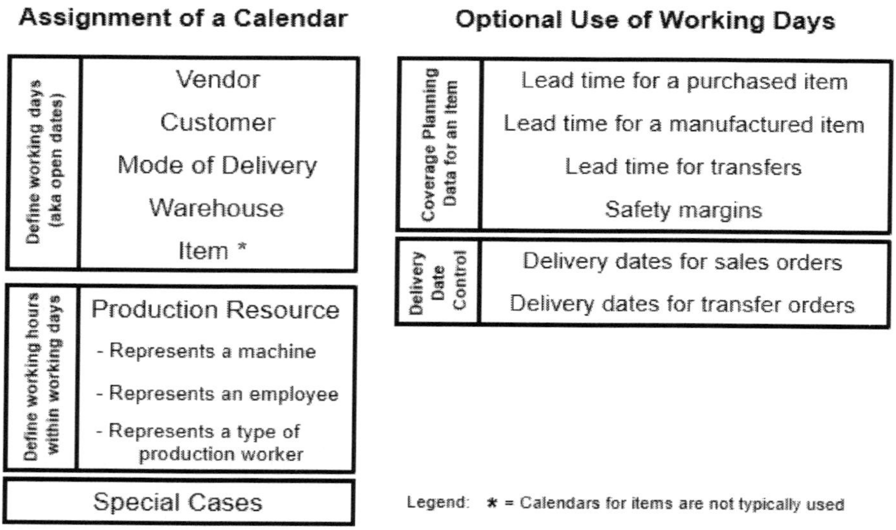

Define Working Days in a Calendar (aka Open Dates) A calendar should be assigned to each vendor, customer, mode of delivery and warehouse, and it defines the open dates (aka working days). An "open" date reflects any calendar date with working hours. Some scenarios require an item-specific calendar. The impacts vary for each type of calendar assignment.

◆ *Calendar for a vendor.* Assigning a "purchase calendar" to a vendor indicates the working days they accept placement of a purchase order. It impacts the order date for planned purchase orders, and the lead time for a purchased item expressed in working days.

◆ *Calendar for a customer.* Assigning a "receipt calendar" to a customer indicates the working days they accept delivery, and it impacts the delivery date on sales order lines.

◆ *Calendar for a mode of delivery.* Assigning a "transport calendar" to a mode of delivery indicates the applicable dates for making deliveries, and it can impact delivery dates on sales orders and transfer orders in cases where the applicable dates differ by warehouse, you can assign a different calendar for the warehouse.

◆ *Calendar for a warehouse.* Assigning a calendar to a warehouse indicates the working days for receiving and shipping. It impacts the delivery dates for planned and actual purchase orders (and transfer orders), and the ship date for sales orders (and transfer orders). The calendar also indicates the working days for delivering completed production orders to the warehouse. It applies whether duration of the production order reflects production lead time or routing data.

◆ *Calendar for an item.* Assigning a calendar to an item represents a special case, and it is not typically specified. An item-specific calendar identifies when it can be received, and it acts as override for the warehouse calendar at the receiving location. It also affects the order date for planned orders. You define the applicable calendar within the Coverage Group assigned to the item.

For a manufactured item with routing data, the item-specific calendar indicates when a production order can be received, but the resource requirements (and related resource calendars) determine the actual scheduled dates for operations.

◆ *Calendar for a legal entity.* The assigned "shipping calendar" for a legal entity acts as a default when a calendar has not been assigned to a warehouse. The figure does not show this option.

Define Working Hours in a Calendar for a Production Resource A calendar should be assigned to each production resource, and it defines the working hours for each date. The working hours often reflect shift patterns, and their significance can differ depending on what the resource represents -- such as a machine, an employee, or a type of production worker. The working hours define the available capacity for a resource, and impact the scheduling logic for production orders.[2] Planned changes to working hours can be modeled by assigning different calendars with different effectivity dates to the resource. Calendar deviations for a given date can be modeled by assigning a different calendar to the date, such as indicating a different number of working hours to reflect downtime or overtime.

Use of Working Days within Coverage Planning Data for an Item The lead time for each purchased item and manufactured item can be expressed in working days or calendar days. You typically define a transfer lead time (aka the transport time) between a warehouse pair, although it can be defined for specific items when they represent a special case. The number of days for safety margins can be expressed in working days or calendar days, as defined by a companywide policy embedded in the Master Planning Parameters. A subsequent chapter

---

[2] A given operation may have time elements for waiting time which can reflect the Gregorian calendar rather than the working hours within a resource calendar, as illustrated in Case 11.8.

provides further explanation of safety margins (Section 6.15) as well as the lead times for purchased items (Section 6.3), manufactured items (Section 6.5) and transfers (Section 6.8).

Use of Working Days within Delivery Date Control For sales orders, the delivery date control policy assigned to the header and line items can enforce several rules, such as consideration of the working days within calendars for the ship-from warehouse, customer receiving point, and mode of delivery. In a similar fashion, the delivery date control policy for a transfer order header and line can enforce rules concerning the calendars for both warehouses and the delivery mode, and the expected transport time. Assigning a policy of "None" will ignore these rules. Subsequent chapters provide further explanation of delivery date control for sales orders (Section 8.4) and transfer orders (Section 14.3).

Special Cases One special case involves subcontracted production at a vendor. In addition to the purchase calendar for the vendor, you also assign a warehouse calendar and a resource calendar to the warehouse and resource that represent the subcontractor. A second special case involves assigning a calendar to an item, as mentioned above. A third special case involves one of the previously described master planning parameters, where a selected calendar can define the basis of the run date when performing the master planning task on weekends (or nightly).

3.8 Summary of Demands and Supplies

The master planning calculations consider different types of demands and supplies, and each type is identified in the net requirements for an item. Figure 3.5 summarizes the common types of demands and supplies. Several additional types can also be considered, as described below.

Additional Types of Demand and Supply based on Master Plan Policies Several additional types of supplies and demands can be considered based on master plan policies. For example, the demands may include supply forecasts, or sales quotations with a high probability for the related opportunity. The supplies may include RFQs or requisitions for purchased material. These master plan policies and their impact are summarized below along with references to more detailed explanations.

◆ *Consider the pipeline of sales quotations as demands.* Some make-to-order scenarios involve sales quotations which ultimately become sales orders. A normal assumption for master planning logic is that only sales orders should be considered as demand, and these sales orders can consume demand forecasts. However, you can override this assumption so that sales quotations with a high probability (of the associated opportunity) will be considered as demand, as illustrated in Case 3.1. These demands do not consume demand forecasts; they are additive.

Figure 3.5 Summary of Demands and Supplies

	Demands (Issues)	Supplies (Receipts)
All Environments	Safety Stock Requirements	On-hand Inventory
	Sales Order	Purchase Order Planned Purchase Order
	Demand Forecast	
	Purchase Order Return to Vendor Transfer Order (Ship-from) Planned Transfer Order Requirement	Sales Order Return from Customer Transfer Order (Ship-to) Planned Transfer Order Receipt
		Consignment Replenishment Order Consignment Inventory
Manufacturing (Un-posted Inventory Journals)	Transfer Journal (From) Count or Adjustment (Minus)	Transfer Journal (To) Count or Adjustment (Plus)
	Picking List Journal (Positive)	
	Component Requirement for a Production/Batch Order	Production/Batch Order Planned Production/Batch Order Co-Product for a Batch Order

◆ *Include supply forecasts as demands.* Some scenarios employ supply forecasts as a push strategy (as described in Section 7.11), but it does not apply to most scenarios.

◆ *Include continuity plans as demands.* Some scenarios involve continuity plans that must be considered as demands.

◆ *Consider purchasing RFQs (Requests for Quote) as supplies.* Some scenarios involve RFQs for purchased material that always result in a purchase order, as illustrated in Case 3.2. A normal assumption for master planning logic is that RFQs should not be considered as supply.

◆ *Consider purchase requisitions as supplies.* Some scenarios involve requisitions for purchased material that always result in a purchase order. A normal assumption for master planning logic is that purchase requisitions should not be considered as supply.

Other Sources of Demand and Supply Additional sources are applicable to project-oriented operations, such as demands stemming from project sales orders, item forecasts and item requirements. Illustrative case studies about these demands are provided in the chapter about project manufacturing. Additional sources also include different types of kanbans in lean manufacturing scenarios, such as fixed kanbans and scheduled kanbans. A subsequent chapter describes the use of master planning to support these two types of kanbans.

3.9 Master Planning by Site vs Site/Warehouse

A fundamental decision involves the choice between master planning by site or by site/warehouse. The book's baseline model assumes master planning by site/warehouse, but some scenarios only require master planning by site. This decision is item-specific. It has multiple considerations and impacts – such as how to model inventory locations and define coverage planning data, and how to treat demands and supplies. Subsequent chapters provide an extended explanation of these key considerations, but it is mentioned here as one of the basics of master planning.

The next chapter covers the key considerations about sites and warehouses, and the significance of sites and warehouses for master planning logic. The following chapter covers the definition of coverage planning data at the site and site/warehouse level.[3]

3.10 Rationale for using Additional Sets of Master Plan Data

The explanation so far has focused on the set of master plan data for managing day-to-day operations. Other purposes can be served by additional sets of master plan data, where each one often reflects different master plan policies and a different set of demand forecasts (aka forecast models). The additional master plans may support one or more of the following purposes. You can copy one master plan to another when applicable.

---

[3] An excellent article by Evert Bos provided an in-depth analysis of master planning by site versus site/warehouse.

- Long-range planning for material or capacity
- Simulations for best-case and worst-case scenarios
- Comparison of plans based on master planning calculations with finite versus infinite capacity of production resources
- Master planning calculations based on just sales order demand (without demand forecasts)

The rationale for using different sets of master plan data and forecast models is also covered in a subsequent chapter about demand forecasts (Section 7.4). An alternative approach to different sets of master plan data employs different sets of forecast plan data generated by the Forecast Scheduling task, as described in a subsequent chapter about demand forecasts (Section 7.12).

3.11 Additional Case Studies

Case 3.1: Master Planning based on Sales Quote Pipeline A fabricated products company designed, quoted and built hundreds of one-time products to customer specifications. They used configurable items to model one-level and two-level custom products, and to define the unique BOM and routing for each configuration. This detailed information provided the basis for calculating estimated costs and a suggested sales price for sales quotations. The high probability sales quotations were used my master planning logic to anticipate material and capacity requirements.

Case 3.2: Master Planning considers Purchasing RFQs as Supplies A manufacturing company often issued an RFQ for needed material, especially for new items. They created an RFQ based on planned purchase orders for the needed material, and sent the RFQ to multiple vendors. The winning vendor reply was used to create a purchase order. The vendor replies were sometimes used to create purchase trade agreement entries for the material, so that future planned purchases orders could simply be firmed – and inherit the trade agreement information.

Case 3.3: Master Planning with Shelf Life Items A food products company produced end-items from raw materials, and both involved batch tracking and expiration dates. Master planning logic assumes that a batch's inventory will no longer be available after its expiration date. This logic also applies to expected receipts, where an expiration date is assigned based on the item's normal expiry period and the expected receipt date. Master planning considers the expiration dates in suggesting planned orders to satisfy demands such as sales orders, demand forecasts, or dependent demands.

In addition, when entering sales orders for a product, the batches of available material are automatically reserved based on first-expired-first-out (FEFO) logic and the customer's requirements about sellable days after they receive the product.

Case 3.4: S&OP Simulations and Different Master Plans A manufacturer employed simulations to assess the impact of changing demands and supplies. Using multiple sets of forecast data to represent various scenarios, and multiple master plans, the management team could analyze the impact of changing demands on material and capacity requirements. For example, the forecast data and master plans could represent best case and worst case scenarios. The master planning task was typically performed using infinite capacity assumptions to anticipate overloaded periods, or identify the need for reduced capacity.

Case 3.5: Master Planning and the use of a Constrained Plan The master scheduler at a manufacturing company used a separate set of master plan data for simulation purposes. She initially ran the master planning task with infinite capacity assumptions to identify overloaded periods on key resources, and then made appropriate adjustments to available capacity or scheduled loads. For example, the planned production orders representing the master schedule could be adjusted and approved, thereby providing a level-loaded master schedule. In addition, the applicable calendars could be updated to indicate overtime or extra working days. The master planning task was then re-run with finite capacity assumptions, and the master scheduler analyzed the resulting set of data to make further adjustments. When satisfied, the master scheduler ran the master planning task for the set of data representing day-to-day operations.

The master scheduler sometimes performed master planning simulations using the calculated delays information to automatically update the requirement dates for planned orders. This approach assumes that the model of their SCM decision making was reasonably realistic, and the master scheduler was not yet comfortable with this assumption.

3.12 Executive Summary

This chapter focused on the basics of master planning for managing day-to-day operations. It covered the one-time setup considerations about master plan policies and the companywide parameters for master planning. For on-going purposes, it covered the options for performing the master planning calculations and considerations about finite capacity and material. The chapter summarized the significance of calendars, the different types of demands and supplies included in the calculations, master planning by site versus site/warehouse, and the rationale for using different sets of master plan data.

Chapter 4

Analyze the Results of Master Planning

The primary engine for coordinating supply chain activities is termed the Master Planning task. Based on several master plan policies, it considers demands and supplies to generate a set of master plan data along with several key outputs that support detailed analysis of the calculations and act as coordination tools. Master planning calculations can also be performed for a single item, as part of performing an explosion, or as part of CTP logic for a sales line. These options were described in the previous chapter.

This chapter focuses on analyzing the results of master planning calculations for managing day-to-day operations. These results include the net requirements, explosion information, and supply schedule for an item, and the use of coordination tools such as planned orders and messages. The results also include the capacity requirements and production schedules for resources. Example screens illustrate the use of these results. These considerations are reflected in the following sections within the chapter.

1. Analyze the Net Requirements for an Item
2. Analyze the Explosion Information for an Item
3. Analyze the Supply Schedule for an Item
4. Planned Production Orders
5. Action Messages
6. Calculated Delay Messages
7. Analyze Capacity Requirements for a Resource
8. Analyze Production Schedules for Resources
9. Coordinate Purchases
10. Coordinate Transfers
11. Workspaces related to Master Planning

4.1 Analyze the Net Requirements for an Item

Information about net requirements can be viewed from several perspectives, such as the net requirements for an item, a sales order line or a supply order. This explanation provides an illustrative example of the net requirements for an item, but the same basic functionality applies to the other perspectives.

The master scheduler and other SCM decision makers can analyze an item's net requirements for a selected set of master plan data. Information about net requirements are displayed in a vertical format with a breakout by site/warehouse. The example screen shown in Figure 4.1 illustrates the Net Requirements page for the item "X1-Product1", which represents a make-to-stock product with demand forecasts. Key points are numbered in the figure and described below.

Figure 4.1 Example Screen of Net Requirements for an Item

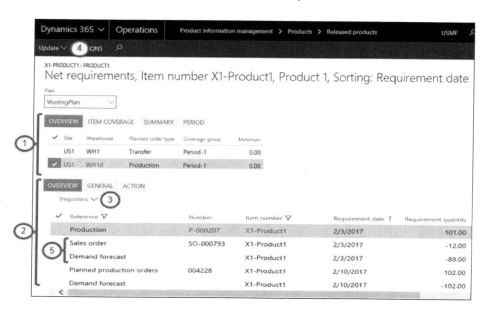

The displayed information consists of two panes. The upper pane displays (1) the applicable sites/warehouses (and variants) for the item, as well as the planned order type, coverage group and safety stock quantity. The example shows two applicable sites/warehouses, where one produces the item and transfers apply to the other. For a selected site/warehouse, three additional tabs display details about the item's coverage planning data, a summary of total demands and supplies, and weekly/monthly time buckets for a selected period template (including a graphic display of the projected available balance).

For a selected site/warehouse in the upper pane, the lower pane displays (2) each supply and demand as a separate line, and the applicable action and/or delay message if any. In this example, the data reflects the item's production orders, demand forecasts and sales orders for the selected production site, and no messages. A complete list of demands and supplies were previously summarized (Section 3.8). For a selected line, you can view the two additional tabs displaying information about the supply or demand, and a summary of action messages if any.

You can optionally perform (3) an inquiry for a selected line in the lower pane, and the types of inquiries can vary by the type of supply or demand. For example, the inquiries for a production order include the BOM and route information, the capacity reservations for resources in the routing, the explosion information about all levels of requirements, and the supply schedule. In contrast, the inquiries for a sales order or demand forecast only include the explosion information and supply schedule.

If needed, you can optionally (4) update the item's net requirements by running the master planning task for the item, as described in the previous chapter (Section 3.4). You can also perform an explosion for a selected order (Section 3.5).

The example data includes (5) one illustration of forecast consumption logic, where a sales order for a quantity of 12 has consumed the original demand forecast of 101, thereby resulting in a remaining demand forecast of 89. A subsequent chapter provides further explanation of forecast consumption logic (Section 7.3).

4.2 Analyze the Explosion Information for an Item

Explosion information displays all levels of requirements calculated for a selected item or order line. You can view the specified item, any lower-level requirements, and the top-level requirement. You can also view detailed information related to each requirement, such as the proposed dates and quantities. Explosion information can be accessed from several starting points, such as the pages for Net Requirements, Planned orders, Production orders, Actions, Calculated Delays and a sales order line.

The example screen shown in Figure 4.2 was accessed from the Net Requirements page for the end-item "X2-Product1" and the selected requirement of a demand forecast. In this simplified example data, the two-level product structure for the end-item consists of the component "X2-Subassembly1" and its component "X2-Raw Material1". Different sections display information about this multilevel bill of material and the pegging to the demand forecast. The displayed information reflects a "down" Explosion view. In contrast, by accessing the Explosion information for the raw material item, an "up" Explosion view would reverse the multilevel format and display pegging to the planned production order for the end-item.

Figure 4.2 Example Screen of Explosion Information

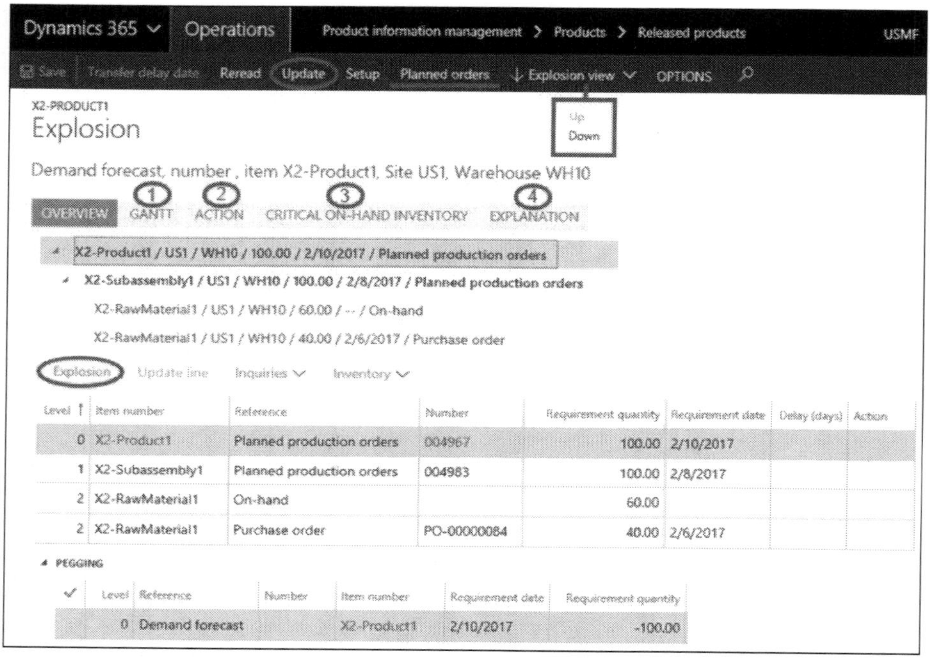

You can optionally access the Planned Orders page to view (and firm) all displayed planned orders. In addition, you can optionally perform an explosion from the Explosion page – using either the Update or Explosion functions highlighted in the figure.

Performing an explosion from the starting point of a sales order line can be used to calculate a promised ship date. You can then transfer the calculated date to the confirmed ship date.

The example screen highlights the explosion information on the Overview Tab. The other tabs display (1) a Gantt chart of all related production orders, (2) action messages if any, and (3) the critical on-hand inventory -- which identifies how requirement quantities are covered by on-hand inventory, supply orders and/or planned orders. The last tab displays (4) an explanation of the master planning calculations after performing an explosion with the logging feature of "enable trace".

The explanation about explosion information consists of several segments, as illustrated in Figure 4.3. These segments include the starting point "preparing for update", the coverage planning logic for each component in the product structure, and the calculated delays and action messages if any. Examples of the detailed explanations for several segments are shown on right side of the figure.

Figure 4.3 Example Screen of the Explanation about Explosion Information

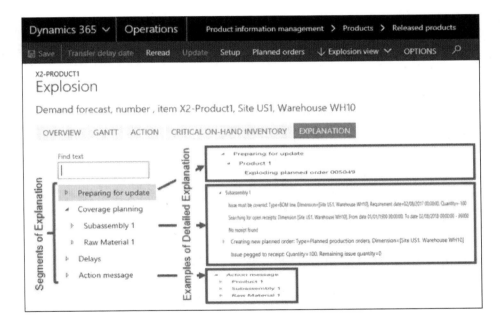

4.3 Analyze the Supply Schedule for an Item

The master scheduler and other SCM decision makers can analyze an item's supply schedule for a selected set of master plan data. Information is displayed in a horizontal format reflecting the time buckets of a selected period template. The information identifies the aggregate companywide demands and supplies without a breakout by site/warehouse. The example screen shown in Figure 4.4 illustrates the Supply Schedule for the item "X1-Product1", which represents a make-to-stock product with demand forecasts. Several key points are numbered in the figure and described below.

Figure 4.4 Example Screen of a Supply Schedule for an Item

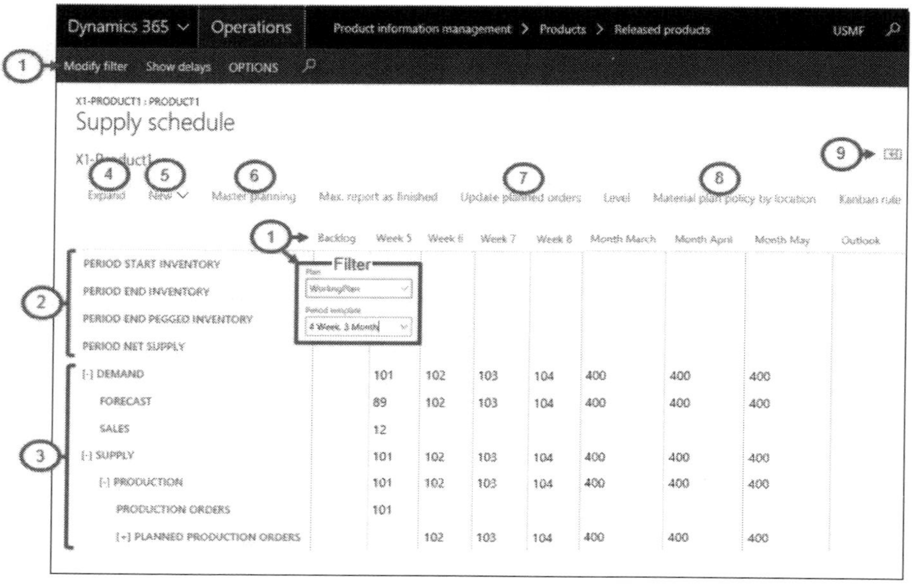

The displayed information reflects (1) the filters for a selected master plan and period template, where the example shows the *WorkingPlan* and a period template consisting of 4 weekly buckets and 3 monthly buckets. The displayed information consists of two major segments. One segment displays (2) the start and ending inventories for each time bucket, which are null in this example because of zero starting inventory, and the supplies exactly match the demands in each time bucket. The second segment displays (3) the demands and supplies within the time buckets defined by the period template. The time buckets include an initial *Backlog* (prior to today's date) and an ending *Outlook* (beyond the time horizon). The example data reflects fully expanded information about demands and supplies. You can (4) expand the level of detail by first selecting a displayed quantity. Conversely, you can collapse the level of detail.

Several actions can be performed from the Supply Schedule. For example, in terms of (5) new orders, you can create a new planned order or a production order. You can (6) run the master planning calculations for the item, (7) view existing planned orders for the item and optionally update them, or (8) view the item's coverage planning data.

When you select a displayed quantity, you can optionally view additional details by toggling (9) the FactBox Pane. The FactBox displays details about the applicable action message and/or delay message if any. Several additional Fast Tabs also provide detailed information about the selected quantity, such as the related sales order or supply order. Figure 4.4 does not include examples of the FactBox or the additional Fast Tabs.

4.4 Planned Production Orders

A firm's S&OP game plans provide the primary driver of production activities. One of the key coordination tools consists of planned production orders (or batch orders), which reflect the model of SCM decision-making embedded in coverage planning data for manufactured items (Section 6.5). They can also reflect scheduling considerations when using routing data (Chapter 11).

The planned orders can be viewed on the Planned Production Orders page for a selected set of master plan data, as illustrated in Figure 4.5 for the *WorkingPlan*. Several key points are numbered in the figure and described below. They can also be viewed on the Planned Orders page. Planned production orders are typically filtered based on selection criteria such as the buyer group and order date, so that the responsible planner can mark and firm the planned orders accordingly.

Figure 4.5 Example Screen for Planned Production Orders

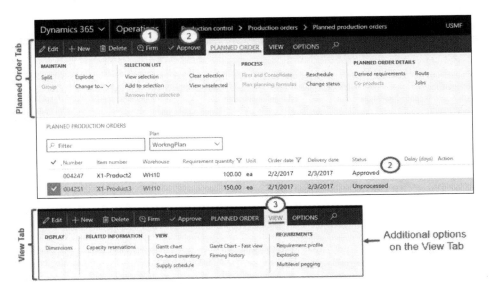

Actual production orders can be created from planned orders via (1) a function termed *firming*. You typically mark the planned orders needing to be firmed. After firming, the actual orders have an automatically-assigned order status based on an item-related policy (embedded in the Coverage Group assigned to the item). An order status of Scheduled is a typical policy. Execution of the firming function automatically deletes the selected planned orders, and creates a log for tracking which planned orders have been firmed and by whom.

In scenarios requiring a level-loaded schedule, the master scheduler role can (2) approve a planned production order to lock the scheduled date and quantity, and prevent it from being deleted by master planning calculations or the Delete Plan task. In addition, this will also lock the BOM and routing information, so that planned changes will not be recognized. An approved planned order must still be firmed to create an actual order. The additional step of approving a planned order may also serve other purposes, such as indicating which planned orders have been agreed upon prior to firming them.

In many cases, you may need to analyze the rationale for a planned production order prior to firming. For example, by accessing information for a selected order on the (3) View Tab, you can view the requirements profile, the explosion information, multi-level pegging to the source of demand, and the item's supply schedule. You can also view the capacity reservations and Gantt chart for resources within the routing. The analysis may lead to one or more of the following actions prior to firming.

♦ *Change a planned order.* You can change the quantity and/or delivery date for a planned order.

♦ *Reschedule a planned production order.* You can reschedule a planned order using a specified scheduling method and scheduling direction, with optional consideration of finite material and capacity.

♦ *Split a planned order.* You can split a planned order using a specified quantity and date.

♦ *Group the planned orders into one order.* You can group together several selected planned orders for the same item, with a total quantity for a single production order. The delivery date reflects the currently selected planned order.

♦ *Change source of supply.* You can identify a different source of supply (such as a purchase or transfer) by changing the planned production order to a planned purchase order or transfer order.

The planned production orders should represent the planner's normal decision making.

4.5 Action Messages

Action messages represent one of the key tools for coordinating activities to meet the S&OP game plans. Master planning calculations can generate action messages (aka *Actions* for short) for planned and actual orders. The logic reflects the action message policies embedded within the coverage group assigned to an item (Section 6.11), or these policies can be defined as part of the master plan policies. Message filters can help eliminate unnecessary messages.

The action messages can be viewed and acted upon in several different ways:

◆ View action messages for a selected item as part of the Net Requirements inquiry.

◆ View action messages for all items on the Actions page, and optionally apply the suggested action for a selected message or access the Action Graph.

◆ View related action messages by accessing the Action Graph, and optionally apply a suggested action

The example screen shown in Figure 4.6 illustrates several action messages on the Actions page. In this example, the end-item "X2-Product1" consists of the component "X2-Subassembly1", and this consists of the component "X2-RawMaterial1". Using the Apply Action function (identified in the figure), you can apply the suggested action for a selected message.

Figure 4.6 Example Screen for Action Messages

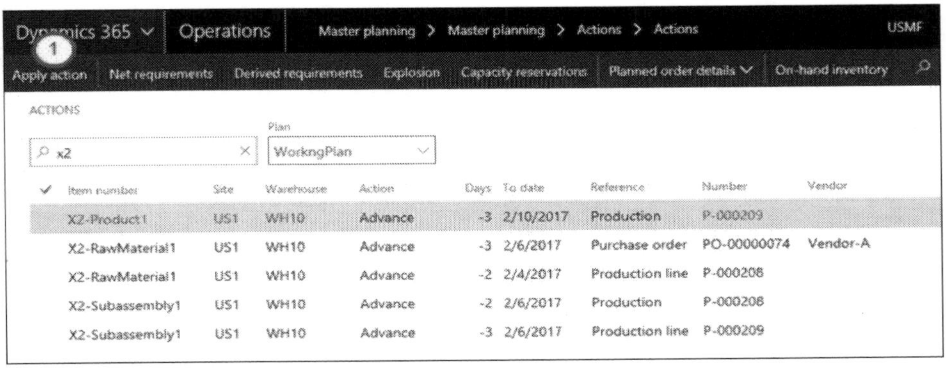

The Action Graph identifies the relationship between action messages, as illustrated in Figure 4.7 with the same data shown in the previous figure. In this example, each order is for a quantity of 100. The display options allow you to focus on just the actionable messages that are related. As a general guideline, you should view related action messages using the Action Graph to understand the context of other orders, and then selectively apply the actions to the relevant messages.

Figure 4.7 Example Screen for the Action Graph

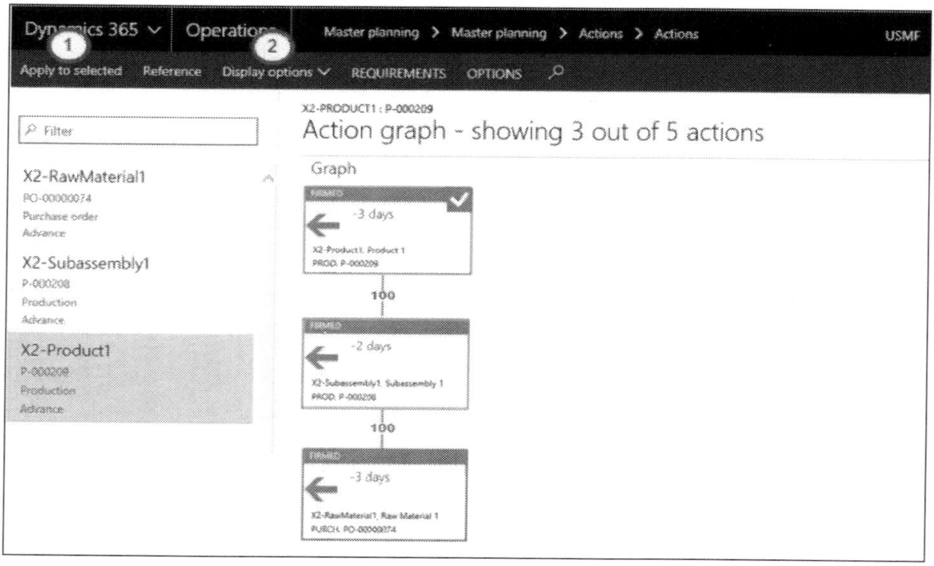

4.6 Calculated Delay Messages

Calculated delay messages represent one of the key tools for coordinating activities to meet the S&OP game plans. Master planning calculations can generate calculated delays (aka *Delays* for short) for planned and actual supply orders as well as for demands stemming from sales orders, demand forecasts and safety stock. The logic reflects the delay message policies embedded within the coverage group assigned to an item (Section 6.12), or these policies can be defined as part of the master plan policies. Message filters can help eliminate unnecessary messages.

The example screen shown in Figure 4.8 illustrates several messages on the Calculated Delays page. In this example data, most of the displayed messages apply to sales orders, and appropriate steps should be taken to meet the demand or to notify the customer of the delayed delivery.

Figure 4.8 Example Screen for Calculated Delay Messages

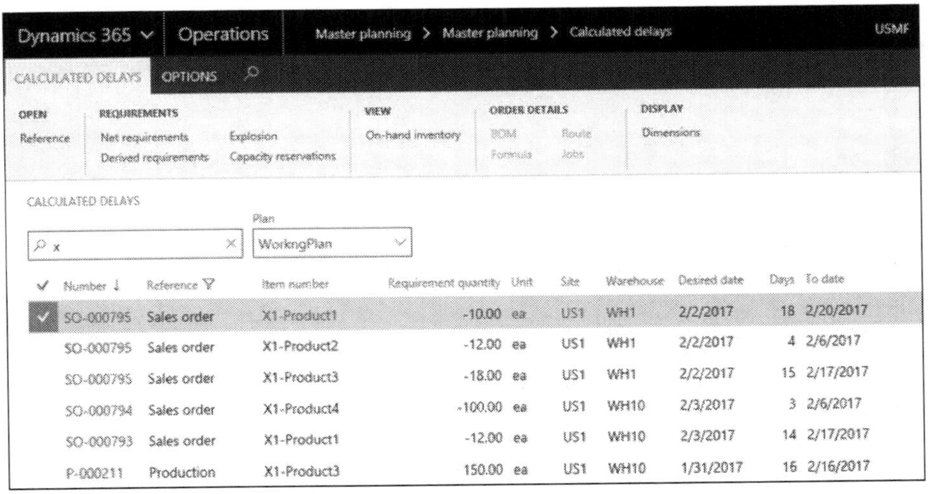

Dynamics 365 ⌄	Operations	Master planning > Master planning > Calculated delays							USMF
CALCULATED DELAYS	OPTIONS 🔎								
OPEN	REQUIREMENTS		VIEW	ORDER DETAILS		DISPLAY			
Reference	Net requirements	Explosion	On-hand inventory	BOM	Route	Dimensions			
	Derived requirements	Capacity reservations		Formula	Jobs				

CALCULATED DELAYS

Plan: WorkingPlan

✓	Number ↓	Reference ▽	Item number	Requirement quantity	Unit	Site	Warehouse	Desired date	Days	To date
✓	SO-000795	Sales order	X1-Product1	-10.00	ea	US1	WH1	2/2/2017	18	2/20/2017
	SO-000795	Sales order	X1-Product2	-12.00	ea	US1	WH1	2/2/2017	4	2/6/2017
	SO-000795	Sales order	X1-Product3	-18.00	ea	US1	WH1	2/2/2017	15	2/17/2017
	SO-000794	Sales order	X1-Product4	-100.00	ea	US1	WH10	2/3/2017	3	2/6/2017
	SO-000793	Sales order	X1-Product1	-12.00	ea	US1	WH10	2/3/2017	14	2/17/2017
	P-000211	Production	X1-Product3	150.00	ea	US1	WH10	1/31/2017	16	2/16/2017

4.7 Analyze Capacity Requirements for a Resource

The production supervisor analyzes the capacity requirements for those resources within their responsibility. The requirements reflect routing data for planned and actual production orders. The analysis typically anticipates overloaded periods for bottleneck resources so that adjustments can be made to capacity or to the load stemming from relevant production orders. The aggregate capacity requirements can also be viewed for a resource group consisting of multiple resources.

Typical analysis tools include graphical capacity requirements, capacity loads and capacity reservations for a resource (or resource group), as illustrated below. The available capacity for a resource can also be adjusted for overbooked periods. These tools can be accessed from the Resources page for a selected resource, or from the Resource Groups page for a selected resource group.

Graphical Capacity Requirements The example screen shown in Figure 4.9 illustrates a graphical analysis of the capacity requirements (in 9 weekly periods) for the resource "X1-Machine1". The figure illustrates a bar chart format indicating the resource capacity (of 40 hours per week) and the loads stemming from planned and actual production orders. In this example, master planning calculations generated planned orders resulting in two overbooked periods based on infinite capacity assumptions.

Figure 4.9 Example Screen of Graphical Capacity Requirements for a Resource

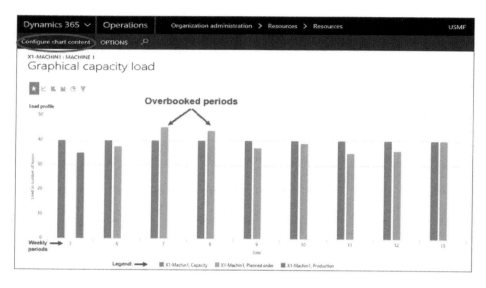

The *Configure chart content* function enables you to tailor the graphical analysis. For example, you can specify the applicable resource (or resource group) and master plan, the date range and time periods, and optionally include planned production orders in the load.

Capacity Loads A detailed analysis of the load is often required. The example screen shown in Figure 4.10 illustrates the Capacity Load page for the same resource and data, where the time periods reflect a period template of 9 weeks. An icon identifies the two overbooked periods. For a selected period (in the top half of the screen), the *Reference* information (at the bottom half of the screen) identifies the applicable production orders.

Figure 4.10 Example Screen of the Capacity Load for a Resource

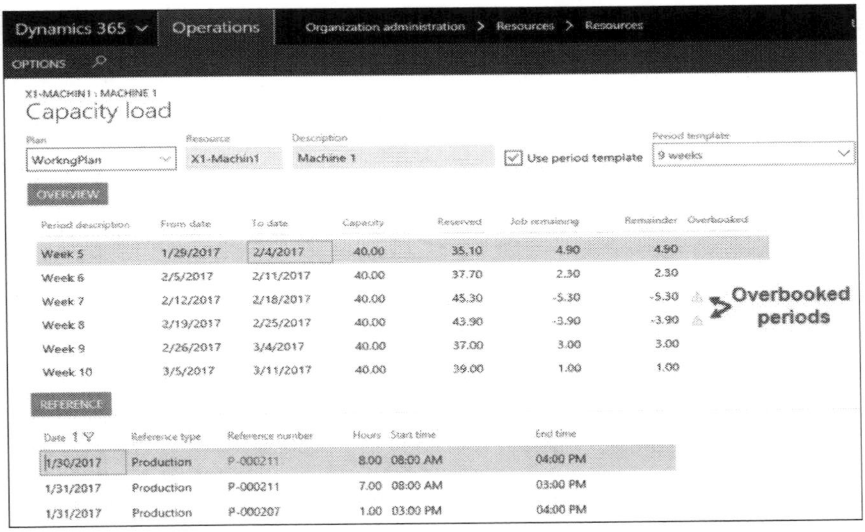

Capacity Reservations The capacity reservations for a resource also provide a detailed analysis of the load. The example screen shown in Figure 4.11 illustrates the Capacity Reservations page for the same resource and data. Each line identifies the required hours for a given date and production order.

Figure 4.11 Example Screen of the Capacity Reservations for a Resource

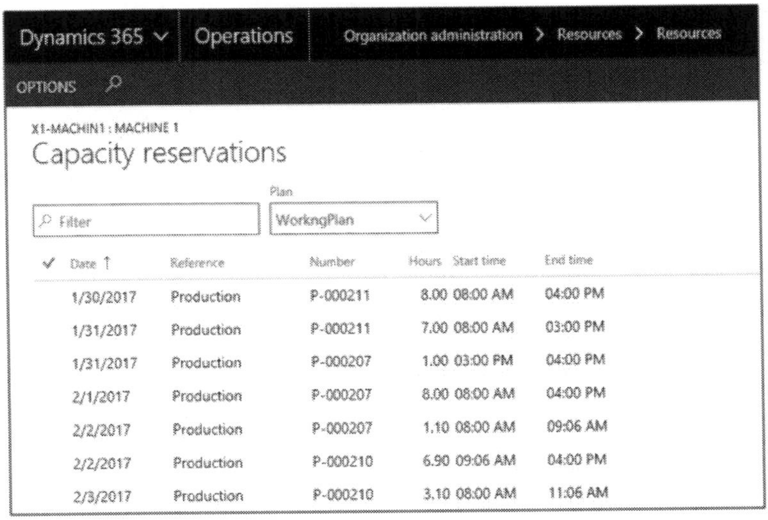

Adjusting the Available Capacity for a Resource You can adjust the available capacity of a resource to handle overbooked periods. As one of the most common approaches, you can define one or more calendars that represent the different approaches to overtime for a resource, and then assign the relevant calendar to selected dates. These are termed calendar deviations for a resource. For example, in the context of previous example screens showing two overloaded periods, you could assign calendar deviations to reflect overtime hours for selected dates in the overloaded periods.

Other approaches are less commonly used. These include changes to the operations scheduling percentage for a resource, or changes to the efficiency percentage for selected dates within the calendar, thereby indicating more work can be scheduled during working hours.

4.8 Analyze Production Schedules for Resources

The production supervisor analyzes the suggested production schedules for those resources within their responsibility. The suggested schedule for a resource reflects master planning calculations with job scheduling. It should be noted that use of operations scheduling will generate schedules for a resource group but not for specific resources.

Many manufacturing scenarios have unique requirements for viewing, modifying and communicating the production schedules for resources. However, the standard software provides several basic tools for production schedule purposes. These include the dispatching capabilities for a resource, the Gantt chart, and the edit job list, as described below.

Dispatching Capabilities for a Resource The Dispatching page displays the suggested schedule for a selected resource, and supports rescheduling based on a manually assigned sequence. The example screen shown in Figure 4.12 illustrates these two aspects of the Dispatching page. The top half of the figure displays the initial list of scheduled orders on the Overview Tab, where this example data reflects master planning logic based on infinite capacity assumptions. Selected orders can then be viewed on the Sequence Tab. You can manually move orders up or down in the sequence, and then schedule the sequenced orders. The bottom half of the figure displays the Sequence Tab with the resulting list after scheduling the sequenced orders, where this example data reflects scheduling with finite capacity assumptions.

Figure 4.12 Example Screen of Dispatching for a Resource

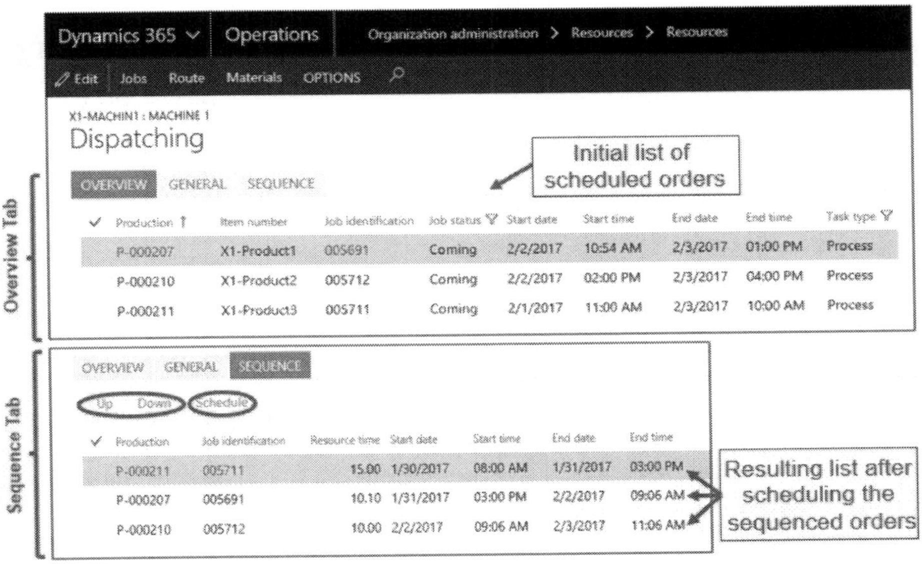

Gantt Chart Capabilities The Gantt chart capabilities provide several ways to view the production schedule for selected resources (and resource groups) and production orders. These capabilities reflect an extensible control framework that lets you add controls by using HTML and JavaScript.[1] The current software version supports interactive scheduling in the Gantt chart, such as drag-and-drop capabilities to move jobs (and their dependent jobs) and to sequence jobs, and to reassign a job to a different resource.

The example screen shown in Figure 4.13 illustrates the resource view of a Gantt Chart for a single resource. The example data reflects the scheduled orders displayed in the previous figure about dispatching (Figure 4.12), where the sequenced orders were scheduled based on finite capacity assumptions.

---

[1] A detailed explanation of the Gantt Development Guide is provided in the Wiki help.

Figure 4.13 Example Screen of a Gantt Chart for a Resource

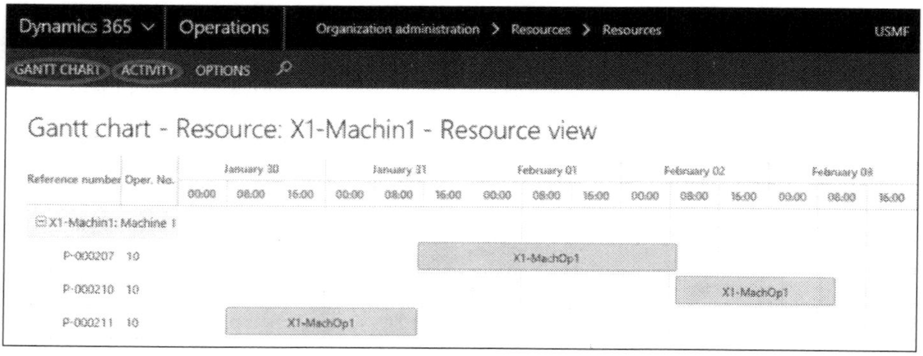

The most basic element of a Gantt chart is the task activity, where each activity is allocated its own row in the chart. In this example, each task activity represents a single operation for three different production orders, where each bar indicates the activity duration and displays the master operation identifier. This example displays a calendar in increments of 8 hours, which simplifies the visualization across a 5-day week. Other scenarios might display a calendar in hourly increments.

Accessing the *Gantt Chart* function provides several options for displaying the information. A basic option for the Gantt chart format consists of the Resource view versus the Order view. Other options include the relevant time scale and content, such as the content about planned and actual production orders.

Accessing the *Activity* function (after selecting a task activity) provides options to drill down into the related production order, operation and job. You can also perform job scheduling and access the dispatching capabilities.

Edit Job List The Edit Job List page provides an alternative approach to basic sequencing when using the MES (Manufacturing Execution System) capabilities. You can use the Edit Job List to adjust the daily schedules, such as re-sequencing or moving jobs, assigning available resources, and designating high priority jobs. You can access information about each production order, the material availability, and capacity loads to support decision making about efficiency and on-time completions. The resulting job list provides the machine operators the sequence to perform their daily tasks.

Production Sequencing for Planned Batch Orders A simple approach for suggested sequencing only applies to planned batch orders. In terms of setup information, you define one or more item characteristics that impact production sequencing, and you assign a value for each characteristic to relevant manufactured items. You also assign the sequencing logic to the resources and resource groups that require production sequencing. This setup information provides the foundation to support production sequencing within master planning calculations. A subsequent chapter about process manufacturing describes a typical process for this approach to production sequencing (Section 18.8).

4.9 Coordinate Purchases

A firm's S&OP game plans provide the primary driver of purchasing activities for material items. The key tools for coordinating these activities include planned purchase orders and messages, which reflect the model of SCM decision-making embedded in coverage planning data for purchased items (Section 6.3). Several other coordination tools can also be employed, such as inquiries/reports about problems in delivery dates.

Planned Purchase Orders The purchasing agent analyzes planned purchase orders for those items and vendors within their responsibility, and typically firms the planned orders to execute the S&OP game plans.

The planned orders can be viewed on the Planned Purchase Orders page for a selected set of master plan data, as illustrated in Figure 4.14 for the *WorkingPlan*. They can also be viewed on the Planned Orders page. Planned purchase orders are typically filtered based on selection criteria such as the buyer group and order date, so that the responsible buyer can select and firm the planned orders accordingly. The bottom of the figure illustrates a filter for orders that need to be placed before 01/31/2017, which reflects a current date of Monday January 30th in the example data.

Figure 4.14 Example Screen of Planned Purchase Orders

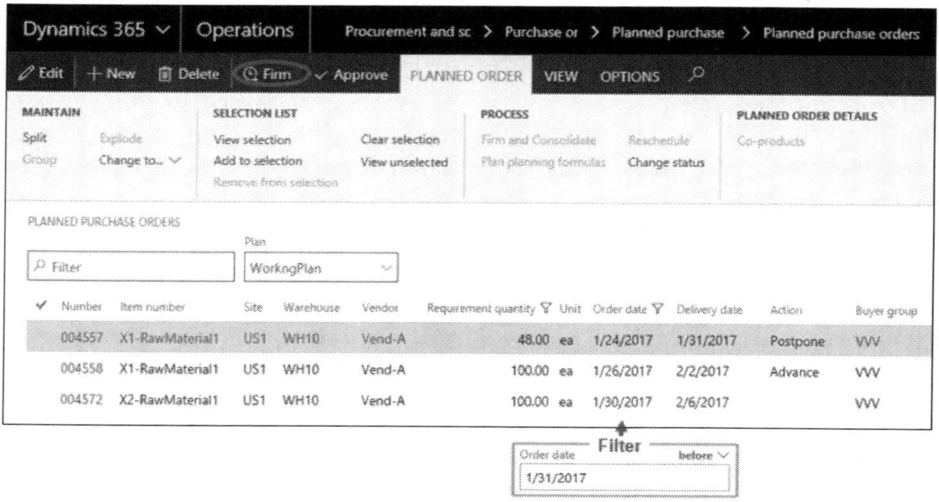

Actual purchase orders can be created from selected planned orders via a function termed *firming*. The firming function creates single-line purchase orders unless you indicate grouping preferences via the firming dialogue. For example, the grouping preferences can reflect the vendor and a period size (such as daily or weekly) in order to generate a multi-line purchase order. Execution of the firming function automatically deletes the selected planned orders, and creates a log for tracking which planned orders have been firmed and by whom.

In many cases, you may need to analyze the rationale for a planned purchase order prior to firming. For example, by accessing information for a selected order on the View Tab, you can view the requirements profile, the explosion information, multi-level pegging to the source of demand, and the item's supply schedule. In addition, the analysis may lead to one or more of the following actions prior to firming.

◆ *Approve a planned purchase order.* Approving a planned purchase order will lock the scheduled date and quantity, and prevent it from being deleted by master planning calculations or the Delete Plan task.

◆ *View and select an alternative vendor.* The selection list for the vendor field identifies the alternative vendors based on the item's approved vendor list, the purchase price trade agreement information, or the vendor item information. The trade agreement information provides the basis for selecting a vendor based on purchase price, quantity breakpoints, and validity dates.

◆ *Change a planned order.* You can change the quantity and/or delivery date for a planned purchase order.

◆ *Split a planned order.* You can split the planned purchase order using a specified quantity and date.

◆ *Group multiple planned orders onto one order.* You can group together several selected planned orders for the same item and vendor, where the delivery date of the firmed order reflects the currently selected planned order.

◆ *Assign a planned order to an existing purchase order.* You can assign a planned order to an existing purchase order so that the firming process adds a line item to the existing order.

◆ *Convert a planned purchase order to a request for quote.*

◆ *Change source of supply.* You can identify a different source of supply (such a transfer or production) by changing the planned purchase order to a planned transfer order or production order.

A standard inquiry identifies the planned purchase orders with an order date of today's date or earlier. The planned purchase orders should represent the buyer's normal decision making and the S&OP game plans.

Analyze the Messages for Purchase Orders The purchasing agent can analyze messages about planned and actual purchase orders to help coordinate supply chain activities for those items within their responsibility. These include Action messages and Calculated Delay messages. A standard inquiry identifies all action messages for purchased items. The action messages to advance and postpone an order merit additional comment.

◆ *Action messages to advance a purchase order.* A standard inquiry identifies the purchase orders with an action message to advance the delivery date, which highlights the need to expedite deliveries.

◆ *Action messages to postpone a planned purchase order.* The suggested date for action messages to postpone delivery of planned purchase orders can optionally act as the requirement date. This helps eliminate unnecessary messages and delays receipt until needed, and requires the master plan policy about action messages for "update postponed date as the requirement date".

The example data in Figure 4.14 included two planned purchase orders with Action messages, where one has a Postpone message and the other has an Advance message.

Identify Potential Problems in Delivery Dates The confirmed delivery date for a purchase line (or a line within a delivery schedule) typically indicates the most realistic up-to-date information from the vendor.   A standard inquiry identifies confirmed purchase orders without confirmed delivery dates, and a second inquiry identifies purchase lines with past due delivery dates. You can also identify purchase-related backorders. These problems typically require action by the purchasing agent and coordination with the vendor.

4.10 Coordinate Transfers

A firm's S&OP game plans provide the primary driver of transfers for material items. The key tools for coordinating these activities include planned transfer orders and messages, which reflect the model of SCM decision-making embedded in coverage planning data for transfers (Section 6.8).   A typical role for coordinating transfers includes a purchasing agent, a DRP coordinator or planner.

Planned Transfer Orders The planned orders can be viewed on the Planned Transfers page for a selected set of master plan data, as illustrated in Figure 4.15 for the *WorkingPlan*. They can also be viewed on the Planned Orders page. Planned transfer orders are typically filtered based on selection criteria such as the ship-from warehouse, order date and/or buyer group, so that the responsible planner can select and firm the planned orders accordingly.

Actual transfer orders can be created from planned orders via a function termed *firming planned orders.* You typically identify the planned orders needing to be firmed. The firming function creates single-line transfer orders unless you indicate grouping preferences via the firming dialogue, such as grouping by a daily or weekly period size. Execution of the firming function automatically deletes the selected planned orders, and creates a log for tracking which planned orders have been firmed and by whom.

Figure 4.15 Example Screen of Planned Transfers

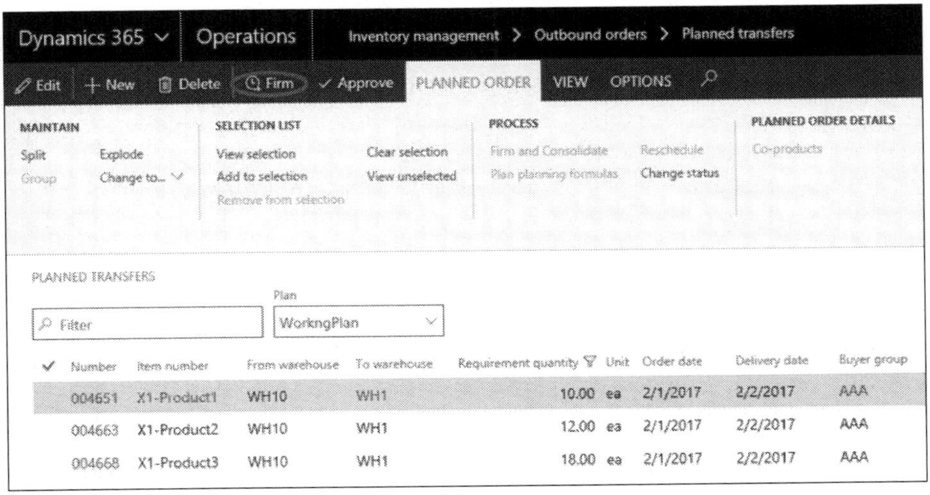

Dynamics 365 ∨	Operations	Inventory management > Outbound orders > Planned transfers

✎ Edit	+ New	🗑 Delete	⟳ Firm	✓ Approve	PLANNED ORDER	VIEW	OPTIONS	🔍

MAINTAIN		SELECTION LIST		PROCESS		PLANNED ORDER DETAILS
Split	Explode	View selection	Clear selection	Firm and Consolidate	Reschedule	Co-products
Group	Change to... ∨	Add to selection	View unselected	Plan planning formulas	Change status	
		Remove from selection				

PLANNED TRANSFERS

Plan

🔍 Filter   WorkngPlan ∨

✓	Number	Item number	From warehouse	To warehouse	Requirement quantity ▽	Unit	Order date	Delivery date	Buyer group
	004651	X1-Product1	WH10	WH1	10.00	ea	2/1/2017	2/2/2017	AAA
	004663	X1-Product2	WH10	WH1	12.00	ea	2/1/2017	2/2/2017	AAA
	004668	X1-Product3	WH10	WH1	18.00	ea	2/1/2017	2/2/2017	AAA

In many cases, you may need to analyze the rationale for a planned transfer order prior to firming. You can view the net requirements and related action messages for a selected planned order. In addition, the analysis may lead to one or more of the following actions prior to firming.

◆ *Approve a planned transfer order.* Approving a planned transfer order will lock the scheduled date and quantity, and prevent it from being deleted by master planning calculations or the Delete Plan task.

◆ *Change the quantity and/or delivery date for a planned transfer order.*

◆ *Split a planned transfer order using a specified quantity and date.*

◆ *Group together several selected planned orders for the same item and warehouse pair.*

◆ *Assign a planned order to an existing transfer order.* You can assign a planned order to an existing transfer order so that the firming process adds a line item to the existing order.

◆ *Change the ship-from warehouse.* This change indicates an alternate source of supply. You can view inventory availability at other sites to support decisions about changing the source of supply.

◆ *Change the source of supply.* You can identify a different source of supply (such as a purchase or production) by changing the planned transfer order to a planned purchase order or production order.

Analyze the messages for Transfer Orders The purchasing agent or DRP coordinator analyzes messages about transfer orders to help coordinate supply chain activities for those items and warehouses within their responsibility. The purchasing agent employs message filters to eliminate unnecessary messages.

4.11 Workspaces related to Master Planning

The Master Planning workspace summarizes several aspects of information about a selected set of master plan data, including planned orders, action messages, and messages about calculated delays. The example screen shown in Figure 4.16 illustrates the Master Planning workspace. Key points are numbered in the figure and described below.

Figure 4.16 Example Screen of the Master Planning Workspace

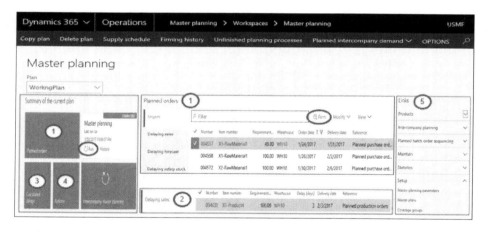

One part of the workspace (shown on the left side of Figure 4.16) displays a summary of topics about the selected master plan. Clicking a topic will display additional information (shown in the middle of the figure). For example, after clicking the (1) planned order topic, you can view and filter the "urgent" planned orders and optionally firm them. You can also view (2) the planned orders that would result in delayed shipment of a sales order, or in delays for meeting requirements for demand forecasts or safety stock. Clicking the other topics about (3) calculated delays and (4) actions would display the related information.

The workspace includes predefined links to key information (5) and the user can add other links. Examples shown on the right side of the figure include links to setup information within the pages for Master Planning Parameters, Master Plans and Coverage Groups. Several functions are also embedded in the workspace, such as running the master planning task or deleting a set of master plan data.

Previous sections provided screen examples for much of the information displayed on the Master Planning workspace.

4.12 Executive Summary

This chapter focused on analyzing the results of master planning calculations for managing day-to-day operations. These results included the net requirements, explosion information, and supply schedule for an item, and the use of coordination tools such as planned orders and messages. The results also included the capacity requirements and production schedules for resources. Example screens illustrated the use of these results.

Chapter 5

Fundamentals of Modeling Inventory Locations

The definition of physical locations containing inventory represents a key part of modeling any supply chain. The fundamental options for modeling these physical locations involve the use of sites and warehouses within a legal entity. In this book, the terms *site* and *warehouse* will be used when explaining system-specific functionality, and the terms of *legal entity* and *company* will be used interchangeably. In addition, we will use the term *bin location* when referring to the locations within a warehouse. We will use the generic terms of *inventory location* or *physical location* for conceptual explanations, as well as the generic term of *multisite operation*.

The model of inventory locations has multiple impacts. It impacts the definition of items, bills of material, resources, routings, product costs, coverage planning data and S&OP game plans. It also impacts master planning logic and the business processes related to inventory, such as sales orders, purchase orders, transfer orders and production orders. These impacts are covered throughout the book. However, the fundamental options for modeling inventory locations are introduced now, and the chapter consists of the following sections.

1. Major Variations for Modeling Inventory Locations
2. Key Considerations about using Sites
3. Key Considerations about using Warehouses
4. Significance of Sites and Warehouses for Master Planning Logic
5. Companywide versus Site- and Warehouse-Level Information for an Item
6. Key Pages for Defining an Item's Planning Data

A graphical portrayal of the inventory locations – termed the operations infrastructure – identifies the multi-level structure of sites and warehouses within legal entities, and provides access to all related information.

5.1 Major Variations for Modeling Inventory Locations

The wide variety of scenarios for supply chain management can be distilled into a few major variations for modeling inventory locations within Dynamics 365 for Operations. Several key factors differentiate the nature of these variations, such as the number of instances, the number of legal entities related to the inventory locations, and the approach for modeling an inventory location via sites and warehouses. Another key factor involves the need for transfers between inventory locations and the solution approach for coordinating transfers. The most common variations and the key factors are summarized in Figure 5.1 and described below.

Figure 5.1 Major Variations for Modeling Inventory Locations

		Major Variations		
		#1	#2	#3
		Multisite Operation Without Transfers	Multisite Operation With Transfers	Multicompany Supply Chain
Key Factors	Number of Instances and Partitions	One		
	Number of Companies (Legal Entities)	One		Multiple
	Approach for Modeling an Inventory Location	Considerations about using Sites and Warehouses for Modeling an Inventory Location		
	Need for Transfers Between Inventory Locations	No	Yes	
Solution Approach for Coordinating Material Transfers		N/A	Transfer Orders	Intercompany Purchase Orders & Sales Orders

The simplest variation consists of a single instance and partition, and a single legal entity with one or more inventory locations. The locations may reflect autonomous sites without transfers, or they may reflect a distribution network with transfers between locations. This simplest variation represents one aspect of the baseline model of operations described in a previous chapter (Section 2.1).

Transfers between locations in a multicompany supply chain represent a more complex variation. You can coordinate transfers via intercompany purchase orders and sales orders, and by master planning logic that generates planned intercompany demand. A subsequent chapter provides further explanation about these capabilities in a multicompany supply chain (Chapter 14).

All these variations involve several considerations about using sites and warehouses for modeling inventory locations. As a key consideration for master planning logic, you can specify whether an item's coverage planning should apply to sites or warehouses, and the planning data can reflect a site- or warehouse-level policy (or a companywide policy). Some unique considerations only apply to sites while other unique considerations only apply to warehouses, as described in the next two sections within this chapter.

Several variations represent less common scenarios and are not included in Figure 5.1. For example, a given enterprise may employ two or more instances, where intercompany trade between locations in each instance can be handled by the Data Import/Export capabilities within the software. The same capabilities also apply to intercompany trade when one of the companies employs a different ERP system. A single instance can also be partitioned with one or more companies in a partition, thereby isolating the information as if separate instances were being used. These other variations fall outside the book's scope.

5.2 Key Considerations about using Sites

Each physical location is typically modeled as a site with one or more warehouses. A site has several unique aspects that are not applicable to a warehouse, as summarized below.

Financial Reporting by Site Each site can have an associated value for a "site" financial dimension, thereby supporting profit and loss statements by site. This approach involves some setup information about the relevant financial dimension on the Dimension Link form, such as the financial dimension for department. The possible values for department must be defined (one for each site) and the applicable value must be assigned to each site. At that point in time, you can activate the financial dimension link.

Site-Specific Standard Costs for an Item The assignment of an item's standard cost can vary by site, especially when standard costing applies to the item. Stated another way, each material item must have an item cost record for each site with inventory. As a special case, an item may be assigned a zero value for its standard cost at a given site.

Site-Specific BOM and Routing Information for a Manufactured Item The BOM and routing information for manufactured items can vary by site.

Site-Specific Labor Rates and Overhead Rates Labor rates and overhead costs can vary by site in manufacturing scenarios.

Site-Specific Policies for Quality Orders The automatic generation of quality orders within a business process – such as production or purchase receiving – provides a key tool for quality management. These policies can be site-specific or companywide.

Other Production Data related to a Site A site is assigned to a resource group and its related resources, so that the resources within the group are assumed to be in close proximity to each other. A site is also assigned to a production unit, which can determine the warehouse source of components for producing an item.

Some Limitations related to Manufactured Items One limitation applies to manufacturing scenarios with a product structure that spans more than one site. More specifically, the warehouse source for a manufactured item's components and the destination warehouse for the item's production order must be within the same site. When a product structure spans two sites, for example, this limitation often means that an item stocked or produced at one site must be transferred to a warehouse within a different site in order to use it as a component.

The same limitation applies to the standard cost calculations and inquiries for a manufactured item, since these can only span a single site. In order to avoid this limitation, some scenarios will use multiple warehouses within a single site to model different inventory locations.

5.3 Key Considerations about using Warehouses

Each physical location is typically modeled as a site with one or more warehouses, as noted in the previous section. The assignment of a warehouse to a site cannot be changed after posting inventory transactions for the warehouse, so that the initial assignments must be carefully considered. Several unique aspects only apply to warehouses.

Use of the Basic versus Advanced Approach to Warehouse Management The choice of a warehouse management approach can be warehouse-specific. The two different approaches have different conceptual models for managing inventory. Examples of these differences include the definition of bin locations within a warehouse, the use of reservation logic, and the impact on business processes involving inventory such as sales orders, purchase orders, transfer orders and production orders.

Warehouse Source of Components for a Manufactured Item The warehouse source of components can be defined in several different ways based on BOM/routing information for a manufactured item. A component's warehouse source indicates where to pick the item for a production order. A subsequent chapter about bill of material information provides more detailed explanations about these options (Section 10.4).

The warehouse source must reflect the previously-mentioned limitation about a product structure than spans more than one site. This consideration is especially important in scenarios with subcontracted production, with tracking of inventory at the subcontractor.

Significance of a Transit Warehouse The need for a transit warehouse only applies when using transfer orders, so that you can track the in-transit inventory. You designate a transit warehouse when creating it, and assign a transit warehouse to each ship-from warehouse.

Warehouse Levels The concept of warehouse levels only applies when using planned transfer orders, where master planning logic performs level-by-level calculations for the destination and refilling warehouses. The levels are normally assigned automatically when defining a destination warehouse and its refilling warehouse, and the levels include the assigned transit warehouse. You can also perform the "update warehouse levels" function on the Warehouses page.

Significance of a Quarantine Warehouse The need for a quarantine warehouse only applies when using the Basic Inventory approach to warehouse management, and when using quarantine orders for reporting inspection.

Designating a Non-Nettable Warehouse A warehouse can be designated with a policy of "manual" item coverage, so that master planning logic views related inventory as non-nettable, and demands for the warehouse do not generate planned supply orders. This historical approach has been used to model non-nettable inventory due to quality problems, but the more recently added capabilities for inventory blocking provide alternative approaches (Section 16.1).

Calendar and Time Zone for a Warehouse   You assign a calendar of working hours to a warehouse, and the warehouse is considered "open" for a given calendar date when its working hours exceed zero.   When applicable, you can optionally indicate whether a given calendar date is closed or open for pickup. You assign the applicable time zone (and the policy about order entry deadlines) to a site, and it applies to all warehouses assigned to the site.

5.4 Significance of Sites and Warehouses for Master Planning Logic

The significance of sites and warehouses for master planning logic is defined by policies within the Storage Dimension Group assigned to an item. A user-defined Storage Dimension Group represents one aspect of the essential information that must be assigned to an item. It consists of several policies which can be broadly segmented into two groups. One group of policies determines the use of site, warehouse, and bin locations. The second group is related to the basic versus advanced approach to warehouse management. The example screen shown in Figure 5.2 illustrates the Storage Dimension Group page and the two groups of policies.

Figure 5.2 Example Screen for a Storage Dimension Group
and its Related Policies

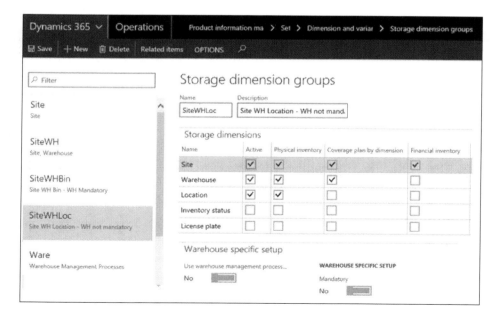

Policies related to the use of Site, Warehouse and Bin Location Most scenarios will track an item's physical inventory by site, warehouse and bin location, while other scenarios simply require tracking by site and warehouse. From a master planning perspective, the critical policies concern (1) the level of coverage planning and (2) the mandatory entry of the relevant warehouse on demands such as sales orders and demand forecasts.[1] The example data shown in Figure 5.2 illustrates coverage planning at the site/warehouse level, but not mandatory entry of the relevant warehouse on demands.

The decision about coverage planning at the site/warehouse level versus the site level has many considerations, some of which are subtle. It directly impacts the number and significance of warehouses that need to be defined. An excellent article by Evert Bos provided an in-depth analysis of the decision about master planning by site versus site/warehouse.

The site information is always a mandatory entry. Enforcing mandatory entry of the relevant warehouse means that master planning logic can determine the site/warehouse from the initial demand. In contrast, when the warehouse is not set to mandatory, it may not be known from the initial demand. This can result in planned orders for a "blank" warehouse even when sufficient supplies exist within the warehouses.

Several policies within the storage dimension group are not directly related to master planning. These include the policies for financial tracking, purchase prices and sales prices.

Policies related to Basic versus Advanced Warehouse Management The policy "use warehouse management processes" indicates a WMS-enabled item, and automatically results in use of the Inventory Status. It also results in the use of License Plates at a WMS-enabled warehouse. These two dimensions – about Inventory Status and License Plates -- are not available for any option which does not include the "use warehouse management process" policy.

5.5 Companywide versus Site- and Warehouse-Level Information for an Item

The concept of companywide versus site/warehouse-level information applies to several aspects of item information. Figure 5.3 summarizes some of the major examples of companywide versus site/warehouse information. The figure does not include the enterprise-level information about an item, such as the basis for item

---

[1] The Wiki Help provides more detailed explanations for all four combinations of these two policies.

identification (item number) and the nature of the item (tangible material versus service item).

Figure 5.3 Companywide versus Site- and Warehouse-Level Information for an Item

Type of Item Information		Level of Information		
		Companywide	Site-Specific	Site/Warehouse-Specific
Basic	Item Identifier	Yes	N/A	
Basic	Inventory UM	Yes	N/A	
Costing	Costing Method (Standard vs Actual)			
Costing	Standard Cost for Item	N/A	Yes	
Costing	Actual Cost for Item	N/A	Yes	
Mfg	BOM for a Manufactured Item	Yes	Yes	N/A
Mfg	Routing for a Manufactured Item	N/A	Yes	N/A
Buy	Approved Vendor for Item	Yes	N/A	
Buy	Purchase Trade Agreements	Yes		
Planning Data	Preferred Vendor	Specify (Act as default)	N/A	Override the default
Planning Data	Primary Source of Supply	Specify (Act as default)	N/A	Override the default
Planning Data	Coverage Group (Set of Policies)	Specify (Act as default)	N/A	Override the default
Planning Data	Lead Time	Specify (Act as default)	Override the default	Override the default
Planning Data	Order Quantity Modifiers	Specify (Act as default)	Override the default	N/A

Page for Maintaining Planning Data: Released Product Details or Default Order Settings   Default Order Settings   Item Coverage

As shown in the top half of Figure 5.3, the examples of an item's companywide information include the item identifier, inventory unit of measure, costing method, and approved vendors. Other aspects can be site-specific (such as costs and BOM/routing information) or applicable to any level (such as purchase trade agreements).

The bottom half of the figure includes several aspects of an item's planning data. Many aspects can be specified as a companywide policy, and optionally overridden at the site- or warehouse-level. As a general guideline, you maintain the data at the highest possible level to minimize data maintenance. The next chapter provides more detailed explanations of the coverage planning data for purchased items, manufactured items, and transfers, and similarly segments the policies into companywide versus site/warehouse-level information.

5.6 Key Pages for Defining an Item's Planning Data

The bottom of Figure 5.3 highlights three key pages for maintaining an item's planning data – consisting of the Released Product Details, the Default Order Settings, and the Item Coverage pages. Information on the Default Order Settings page can represent companywide or site-specific planning data, where you identify the relevant site to provide overrides for site-specific policies. Information on the Item Coverage page can represent warehouse-specific policies when coverage planning applies to a warehouse, or it can represent site-specific policies when coverage planning only applies to a site.

The example screens shown in Figure 5.4 illustrate these three key pages for a purchased item's planning data, and how they can be used to define companywide policies as well as the overrides for site- and warehouse-specific policies. From the starting point of the Released Product Details page, the figure highlights how to access the Default Order Settings and Item Coverage pages. The example data illustrates the warehouse-specific overrides for a preferred vendor, purchase lead time, and coverage group.

Figure 5.4 Example Screens for Defining an Item's Planning Data

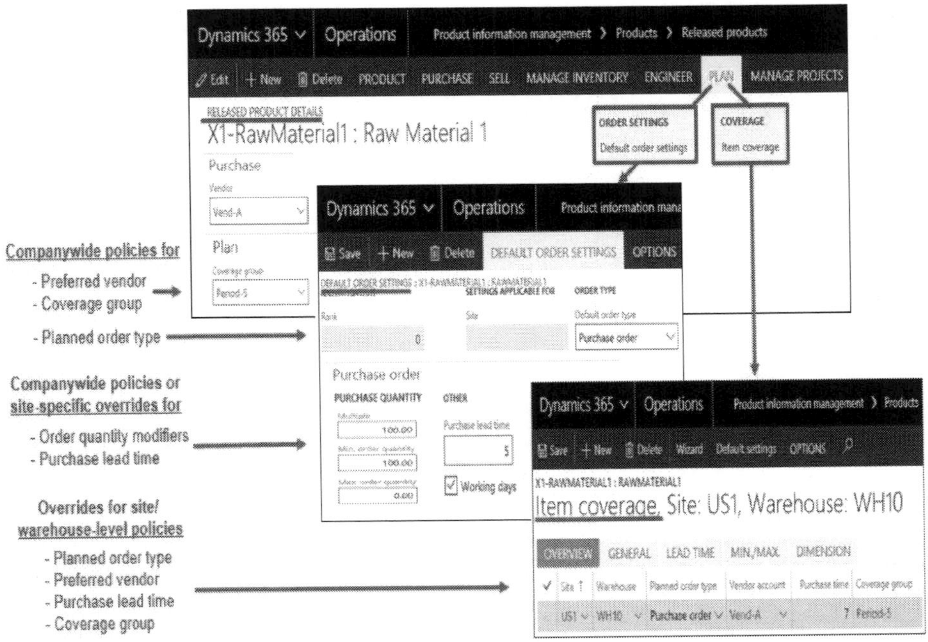

The next chapter provides further explanation about coverage planning data, including the key planning data for purchased items (Section 6.3) and the approaches for maintaining planning data (Section 6.10).

5.7 Executive Summary

The definition of inventory locations represents a key part of modeling any supply chain, and there are several fundamental options for modeling these locations within Dynamics 365 for Operations. These options include the use of sites and warehouses to model inventory locations within a legal entity, and the chapter highlighted several considerations about using sites and warehouses. In addition, it reviewed the significance of sites and warehouses for master planning logic, which determines the level of coverage planning and mandatory entry of a warehouse on demands. It also summarized the companywide versus site- and warehouse-level information for an item, and provided example screens for maintaining an item's planning data. Choices about these fundamental options have multiple impacts described throughout the book.

Chapter 6

Coverage Planning Data to Model SCM Decision Making

Planned orders communicate the need to replenish an item's inventory, and are generated by master planning calculations based on an item's coverage planning data and related S&OP game plans. The coverage planning data (or planning data for short) represents a model of decision making about coordinating the supply chain. The planning data differs for purchased items, manufactured items and transfers. Much of this planning data can be assigned as a companywide policy for an item, and optionally overridden as a site-specific or site/warehouse-specific policy. The key planning data includes the coverage group assigned to an item. Each user-defined coverage group consists of multiple policies such as the applicable coverage code and use of action messages. These messages work in conjunction with planned orders and actual orders to coordinate supply chain activities to meet the S&OP game plans.

This chapter focuses on coverage planning data. The chapter starts with the significance of coverage groups and the options for a coverage code, and then explains the key planning data for purchased items, manufactured items, and transfers. It addresses several topics within the coverage planning data, ranging from policies about action messages to time fences. These considerations are reflected in the following sections within the chapter.

1. Significance of Coverage Groups
2. Options for a Coverage Code
3. Planning Data for Purchased Items
4. Special Cases for Purchased Items
5. Planning Data for Manufactured Items
6. Significance of a Single Production Order
7. Special Cases for Manufactured Items

8. Planning Data for Transfers
9. Planning Data for the Master Scheduler Role
10. Maintain Coverage Planning Data for Items
11. Action Messages and Related Policies
12. Calculated Delay Messages and Related Policies
13. Negative Days and the Rescheduling Assumption
14. Positive Days and Assumptions about Current Inventory
15. Safety Margins
16. Time Fence Policies

6.1 Significance of Coverage Groups

A coverage group consists of multiple policies that provide a model of decision making about coordination of an item's supply chain activities. Each coverage group has a user-defined identifier and name, and a typical company will employ different coverage groups to model the differences in decision-making logic. For example, key aspects of decision-making logic involve the generation of planned supply orders to meet demands, and the use of action messages to coordinate supply orders.

As an explanatory approach, the various policies within a coverage group will be segmented into different topics and covered by different sections within the book. The various aspects of coverage group policies are summarized here along with references to more detailed explanations.

◆ Options for a coverage code (Section 6.2)

◆ Action messages and related policies (Section 6.11)

◆ Calculated delay messages and related policies (Section 6.12)

◆ Negative days (Section 6.13)

◆ Positive days (Section 6.14)

◆ Safety margins (Section 6.15)

◆ Time fence policies (Section 6.16)

◆ Demand forecasts for salable end-items (Sections 7.2 thru 7.4)

◆ Demand forecasts for stocked components (Section 7.8)

◆ Calendar for an item (Section 3.7)

◆ BOM versions and route versions for a manufactured item, where the versions represent non-interchangeable inventory (Sections 10.1 and 11.6)

As already noted, different coverage groups can model the differences in decision-making logic, and Case 6.1 provides an illustration.

6.2 Options for a Coverage Code

The coverage code represents a key part of the decision-making logic about generating planned supply orders for an item. It is embedded within the coverage group assigned to an item, but its importance merits a separate explanation. The term coverage code has several synonyms and different ERP systems employ different terms and provide different options. The options for a coverage code are summarized in Figure 6.1 and described below.

Figure 6.1 Options for a Coverage Code

Logic Basis	Coverage Code and its significance	Planning Data		
		Primary Planning Data	Order Qty Modifiers**	Safety Stock Approach
Period Lot Size	Period Suggested order quantity covers multiple demands within the period subject to order quantity modifiers	Period Size (in days)	Minimum Multiple Maximum	Minimum Quantity*
Order Driven	Requirement Suggested order quantity covers one demand subject to order quantity modifiers		Minimum Multiple Maximum	Minimum Quantity*
Order Point	Min-Max Suggested order quantity achieves maximum inventory quantity subject to order quantity multiple	Minimum Quantity* Maximum Quantity	Multiple	N/A
Manual Planning	Manual No suggested orders	N/A	N/A	N/A

*   = The minimum quantity represents a site/warehouse-specific safety stock quantity, and differs from the order quantity modifiers for a minimum.

** = Three different sets of order quantity modifiers can be defined for an item: for sales orders, purchase orders and for production/batch orders. Planned transfer orders use the order quantity modifiers related to production/batch orders.

As shown in Figure 6.1, the four options for a coverage code include period (aka period lot-sizing logic), requirement, min-max and manual. The most commonly used options include period and requirement. Each option can be characterized by its primary planning data, order quantity modifiers, and a safety stock approach. The left-hand columns characterize each option in terms of its underlying logic, such as order point or period lot-sizing logic.

Period (also known as Period Lot Size) When an item's projected inventory reaches zero (or its minimum quantity), master planning calculations will suggest a planned order with a quantity that covers demands over the period size, subject to order quantity modifiers. The period size reflects the frequency of replenishment (such as daily, weekly or monthly) and different coverage codes must be defined for each period size. Examples of the user-defined values for a coverage code include *Period-1Day*, *Period-7Days* and *Period-30Days*, where the associated period size reflects the frequency of daily, weekly and monthly replenishment.

The item's minimum quantity for a given site/warehouse represents an explicit inventory plan or safety stock. An implied inventory plan reflects the extent to which the order quantity modifiers (for minimum and multiple) inflate the suggested order quantity so that it exceeds the requirements.

Requirement (also known as Order-Driven or Lot-for-Lot) When an item's projected inventory reaches zero (or its minimum quantity), master planning calculations will suggest a planned order and quantity that covers each individual demand, subject to order quantity modifiers. As noted above, the minimum quantity and the order quantity modifiers represent explicit and implied inventory plans respectively.

Min-Max When an item's projected inventory falls below its minimum quantity, master planning calculations will suggest a planned order with a quantity that achieves the item's maximum quantity, subject to an order quantity modifier for a multiple. The projected inventory reflects future demands and scheduled receipts for the item. The values for minimum and maximum quantity are typically specified using a fixed approach, but a variable approach can be used. The fixed approach consists of a single value for each quantity, whereas the variable approach employs a pattern for each quantity such as different quantities for each month to reflect seasonality or trends. Each pattern is termed a minimum/maximum key.

Manual Master planning calculations will not suggest planned orders, but it does calculate requirements to support manual planning efforts.

Assignment of the Coverage Code to an Item The coverage code is embedded within the coverage group assigned to an item. You assign the coverage group as part of the item master information, but it can be overridden as part of the site/warehouse information for an item. Alternatively, you can just override the coverage code (rather than the coverage group) as part of the site/warehouse information for an item.

Order Quantity Modifiers Three different sets of order quantity modifiers can be defined for an item -- for sales orders, purchase orders and production/batch orders. Planned transfer orders use the order quantity modifiers related to production/batch orders. These order quantity modifiers involve several considerations for planned supply orders.

◆ *Minimum.* The minimum represents the smallest suggested order quantity.

◆ *Multiple.* The suggested order quantity will always reflect the multiple, even if it exceeds the maximum.

◆ *Maximum.* The maximum represents the largest order quantity, so that master planning calculations will generate multiple planned orders to cover requirements exceeding the maximum.

Some situations require a fixed order quantity, perhaps reflecting considerations about batch tracking, transportation, production or some other factor. In these situations, use the same values for minimum, maximum and multiple so that master planning calculations will generate multiple planned orders for the fixed quantity.

6.3 Planning Data for Purchased Items

Master planning calculations will generate planned purchase orders based on an item's planning data. Figure 6.2 summarizes the planning data for purchased items, and highlights the companywide versus site-specific and site/warehouse policies. The information reflects the book's baseline model, where coverage planning applies to the combination of site and warehouse. The bottom of the figure also highlights the three key pages for maintaining an item's planning data, and the previous chapter illustrated their use (Section 5.6). Further explanation covers each aspect of planning data within the figure.

Primary Source of Supply A planned order type of Purchase Order indicates the primary source of supply for an item, so that master planning calculations will generate planned purchase orders. An item's planned order type (aka default order type) can be specified as a companywide policy, and optionally overridden for a given site/warehouse. For example, a purchased item may be replenished via purchase orders at one warehouse, but replenished via transfer orders at a different warehouse.

Preferred Vendor An item's preferred vendor can be specified as a companywide policy, and optionally overridden for a given site/warehouse. It must reflect one of the item's approved vendors when enforcing the policy for approved vendors. Master planning calculations assign the preferred vendor to planned purchase orders for the item.

The approach to defining an item's preferred vendor differs slightly for buy-to-order components, or when sourcing to the vendor with the lowest price or delivery lead time. The next section provides further explanation of these special cases for purchased items.

Figure 6.2 Key Planning Data for Purchased Items

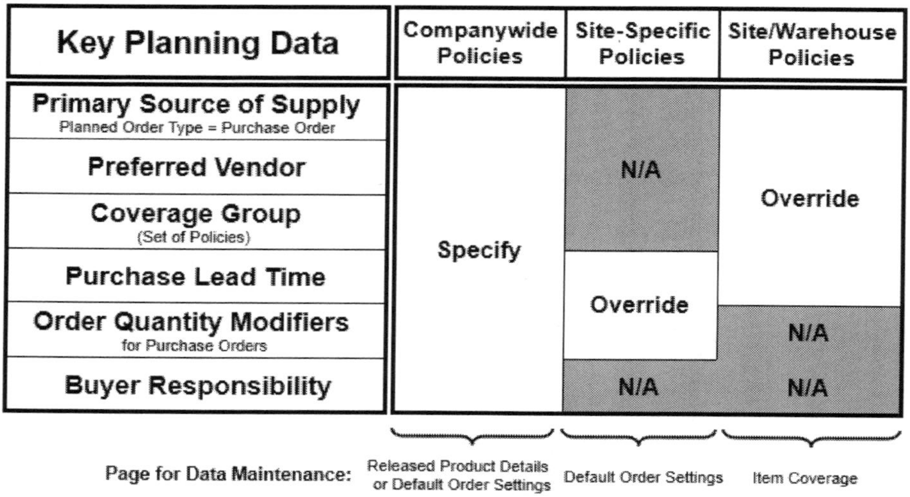

Key Planning Data	Companywide Policies	Site-Specific Policies	Site/Warehouse Policies
Primary Source of Supply Planned Order Type = Purchase Order	Specify	N/A	Override
Preferred Vendor	Specify	N/A	Override
Coverage Group (Set of Policies)	Specify	N/A	Override
Purchase Lead Time	Specify	Override	Override
Order Quantity Modifiers for Purchase Orders	Specify	Override	N/A
Buyer Responsibility	Specify	N/A	N/A

Page for Data Maintenance: Released Product Details or Default Order Settings | Default Order Settings | Item Coverage

Coverage Group The coverage group consists of multiple policies that provide a model of the decision-making logic about coordination of an item's supply chain activities, as described in the previous section. The companywide policy for an item's coverage group can be overridden for a given site/warehouse. As an alternative approach for overriding the coverage group, you can override selected policies such as the coverage code and period lot size.

Purchase Lead Time An item's purchase lead time can be specified as a companywide policy, and optionally overridden as a site-specific or site/warehouse-specific policy. It can be expressed as working days or calendar days. This lead time typically represents the average number of days to receive material after placing a purchase order. Master planning logic uses this lead time to suggest an order date for planned purchase orders. It is also used when manually creating a purchase order to initially calculate the delivery date for the item.

An item's purchase lead time can be optionally specified in purchase trade agreements. However, this information only applies to several special cases described in the next section.

Order Quantity Modifiers for Purchasing   The order quantity modifiers consist of a minimum, maximum and multiple. They are expressed in the item's default purchase UM (if specified) otherwise they reflect the item's inventory UM. The order quantity modifiers impact planned purchase order quantities. They are also considered when manually creating or maintaining a purchase order for the item, where a soft warning will be displayed when you enter a quantity that does not meet these criteria. The item's standard purchase order quantity also reflects considerations about these order quantity modifiers, and it acts as a default value when manually entering a purchase order line for the item.

Buyer Responsibility   The concept of buyer responsibility provides an organizing focus for communicating the need to synchronize supplies with demands. The concept of buyer responsibility is typically based on the buyer group field; an alternative basis could be the item group field. A user-defined buyer group can be assigned to an item to indicate responsibility for maintaining planning data, whereas the buyer group assigned to a vendor indicates responsibility for coordinating purchases. Master planning calculations generate planned orders identified with the buyer group associated with the vendor. A purchase order header contains a buyer group that applies to all purchase order line items.

6.4 Special Cases for Purchased Items

The previous section focused on the key planning data for purchased items, and several special cases involve additional considerations. These special cases include buy-to-order components, purchase lead times within purchase price trade agreements, the suggested vendor for planned purchase orders based on lowest price or delivery lead time, purchased items requiring internal production, and the use of default ship-to locations.

Buy-to-Order Component for Material   A purchased item can be designated as a but-to-order component in the BOM information of its parent item, where you specify a BOM line type of Vendor. The preferred vendor for a buy-to-order component can be optionally overridden as part of the component information otherwise it reflects the companywide or site-specific preferred vendor for the item.

Master planning calculations will calculate requirements for a buy-to-order component, and even generate planned orders based on the item's planning data.[1]

---

[1] You typically assign a coverage code of Requirement or Period to a purchased item that has buy-to-order requirements.

The logic ignores on-hand inventory for meeting the buy-to-order requirements. However, the planned orders simply provide visibility about these requirements, and they cannot be firmed for creating a purchase order. Instead, the system will automatically create a linked purchase order for a buy-to-order component when you update the status of the parent item's production order, such as updating the status to Estimated or Scheduled. The quantity for the linked purchase order reflects the production order quantity and the BOM information about the component quantity. Deleting the parent item's production order will delete the linked purchased order. Case 6.4 illustrates a buy-to-order component.

Buy-to-Order Component for a Subcontracted Service The approach to subcontracted production employs a buy-to-order component to represent the subcontracted service. The above explanation also applies to these buy-to-order components.

Purchase Lead Times within Purchase Price Trade Agreements An item's purchase lead time can be optionally specified within the entry for a purchase price trade agreement, such as specifying a longer lead time for a lower purchase price. However, you must explicitly designate usage of this lead time information as part of the entry. When explicitly designated for use, the lead time will be inherited by a manually entered purchase order line that meets the criteria for the trade agreement entry. It will also be inherited by the planned purchase order.

Suggested Vendor based on Lowest Price or Delivery Lead Time Some scenarios will source a purchased item based on price or delivery considerations rather than a preferred vendor. In this case, the preferred vendor field should be left blank to support automatic vendor assignment on planned purchase orders based on trade agreement information for lowest price or delivery lead time.[1] The previous point explained the additional consideration for using the purchase lead time associated with trade agreement entries. Case 6.3 illustrates suggested vendors based on lowest price.

Purchased Items Requiring Internal Production Some scenarios involve internal production or rework of a purchased item. Internal production may reflect an intermittent basis or a planned change. In this case, the item must be designated with a production type of BOM. The item should also have bill of material information to support the use of production orders. When you primarily purchase the item, you assign a planned order type of Purchase Order. You may also need

---

[1] A companywide policy (defined in the Master Planning Parameters) determines whether master planning logic can use the purchase price trade agreement information to suggest a vendor for purchased items (when a preferred vendor has not been specified). A related policy specifies whether price or delivery lead time serves as the basis for suggesting a vendor.

to assign a standard cost reflecting the item's purchase price rather than calculating the item's manufacturing cost. The cost calculations for higher level items should also employ the item's purchase cost, which requires a *stop explosion* policy in the calculation group assigned to the item.

Default Ship-To Location You can optionally specify a default ship-to location for a purchased item (consisting of a specified site or a specified site/warehouse), and even mandate use of the ship-to location. This approach typically reflects a scenario where the purchased item is only used at the specified location. Alternatively, the default ship-to location can be assigned to a vendor.

6.5 Planning Data for Manufactured Items

Master planning calculations will generate planned production orders based on the planning data for a manufactured item. Figure 6.3 summarizes the key planning data for a manufactured item, and highlights the companywide versus site-specific and site/warehouse-specific policies. The information reflects the book's baseline model, where coverage planning applies to the combination of site and warehouse. The bottom of the figure also highlights the three key pages for maintaining an item's planning data, and the previous chapter provided screen examples illustrating their use (Section 5.6). Further explanation covers each aspect of planning data within the figure.

Figure 6.3 Key Planning Data for Manufactured Items

Key Planning Data	Companywide Policies	Site-Specific Policies	Site/Warehouse Policies
BOM Version	Specify BOM as Companywide	Specify BOM as Site-Specific	N/A
Route Version	N/A	Specify Route as Site-Specific	N/A
Primary Source of Supply Planned Order Type = Production	Specify	N/A	Override
Coverage Group (Set of Policies)	Specify	N/A	Override
Production Lead Time	Specify	Override	Override
Order Quantity Modifiers for Production Orders	Specify	Override	N/A
Planner Responsibility	Specify	N/A	N/A
Page for Data Maintenance:	Released Product Details or Default Order Settings	Default Order Settings	Item Coverage

BOM Version The BOM versions for a manufactured item can be site-specific or companywide. Master planning calculations will use an item's site-specific BOM version (if it exists) based on the site of the item's requirements. If a site-specific BOM version does not exist, master planning calculations will use the companywide BOM version (if it exists).

Route Version Master planning calculations will use an item's site-specific route version (if it exists) based on the site of the item's requirements. The routing data will be used to calculate the lead time for planned and actual production orders, but only within the capacity time fence employed by master planning calculations.

Primary Source of Supply A planned order type of Production indicates the primary source of supply for a manufactured item, so that master planning calculations will generate planned production orders. An item's planned order type (aka default order type) can be specified as a companywide policy, and optionally overridden for a given site/warehouse. For example, a manufactured item may be replenished via production orders at one warehouse, but replenished via transfer orders at a different warehouse.

Coverage Group The coverage group consists of multiple policies that provide a model of the decision-making logic about coordination of an item's supply chain activities, as described in a previous section (Section 6.1). The companywide policy for an item's coverage group can be overridden for a given site/warehouse. As an alternative approach for overriding the coverage group, you can override selected policies such as the coverage code and period lot size.

Production Lead Time An item's fixed production lead time (expressed in days) can be specified as a companywide value, and optionally overridden as a site-specific or site/warehouse policy. It is typically expressed as working days but it can reflect calendar days. Master planning calculations will use this fixed lead time when routing data does not exist, or when ignoring the routing data beyond the capacity time fence. In addition, the fixed lead time can be used to determine the due date of safety stock requirements, and to calculate safety stock requirements based on historical usage (Section 7.7).

Alternatively, routing data can be used to calculate a variable elapsed time for each production order, where several other factors also impact the calculated time (such as order quantity and capacity availability). The calculated time only applies to production orders within the capacity time fence employed by master planning calculations. In a typical scenario, master planning calculations will calculate the variable elapsed time in the near-term horizon defined by the capacity fence, and use the fixed lead time beyond this time horizon.

Order Quantity Modifiers for Production   The order quantity modifiers consist of a minimum, maximum and multiple. They are expressed in the item's inventory UM. The order quantity modifiers impact planned production order quantities. They are also considered when manually creating or maintaining a production order for the item, where a soft warning will be displayed when you enter a quantity that does not meet these criteria. The item's standard production order quantity also reflects considerations about these order quantity modifiers, and it acts as a default value when manually creating a production order for the item.

Planner Responsibility   The concept of planner responsibility provides an organizing focus for communicating the need to synchronize supplies with demands. The concept of planner responsibility is often based on the production pool or buyer group assigned to a manufactured item. For example, master planning calculations generate planned production orders identified with the buyer group, so that a planner can selectively view and mark planned orders for which they have responsibility. In addition, production orders inherit the item's production pool thereby enabling the planner to selectively view orders for which they have responsibility. Changes to the order status of production orders can be based on the production pool, and a planner can selectively view action messages by production pool.

6.6 Significance of a Single Production Order

The significance of a single production order can vary in different scenarios. For example, the order quantity may represent a single production run (aka physical batch) in some scenarios, multiple production runs in other scenarios, or a production run for a given time period such as shift, day or week   This impacts the use of order quantity modifiers and quantity-sensitive route versions (and BOM versions) for a manufactured item, so that planned production orders correctly reflect the planner's decision making. It can impact the period lot size for the item's coverage code, which may also reflect the frequency of production. It also impacts the fixed lead time assigned to a manufactured item, since this represents the average lead time for an average order quantity under normal conditions.

A single production order may also reflect requirements stemming from a single sales order line, which argues for a coverage code of Requirement to correctly generate planned orders for the manufactured item. In addition, a single sales order can be linked to a sales order line, either by firming a planned order with marking or by creating it from the sales order line. In some scenarios, the applicable BOM version and Route version are assigned to the sales order line, which will override use of the active versions for the item's production order.

Several related issues apply to the significance of a single production order.

♦ *Reservation logic.* The reservation policy for a production order determines when components will be reserved relative to order status.

♦ *Prevent rescheduling.* You can lock a production order to prevent rescheduling.

♦ *Prevent changes to order status.* You can assign a stop flag to a production order, thereby preventing changes to order status prior to reporting the order as started.

♦ *Impacts on reporting and the production picking list journal(s).* The significance of a single production order can impact the reporting of a started quantity (and/or started operations) or the finished quantity, and the related creation and posting of a picking list journal. In a simple scenario, for example, the picking list journal will be created for the entire order quantity and all components after reporting the order as started. When using advanced warehousing, the creation of raw material picking work upon order release will reflect the entire order quantity and all components.

6.7 Special Cases for Manufactured Items

A previous section focused on the planning data for manufactured items, and several special cases require additional considerations. These special cases include phantoms, make-to-order components, configure-to-order manufactured products, subcontracted production, and assigning a specific BOM version and/or route version to a manufactured component.

Phantoms A manufactured item can be designated as a phantom component in the BOM information of its parent item, where you specify a BOM line type of *Phantom.* Master planning calculations will calculate requirements for the phantom and ignore its on-hand inventory. The logic will also generate a planned order for the phantom, but the planned order cannot be firmed.

Make-to-Order Components A manufactured item can be designated as a make-to-order component in the BOM information of its parent item, where you specify a BOM line type of *Pegged Supply.* Master planning calculations will calculate requirements for a make-to-order component, and even generate planned orders based on the item's planning data.[2] The logic will ignore on-hand inventory for meeting the make-to-order requirements. However, the planned orders simply provide visibility about these requirements, and these planned orders cannot be

---

[2] You typically assign a coverage code of Requirement or Period to a manufactured item that has make-to-order requirements.

firmed (for creating a production order). Instead, the system automatically creates a linked production order for a make-to-order component when you update the status of the parent item's production order to an *Estimated* status or higher. The quantity for the linked production order reflects the parent item's production order quantity and the BOM information about the component quantity. Deleting the parent item's production order will delete the linked production order.

Configure-to-Order Manufactured Products   Different types of configuration technologies can support configure-to-order manufactured products. One type consists of the constraint-based configuration technology with the standard software. Other sections have described this approach in terms of defining a configurable item (Section 9.7), the BOM considerations (Section 10.2), the route considerations (Section 11.6), and sales orders for the configurable item (Section 8.9).

Subcontracted Production   The planning data for a subcontracted item are the same as an internally manufactured item. There are differences in the item's route version (containing one or more outside operations), and the resulting calculation of lead time for a production order. The manual entry for the item's production lead time should reflect the normal turnaround time at the subcontractor as well as the relevant variation of coordinating supplied material and the finished quantities.

Assign a BOM Version or Route Version to a Manufactured Component   The assignment of a BOM version to a manufactured component (termed a sub-BOM) will override the normal use of the active BOM version for the item. You can also assign a route version to a manufactured component (termed a sub-route), which will override the normal use of the active route version for the item. The use of sub-BOMs and sub-routes for manufactured components generally applies to custom product manufacturing scenarios.

BOM Versions (and/or Route Versions) represent Non-interchangeable Inventory of a Manufactured Item   In some scenarios, the production of different BOM versions represents non-interchangeable inventory of a manufactured item. This is sometimes termed significant revision levels. As noted in the previous point, you may specify an approved-but-not active BOM version in the sub-BOM field for a sales order line, or as part of the BOM line information for a manufactured component. To satisfy demand, master planning calculations will ignore available inventory and generate planned production orders for the specified BOM version. This approach requires an item-specific policy (embedded in the Coverage Group assigned to the item) labeled "Use the specified BOM version". The production of different route versions can also represent non-interchangeable inventory of a manufactured item, as defined by a similar policy labeled "Use the specified route version."

6.8 Planning Data for Transfers

Master planning calculations will generate planned transfer orders based on an item's planning data. Figure 6.4 summarizes the key planning data for transfers of an item, and highlights the companywide versus site-specific and site/warehouse policies. The information reflects the book's baseline model, where coverage planning applies to the combination of site and warehouse. The bottom of the figure also highlights the three key pages for maintaining an item's planning data, and the previous chapter illustrated their use (Section 5.6). Further explanation covers each aspect of planning data within the figure.

Figure 6.4 Key Planning Data for Transfers

Key Planning Data	Companywide Policies	Site-Specific Policies	Site/Warehouse Policies
Primary Source of Supply Planned Order Type = Transfer	N/A	N/A	Specify
Refilling Warehouse			Specify
Coverage Group (Set of Policies)	Specify		Override
Transfer Lead Time	Specify transport time between warehouse pairs		Override
Order Quantity Modifiers for Transfer Orders	Specify	Override	N/A
Planner Responsibility	Specify	N/A	N/A

Page for Data Maintenance: Released Product Details or Default Order Settings   Default Order Settings   Item Coverage

Primary Source of Supply   Replenishment based on transfers must be designated in the item's site/warehouse-specific coverage data, where you indicate a planned order type of *transfer* so that master planning calculations will generate planned transfer orders. A related field defines the preferred refilling warehouse.

Refilling Warehouse   The preferred refilling warehouse can be defined for transferring individual items to a warehouse (as part of each item's site/warehouse-specific coverage planning policies). Alternatively, it can be defined for an entire warehouse, which indicates that all warehouse inventory will be replenished from one refilling warehouse unless specifically overridden for an individual item.

Coverage Group The coverage group consists of multiple policies that provide a model of the decision-making logic about coordination of an item's supply chain activities, as described in the previous section. The companywide policy for an item's coverage group can be overridden for a given site/warehouse. As an alternative approach for overriding the coverage group, you can override selected policies such as the coverage code and period lot size.

Transfer Lead Time The transfer lead time (aka transportation time or transport days) is expressed in calendar days. It can reflect a warehouse viewpoint or an item viewpoint. With a warehouse viewpoint, you specify the transport days between a pair of warehouses on the Transport page. It reflects a companywide policy for all transfers between the warehouse pair. The item viewpoint supports an item-specific transfer time for handling unusual situations, and is defined as part of the item's site/warehouse-specific coverage planning policies. Most scenarios simply use the warehouse viewpoint.

Order Quantity Modifiers for Transfer Orders The order quantity modifiers consist of a minimum, maximum and multiple. They are expressed in the item's inventory UM. The order quantity modifiers impact planned transfer order quantities. They are also considered when manually creating or maintaining a transfer order line for the item, where a soft warning will be displayed when you enter a quantity that does not meet these criteria. The item's standard order quantity also reflects considerations about these order quantity modifiers, and it acts as a default value when manually entering a transfer order line for the item.

Planner Responsibility The concept of planner responsibility for transfer orders is often based on the ship-from or ship-to warehouse, or the buyer group assigned to the item. For example, master planning calculations generate planned transfer orders identified with the buyer group and the ship-from/ship-to warehouses, so that a planner can selectively view planned orders for which they have responsibility.

Special Cases for Transfers Some scenarios have adjacent warehouses where planned transfer orders between the warehouses are used to communicate requirements, but without the need for tracking in-transit inventory. Actual transfers between warehouses can be handled through a transfer journal rather than a transfer order. In this case, planned transfers can be used to communicate requirements, but firming the planned orders generates a transfer journal which can be subsequently posted after physically moving the material. This approach requires a site-specific policy termed "Use transfer journals for movements within site" otherwise firming a planned order results in a transfer order.

6.9 Planning Data for the Master Scheduler Role

A master scheduler role is typically responsible for entering and maintaining the S&OP game plans in manufacturing companies. In most cases, the master scheduler is also responsible for maintaining the planning data for relevant end-items and even stocked components within the S&OP game plans. An additional aspect of planning data involves forecast consumption logic, as defined by several policies within the Coverage Group assigned to these items. Another aspect involves the delivery date control policy assigned to salable items, such as ATP or CTP logic. Subsequent chapters provide further explanation of forecast consumption logic (Section 7.3) and the delivery date control policy (Section 8.4).

6.10 Maintain Coverage Planning Data for Items

The coverage planning data for an item is spread across multiple pages, including the pages for Released Product Details, Default Order Settings and Item Coverage. Planning data on the Released Product Details page represents companywide policies, and it can be populated via a template. Planning data on the Default Order Settings page can be companywide or site-specific, and planning data on the Item Coverage page can be site- or warehouse-specific. As a general guideline, you maintain the coverage planning data at the highest possible level unless warranted; this approach reduces the level of data maintenance.

Information on the Item Coverage page can be maintained directly, or you can use a mass maintenance approach using the Item Coverage Setup page. Use of the Item Coverage Setup page provides several advantages.

◆ View items without any item coverage records, thereby making initial data maintenance easier.

◆ View a subset of items by filtering on the item group or buyer group, or the currently assigned coverage group or storage dimension group.

◆ Use the default settings (of a selected record of one item's coverage data) as the copy basis for initially creating a new record for selected items without data.

◆ Delete the item coverage data records for selected items, so that you have a fresh start at maintaining the data.

6.11 Action Messages and Related Policies

Action messages represent one of the key tools for coordinating supply chain activities to meet the S&OP game plans. However, many companies struggle with effective use of action messages because the volume can easily overwhelm the planner so that the messages become meaningless. This section summarizes the action messages and provides some guidelines for effective usage.

Several action message policies are embedded within the coverage group assigned to an item, and master planning calculations can generate action messages for planned and actual supply orders. The various types of action messages and related policies are summarized in Figure 6.5. The figure includes information for messages about calculated delays, and these will be covered in the next section.

Figure 6.5 Significance of Action Messages

Type of Message		Significance of Message	Message Filters		
			Suppress	Tolerance	Horizon
Action Messages	Advance	Expedite the order to an earlier date	Yes/No	Advance Tolerance (in days)	Look-Ahead Horizon (in days)
	Postpone	De-expedite the order to a later date	Yes/No	Postpone Tolerance (in days)	
	Increase	Increase order to a suggested quantity	Yes/No		
	Decrease (or Cancel)	Decrease order to a suggested quantity	Yes/No*	N/A	
		Cancel order			
	Derived Actions Policy	Transfer the action message related to a production order to its component items	Yes/No		
	Delay	Projected completion date does not meet requirement date	Yes/No	N/A	Look-Ahead Horizon (in days)

* = Suppressing the decrease message will also suppress the cancel message.

Summary of Action Messages An action message indicates a suggestion to advance/postpone an order's delivery date, to increase/decrease an order quantity, or to cancel a supply order. Message filters can eliminate unnecessary action messages, such as a look-ahead horizon to limit the number of messages and tolerances for the advance and postpone messages. The look-ahead horizon can be specified within a coverage group, or as one of the policies for a set of master plan data. If used, the master plan policies will override the item-specific policies.

In many cases, the "advance" action message reflects the rescheduling assumption about an item, where it is generally easier to reschedule an existing supply order than create a new one. That is, master planning calculations will generate an advance message for an existing order rather than generating a new planned order to cover a requirement that occurs within a relevant time horizon (such as the item's lead time). A subsequent section provides further explanation of the rescheduling assumption and the definition of the relevant time horizon (Section 6.13).

The action message policy about "derived actions" means that an action message related to a planned or actual production order should be transferred to its component items. It represents a prerequisite for analyzing the multi-level format about action messages using the Action Graph capabilities described in the next point.

Analyzing Action Messages Action messages can be viewed from several different pages for a specified set of master plan data. For example, you can view the action messages for a single item on the Net Requirements page or for all items on the Actions page. The Actions page enables you to apply the suggested action for a selected message, where the applied action depends on the message and the type of supply order, and whether it represents a planned or actual supply order. An associated Apply Action dialogue enables you to specify an additional-but-related impact. When applying an advance message related to production, for example, you can also reschedule the actual production order or indicate the planned production order should be approved. When applying a cancel message for a purchase order line (which will delete the line), you can choose to delete the entire purchase order if it was the last line on the order.

From the Actions page, you can also access the Action Graph page to view a graphic analysis of related action messages for a selected message. The related action messages are displayed in a multi-level format when the selected item reflects any part of a supply chain involving production orders and/or transfer orders. The multi-level format involving production orders requires the "derived actions" policy described in the previous point. In this way, you can analyze the action message for the top-level item that impacts lower level items, such as the need to advance the production order for the top-level item. You can also apply a suggested action as described above.

Guidelines for Effective Use of Action Messages Many companies struggle with effective use of action messages, often because of the sheer volume of messages and the resulting difficulties in taking action. To really be effective, you should consider ways to reduce the number of messages so that you achieve a target "hit rate" of more than 90% for taking action on the messages.

As a starting point, you can reduce the number of messages by reducing the look-ahead window for each type of message, and/or by adjusting the message filters for advance/postpone messages. One guideline involves minimizing the degree to which you create actual supply orders for future periods (in advance of the order date), since this results in additional messages when demands change. In contrast, the use of planned orders will automatically adjust to demand changes. A high volume of messages often stems from poor S&OP game plans and unrealistic promise dates on sales orders, and a previous chapter provides guidelines for effective S&OP game plans (Section 2.5).

An additional approach to improve effective use of action messages only applies to planned purchase orders and the postpone message. The suggested date for these postpone messages can optionally act as the requirement date. This helps eliminate unnecessary messages and delays receipt until needed. It requires the master plan policy about action messages for "update postponed date as the requirement date".

6.12 Calculated Delay Messages and Related Policies

Messages about a calculated delay represent one of the tools for coordinating supply chain activities to meet the S&OP game plans. The messages indicate that the projected completion date for a supply order will cause a delay in meeting a requirement. This is especially relevant for a sales order requirement, but it also applies to a requirement stemming from a demand forecast and/or safety stock. A related supply order typically has an associated "advance" action message. However, the messages about calculated delays also represent one of the more complex aspects of master planning calculations, and they are suppressed in many scenarios. This section summarizes the messages about calculated delays and provides some guidelines for effective usage.

Summary of Messages about Calculated Delays The policy about using calculated delay messages is typically embedded within the coverage group assigned to an item, and master planning calculations can generate messages for planned and actual supply orders. As previously summarized in Figure 6.2, you can specify a look-ahead window to limit the number of messages or simply suppress them. The look-ahead horizon can also be specified as one of the policies for a set of master plan data, which acts as an override to the value within a coverage group.

The messages can be communicated across a multi-level product structure, thereby indicating the impact of delays for key components on the projected completion for end-items. This requires assignment of the message policy to the end-item and to each key component in the end-item's product structure. The relevant items typically have long lead time or delivery issues, and they comprise the critical paths to produce the end-item.

Designating Finite Material based on use of the Calculated Delay Message The use of calculated delay messages represents one way to designate an item as finite material. This makes it easier to say "perform master planning with finite material". The master planning calculations will generate messages about calculated delays for items designated as finite material.

Analyzing Messages The messages about calculated delays can be viewed from several different pages for a specified set of master plan data. For example, you can view the messages for a single item on the Net Requirements page.

Guidelines for Effective Use of Calculated Delay Messages Many companies struggle with effective use of messages about calculated delays, often because of the sheer volume of messages. As a starting point, you can reduce the number of messages by reducing the look-ahead window. You can also reduce the number of messages by only assigning the message policy to the key components within the product structure of end-items. The messages can be completely suppressed by performing. A high volume of messages often stems from poor S&OP game plans and unrealistic promise dates on sales orders, and a previous chapter provided guidelines for effective S&OP game plans (Section 2.5).

Another common problem concerns the degree to which you have accurately modeled your supply chain and SCM decision making. If the model is inaccurate or incomplete, then it is difficult to trust the messages about calculated delays.

Using Calculated Delays Information to update Requirement Dates for Planned Orders When the calculated delays for planned orders represent an accurate model of the supply chain, and the delays cannot be reduced, the master planning task can optionally update the requirement dates with the calculated delay information. Separate master plan policies indicate whether the updates should apply to planned production orders, planned purchase orders and/or planned transfers. These policies are rarely used.

6.13 Negative Days and the Rescheduling Assumption

One of the more confusing aspects of planning data involves the significance of negative days and the related policy of dynamic negative days. These policies directly impact the generation of planned orders for an item, and the action messages to advance existing supply orders. A key part of the logic for these "advance" messages is commonly termed the rescheduling assumption.

The rescheduling assumption represents a key aspect of planning calculations in every ERP system. In summary, it is typically easier to expedite an item's existing supply order (to meet demand within the item's lead time) rather than generating a new order. Stated another way, the master planning calculations should generate an action message to expedite or "advance" an item's existing supply order to meet demand within the item's lead time, or generate a new planned order if that is not possible. There are two basic options for this rescheduling assumption. The first option reflects dominant business practices and the second option represents a special case.

Option #1: Rescheduling Assumption based on Item Lead Time. Most firms employ a companywide policy to indicate rescheduling assumptions should be based on each item's lead time. You define this policy -- labeled Use Dynamic Negative Days – on the Master Planning Parameters page. However, many scenarios will create supply orders for delivery in future periods (beyond the item's lead time), so that the rescheduling assumption should be based on a longer time horizon and apply to all existing orders. With a longer horizon, you can avoid the confusion associated with action messages to "cancel" existing orders, while getting new planned orders at the same time. You specify the longer time horizon with a large value (such as 365 days) for the Negative Days field embedded within every coverage group, and this value will be automatically added to the item's lead time.

Several considerations apply to the rescheduling assumption. First, the rescheduling assumption only applies when the item's replenishment reflects a coverage code of Period or Requirement; it does not apply to the coverage codes for Min/Max or Manual. Second, the "advance" action message communicates the need to expedite an existing supply order. The message can be generated for planned and actual supply orders. Third, the combined action message of "Advance and Increase" can also be generated, although my personal preference is to suppress the increase message.

Special Case: Limited Ability to Reschedule Existing Supply Orders.
Some scenarios require a different basis for the rescheduling assumption (rather
than the item's lead time), such as a purchased item or transfer item with delivery
via ocean vessel. In these scenarios, it is impossible to expedite an item's existing
supply orders within lead time, so that a new planned order should always be
generated. Rather than using the policy for dynamic negative days, you typically
specify a zero value for negative days but still specify the item's lead time.

6.14 Positive Days and the Assumptions about Current Inventory

With normal netting logic, an item's requirements can be met with current
inventory even when the requirement date is in the distant future. Most scenarios
will employ this logic, which means that a large value should be used for positive
days -- such as 365 days.

Some scenarios prefer to use current inventory only for near-term sales orders, so
that sales orders for future shipment dates should be fulfilled by the generation of
planned supply orders. This represents an exception to normal netting logic. A
classic example involves perishable inventory such as fresh fruits or fish, where
current inventory should only be sold for today's sales orders, and sales orders for
future shipment dates should be fulfilled by planned supply orders. A time horizon
of 1 day (for positive days) might apply in this example. An appropriate time
horizon depends on several factors, such as an item's inventory plan, frequency of
replenishment, and rate of sales.

6.15 Safety Margins

A safety margin may be employed when you require significant time (such as one
or more days) for processing receipts or shipments, or creating supply orders.
These correspond to the three possible values for a safety margin labeled receipt,
issue and reorder. The value(s) for a safety margin can be defined within the
coverage group assigned to an item. Different coverage groups may be needed to
reflect differences in the use of a safety margin, as illustrated by these examples.

◆ *Receipt Safety Margin for a Purchased Item.* A receipt safety margin often
applies to purchased material with significant time requirements for receiving
inspection or simply processing the incoming material, so that master planning
calculations will schedule a delivery prior to the required date.

◆ *Reorder Safety Margin for a Purchased Item.* A reorder safety margin indicates the number of days to arrange a purchase order, so that master planning calculations will suggest planned orders with an earlier order date that also reflects the item's lead time and the required date.

◆ *Issue and Receipt Margins related to Transfer Orders.* The issue safety margin reflects the preparation time for picking/shipping a transfer order at the ship-from location, so that the master planning calculations will generate planned supply orders to arrive prior to the ship date. Master planning logic also uses the receipt safety margin to schedule delivery prior to the required date at the ship-to location.

◆ *Issue Safety Margin for a Salable Item.* An issue safety margin reflects the preparation time for picking/shipping a salable item, so that the master planning calculations will generate planned supply orders to arrive prior to the ship date.

Safety margins may also apply to a manufactured item, such as significant time requirements for issuing components to a production order or the inspection of finished quantities.

As an additional consideration, the number of days for the three safety margins can be defined as part of the policies for a set of master plan data, and these will be added to the values defined within coverage groups (if defined). However, these additional days can significantly increase total lead times, and their use is not generally recommended.

6.16 Time Fence Policies

Master planning logic uses several time fences that serve different purposes. Many scenarios can define these time fences as part of the master plan policies, since that is the simplest approach and the easiest to understand and maintain. The time fences reflect the purpose of the master plan data, such as the master plan for day-to-day operations versus a master plan for long-range planning purposes. In other scenarios, some of time fence policies may vary for different items (such as a capacity time fence and its time horizon), so they should be defined as part of a coverage group assigned to these items. It should be noted that use of selected time fences in the master plan policies will override the item-specific time fences.

Time Fence Policies for Day-to-Day Operations The significance of time fences can be grouped into several topics, and the following explanation focuses on the master plan data that supports day-to-day operations in a manufacturing operation. The example screen shown in Figure 6.6 illustrates the master plan policies for time fences.

◆ *Planning horizon and related time fence policies.* The planning horizon for manufactured items must extend beyond the cumulative manufacturing lead times to provide visibility about requirements for purchased items. This planning horizon should be reflected in the time fences for coverage, forecast plans, and explosion. Example data within the figure illustrates a 365-day planning horizon.

◆ *Capacity time fence and the use of routing data.* The capacity time fence determines when routing data for manufactured items should be ignored by master planning logic. For example, routing data may be used for near-term scheduling purposes within the next 30 days, and then ignored after the 30-day time fence so that a fixed lead time applies to manufactured items.

Figure 6.6 Example Screen of Time Fences within the Master Plan Policies

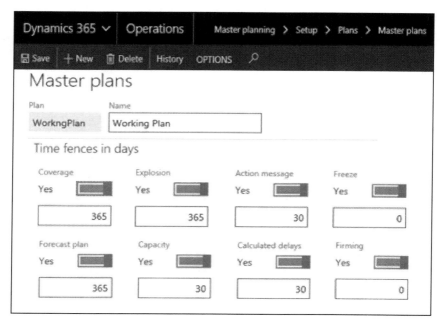

◆ *Freeze time fence and the use of a frozen period.* The concept of a frozen period (termed a *freeze time fence*) is typically employed by the master scheduler role to ensure stability of the near-term schedule, where planned production orders should not be automatically scheduled within the frozen period. When the required date for a planned order falls within the freeze time fence, master planning calculations will place the due date at the end of the frozen period, and the master scheduler can determine how to handle it. Example data within the figure illustrates a value of 0 for this time fence, which means a frozen period does not apply.

To support selective use of a freeze time fence, it should be defined in the coverage group assigned to those items within the responsibility of the master scheduler role.

◆ *Time fence policy for automatic firming.* The concept of automatic firming is typically employed in more mature implementations, where it typically applies to selected items with planned orders that always represent the decision-making logic of the planner or buyer. Automatic firming of planned orders within a specified horizon (for the firming time fence) reduces the need for manual intervention. Example data within the figure illustrates a value of 0 for this time fence, which means automatic firming does not apply.

Automatic firming of planned purchase orders, for example, will reflect the preferred vendor and result in multi-line purchase orders based on grouping preferences. To support selective use of the firming time fence and its time horizon, it should be defined in the coverage group assigned to those items within the responsibility of the purchasing agent.

Automatic firming may also apply to selected manufactured items and transfers, so that selective use should be reflected in the definition and assignment of coverage groups assigned to the relevant items.

◆ *Time fence policies for Action Messages and Calculated Delay Messages.* These time fence policies and their time horizons were described in previous sections (Sections 6.11 and 6.12). Example data within the figure illustrates a 30-day look-ahead window for filtering these messages.

6.17 Additional Case Studies

Case 6.1: Different Coverage Groups to Model SCM Decision Making
A manufacturing company employed several different coverage groups within AX to model the SCM decision making of different roles, such as master schedulers, production planners, buyers and DRP coordinators for transfer orders. As a starting point, they defined several coverage groups to reflect the different values for a coverage code reflecting differences in period lot sizes (such as daily, weekly, bi-monthly and monthly), and the use of requirements and min-max logic as a coverage code. Additional coverage groups were needed for several purposes. First, the master scheduler employed additional coverage groups to support differences in forecast consumption logic for salable end-items versus stocked components. Second, buyers and planners employed different groups to support

differences in filtering of action message policies, thereby improving the usefulness of action messages. Third, additional groups were needed to identify different safety margins when an item required significant time for picking/shipping or receiving/inspection activities.

Case 6.2 Measuring Improvements in the Models of SCM Decision Making

A manufacturing company wanted to improve the effectiveness of system usage based on macro-level quality metrics and periodic sampling. They identified several usage characteristics as the basis for the macro-level metrics, and performed sampling on a weekly basis to measure improvements. Examples of the usage characteristics for different roles such as buyers and planners included (1) the percentage of planned orders that reflected the actual SCM decision making, (2) the number of action messages and the percentage that were actually useful, and (3) the number of supply orders and sales order lines with unrealistic or past due dates. These metrics indicated the actual usefulness of the formal system to support SCM decisions, and helped guide incremental efforts to improve system usage.

Case 6.3: Suggested Vendor based on Lowest Price

A manufacturer purchased several components from the vendor offering the lowest price, whereas other purchased components were always sourced from a single preferred vendor. Each vendor provided price quotes for selected items (with date effectivities), and the quotes were used to update purchase price trade agreement information. Using this information, master planning calculations generated planned purchase orders for the selected items, where the suggested vendor reflected the one with the lowest price.

Case 6.4: Buy-to-Order Component

A manufacturer produced configure-to-order products which included a specialized purchase component requiring delivery that was closely synchronized with the parent item's production order. Due to its size and specialized nature, it was critical for the purchased component to be delivered when actually required, and to identify the related production order at the time of receipt. By designating the item as a buy-to-order component for the parent item, a linked purchase order was automatically created after scheduling the parent item's production order, and also synchronized automatically as the schedule changed.

6.18 Executive Summary

Planned orders communicate the need to replenish an item's inventory, and are generated by master planning calculations based on an item's coverage planning data and related S&OP game plans. An item's preferred source of supply -- defined on a companywide or site/warehouse-specific basis -- determines whether it reflects a purchase, transfer or production order. This chapter summarized the coverage planning data related to generation of planned orders and the use of action messages and messages about calculated delays.

Chapter 7

Using Demand Forecasts

Demand forecasts represent a critical element in many S&OP game plans for stocked products. They can also apply to stocked components in the S&OP game plans for make-to-order products. Another critical element consists of safety stock requirements, typically to anticipate variations in actual demand and achieve the desired service levels.

This chapter focuses on using demand forecasts to support day-to-day operations. It reviews the basics of demand forecasts and the related topic of forecast consumption logic. It covers different approaches to maintain demand forecasts, and different approaches to safety stock requirements. It includes several typical business processes to maintain the S&OP game plans using demand forecasts and safety stock. These considerations are reflected in the following sections within the chapter.

1. S&OP Game Plans using Demand Forecasts for Make-to-Stock Products
2. Basics of Demand Forecasts
3. Basics of Demand Forecast Consumption
4. Additional Considerations about Demand Forecasts
5. Maintain Demand Forecasts using Microsoft Excel
6. Calculate Demand Forecasts based on Historical Data
7. Safety Stock Requirements
8. Demand Forecasts for Stocked Components
9. S&OP Games Plans using Demand Forecasts for Stocked Components
10. S&OP Games Plans using Demand Forecasts in a Distribution Network
11. Using Supply Forecasts
12. Using the Forecast Scheduling Task and Forecast Plan Data
13. Additional Case Studies

7.1 S&OP Game Plans using Demand Forecasts for Make-to-Stock Products

The S&OP game plans for a make-to-stock product often involve a combination of demand forecasts and actual sales orders that drive the item's master schedule, which consists of planned and actual production orders. The term master schedule generally applies to the highest possible stocking level for manufactured items, which consists of saleable end-items items in this scenario. The master schedule provides the basis for making delivery promises on sales orders using available-to-promise (ATP) logic.

A typical business process to maintain the S&OP game plans consists of multiple steps performed by different roles, as summarized in Figure 7.1 and described below. A key role is often called the master scheduler. The master scheduler role typically maintains the game plans and obtains management agreement. This role requires an in-depth understanding of sales and supply chain capabilities, as well as the political power to achieve agreed-upon game plans.

Figure 7.1 Typical Process to Maintain S&OP Game Plans using Demand Forecasts for a Make-to-Stock Product

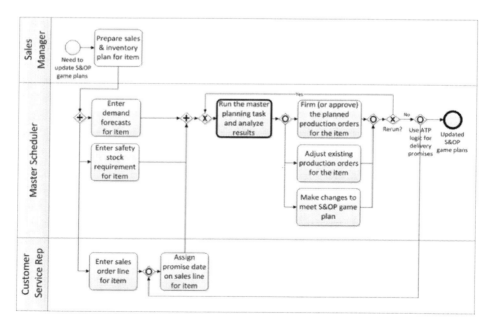

Overview The business process starts with the periodic analysis of historical and projected demands in order to prepare a sales plan and inventory plan for each product. The sales plan is typically expressed in monthly increments. The inventory plan covers higher-than-anticipated sales order demands to meet desired customer service levels. The master scheduler translates this information into entries for the item's demand forecast and safety stock requirements. After the master planning task has been performed, the master scheduler analyzes the results to determine the need for adjustments, and to firm (or approve) planned orders that represent the master schedule. The master schedule provides the basis for realistic promised delivery dates using available-to-promise logic, typically in the context of customer service reps entering sales order lines for the item. In this scenario, actual sales orders consume the item's demand forecast within user-defined forecast periods.

For most scenarios, coverage planning applies to the site/warehouse level, and period lot sizing logic applies to the coverage code assigned to stocked items and their components. The period lot size (expressed in days) represents the frequency of replenishment, and the planned order quantities and dates reflect the time increments and due dates for demand forecasts.

Prepare a sales plan and inventory plan for the item A sales manager role generally has responsibility for analyzing historical and projected demands for the item in order to prepare a sales plan by ship-from location, typically expressed in monthly increments. In many cases the master scheduler must assume this responsibility. The analysis also results in an inventory plan for the item (by ship-from location) to meet the desired customer service levels when actual demands exceed forecast. The analyses may reflect a statistical forecasting technique or some other method.

Enter demand forecasts for the item The master scheduler translates the item's sales plan into entries for demand forecasts, typically expressed in weekly increments (or even daily increments) in the near term. In this scenario, actual sales orders for an item will automatically consume the item's demand forecast within the user-defined forecast periods.

Enter safety stock requirements for the item The master scheduler translates the item's inventory plan into entries for a safety stock requirement. The safety stock requirements can be entered as a single value, and the value can be calculated based on historical usage. A subsequent section provides further explanation about calculating safety stock requirements (Section 7.7). The safety stock requirements can also be defined as a pattern of multiple values for different time periods.

Run the master planning task and analyze results This activity represents a sub-process with multiple steps and roles. After running the master planning task, the master scheduler analyzes the results to identify potential constraints related to material or capacity, and potential problems in meeting demands. The results include planned orders, action messages and net requirements for material items, and capacity requirements for resources. A previous chapter covered the options for performing the master planning calculations (Section 3.4).

Firm (or approve) the planned production orders for the item The master schedule consists of the item's production orders, both planned and actual. Planned orders can be approved or firmed, and the suggested quantities and/or dates may be adjusted to ensure a realistic master schedule.

◆ *Approve a planned production order.* By assigning a status of "Approved" to a planned order, master planning logic will treat the planned order as if it has been scheduled for the specified quantity and due date. It also locks the BOM/route information (so that planned changes will not be recognized) and prevents deletion when deleting a set of master plan data (unlike other planned orders). An approved planned order must still be firmed to create an actual production order.

◆ *Firm a planned production order.* Firming a planned order generates an actual production order (typically with a scheduled status) for the specified quantity and due date. It also results in the initial assignment of the Production BOM and route information for the production order.

For example, the master scheduler may firm (or approve) the planned orders to represent a level-loaded schedule, or to account for material or capacity constraints. Alternatively, the master scheduler may simply use planned orders to represent the master schedule, and ultimately firm them just prior to starting production. This alternative approach assumes the planned orders reflect the anticipated master schedule.

Adjust existing production orders for the item The master scheduler may adjust existing production orders to reflect the master schedule, such as changing the quantity or due dates.

Make changes to meet the S&OP game plan The master scheduler may need to coordinate several types of changes to meet the master schedule. For example, the changes often involve working with purchasing agents to expedite purchase orders for components, or working with production supervisors to adjust capacity or schedules. The changes may also involve working with customer service representatives to delay the promised delivery date on sales orders. These changes often involve trade-offs between conflicting objectives.

Enter sales order line for item The customer service rep enters sales orders for the item, where each sales line indicates a quantity, ship-from location, and a requested ship date and delivery date. Based on forecast consumption logic, the actual sales orders for an item will automatically consume the item's demand forecast within the forecast period.

Assign promise date on sales line for the item When the customer service rep creates a sales order line for the item, the earliest possible dates for shipment and delivery are automatically assigned based on available-to-promise (ATP) logic. The ATP logic reflects the master schedule for the item, which helps align actual sales orders to the S&OP game plans. The customer service rep can view available to promise information to answer questions about availability, or disable the delivery date control logic to assign an unrealistic promise date. The next chapter provides further explanation of the delivery date control logic, and the assignment of requested and confirmed dates to a sales order line.

7.2 Basics of Demand Forecasts

Demand forecasts often represent one of several key elements in the business process to maintain S&OP game plans. The basics of demand forecast information include the identifier for a set of forecast data, how to enter a demand forecast for an item, and using the demand forecasts in master planning calculations.

Forecast Models and the Identifier for a Set of Forecast Data A set of forecast data has a user-defined identifier termed a forecast model. You specify the forecast model identifier when entering the forecasted quantities and dates for an item. You also specify the relevant forecast model for use in the master planning task. Different sets of forecast data can be identified by different forecast models, but we'll focus on the forecast model containing the current forecast continuously updated as part of the S&OP game plans. A typical identifier for the forecast model could be *CurrentForecast* or simply *Forecast*.

An alternative approach to demand forecasts consists of a two-level forecast model, which requires multiple forecast model identifiers. As an example, the forecast model identifier representing the companywide forecast can be associated with several forecast model identifiers representing regional forecasts. Each forecast entry has a forecast model corresponding to a regional forecast. However, you specify the companywide forecast model for use in the master planning task, and the regional forecast models will be automatically rolled up into the companywide forecast model.

Entering a Demand Forecast for a Saleable Item A saleable item may represent an end-item or a component, and each forecast entry minimally consists of the forecast model, the item identifier, quantity, date, and ship-from site/warehouse. The example screen shown in Figure 7.2 illustrates these demand forecast entries for an item, where the entries reflect weekly increments (for 4 weeks) and monthly increments thereafter (for 3 months). All forecast entries with the same forecast model comprise a set of forecast data.

Figure 7.2 Example Screen for Demand Forecasts by Item

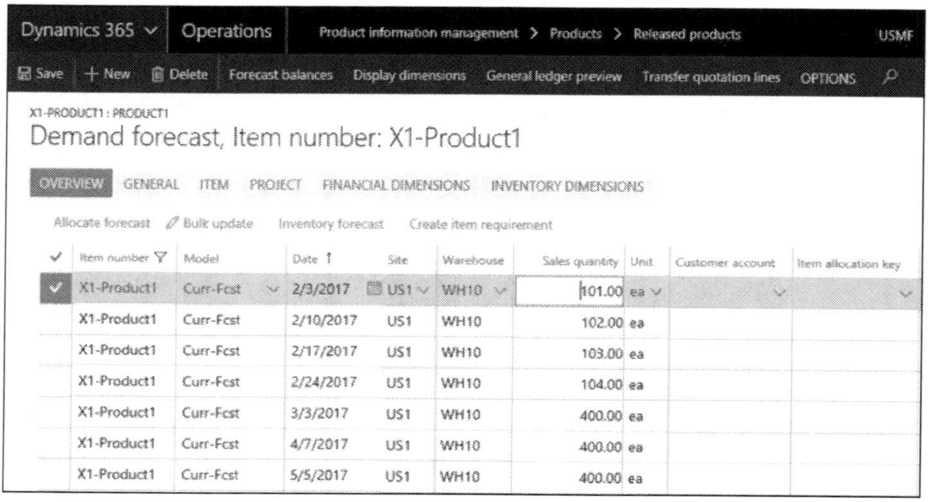

Other approaches to a demand forecast require additional information. Examples include a demand forecast by customer, a demand forecast for a group of items, and translating monthly or weekly demand forecasts into daily increments. These approaches are described in a subsequent section about additional considerations for demand forecasts.

Using Demand Forecasts in the Master Planning Calculations One master plan policy indicates whether to consider demand forecasts in master planning calculations, and a second policy specifies the relevant forecast model.

A third related policy (termed the reduction principle) indicates the primary option for forecast consumption, as described in the next section.

Using Demand Forecasts in the Forecast Scheduling Task While the set of master plan data reflects net requirements and provides coordination for supply chain management, it is sometimes helpful to calculate gross requirements that only reflect forecasted demand. The forecast scheduling task calculates these gross requirements and generates a set of *forecast plan data* based on a specified forecast model. A subsequent section provides further explanation of using the forecast scheduling task and forecast plan data.

7.3 Basics of Demand Forecast Consumption

The combination of demand forecasts and actual sales orders must be considered to avoid doubled-up requirements for an item. These considerations are commonly termed forecast consumption logic. A basic choice concerns the reduction principle option within the master plan policies. The choice may include the use of a reduction key. The four major options for the reduction principle are summarized in Figure 7.3 and described below.

Figure 7.3 Summary of Forecast Consumption Policies

Reduction Principle and Description	Related Policies for an Item		
	Applicable Reduction Key	Reduce Forecast By = Sales Orders	Estimated Usage
1 Transactions – Reduction Key Sales orders consume demand forecasts within specified forecast periods	Yes	Yes	> 70%
- Using a Reduction Key with a fixed start date - Using a Reduction Key with a floating start date			< 5%
2 Transactions – Dynamic Period Sales orders consume demand forecasts within implied forecast periods	N/A	Yes	~ 20%
3 Percent – Reduction Key Automatically reduce demand forecasts within specified forecast periods	Yes	N/A	< 1%
4 None Manually adjust demand forecasts to reflect forecast consumption	N/A	N/A	< 5%

Legend: ▨ = Dominant Business Practices

The major options of a reduction principle summarized in Figure 7.3 include two related policies for an item. The need for these two related policies depends on the selected option for a reduction principle, as indicated by "Yes" versus "N/A" in the figure. You define these additional policies as part of the coverage group assigned to an item. One policy indicates the applicable Reduction Key, which will be described shortly. The second policy -- labeled *Reduce Forecast By* -- indicates whether a demand forecast should be consumed by all types of demand or just by sales order demand for the item.

The figure also indicates the estimated usage for each option. As shown by shading for Option #1, the dominant business practices consist of forecast consumption by transactions based on a reduction key with a fixed start date, typically with fixed monthly forecast periods.

Option #1: Sales Orders Consume Demand Forecasts within Specified Forecast Periods   The reduction principle is *Transactions - Reduction Key,* and the option requires the two related policies for an item. One of these policies indicates the applicable reduction key, which defines the time buckets for forecast consumption purposes. The second "Reduce Forecast By" policy indicates that sales orders (rather than all types of demands) should consume the demand forecasts.

As an explanatory approach, we will focus on a reduction key comprised of fixed monthly time buckets and weekly forecast increments. This also represents dominant business practices. In this example, any sales orders with ship dates within a monthly time bucket will consume the item's demand forecasts within the same monthly bucket, starting with the earliest unconsumed forecast and consuming forward. The demand forecasts within a given month can be over-consumed; there is no carry-forward effect to consume forecasts within a future time bucket. Changing the sales order ship date to another month (especially the confirmed ship date) will consume demand forecasts in the relevant month.

Definition of a Reduction Key   A reduction key defines the time buckets for forecast consumption purposes. The time buckets are sometimes called forecast periods. Examples of a reduction key include monthly periods, or a combination of weekly periods for several weeks and monthly periods thereafter. The two basic approaches for defining a reduction key consist of a fixed start date and floating start date.

◆ *Reduction Key with a Fixed Start Date.* In a typical example, the fixed start date is specified as January 1st of the current year, and the reduction key defines 12 or more monthly periods. As time progresses, this approach requires additions to the monthly periods within the reduction key or a change in the fixed start date. This approach is the simplest to understand.

◆ *Reduction Key with a Floating Start Date.* The current date (for running the master planning task) acts as the floating start date. This approach is slightly more complex to understand because the forecast periods are relative to the current date, but it provides greater flexibility and granularity in modeling some forecast consumption scenarios.

To simplify forecast consumption logic, most scenarios will start with just one reduction key (such as fixed monthly forecast periods), and assign it to every coverage group assigned to saleable items. The need for additional reduction keys, and the assignment of different reduction keys to different items, reflects increasing sophistication and complexity in modeling forecast consumption logic.

Option #2: Sales Orders Consume Demand Forecasts within Implied Forecast Periods The reduction principle is *Transactions - Dynamic Period,* and the option requires the "Reduce Forecast By" policy indicating that sales orders (rather than all types of demands) should consume the item's demand forecasts. This option employs implied forecast periods defined by the due dates of forecast entries. It does not employ a reduction key. An implied forecast period ends with the next forecast date for the item and ship-from site/warehouse.

Option #3: Automatically Reduce Demand Forecasts by a Percentage The reduction principle is *Percent - Reduction Key,* and my research suggest the option is rarely used. This option uses a reduction key but with a specified reduction percentage for near-term time buckets. It does not support forecast consumption by sales orders. As one example, you might define a reduction percentage of 100% for the first monthly forecast period within the reduction key, so that only sales orders should be considered during the month. Otherwise the demand forecast and sales orders will be added together within each forecast period. The reduction key can employ a fixed or floating start date.

This concept is often called a demand fence in other ERP systems, where only sales orders are considered as demand within the demand fence. The concept typically applies to scenarios with a fully-booked sales order backlog over the near-term horizon (defined by the demand fence), where the near-term forecasts can be ignored or factored down. The concept can also be implemented by manual adjustments to the demand forecasts, rather than using reduction percentages within the reduction key.

Option #4: Manually Adjust Demand Forecast to reflect Forecast Consumption The reduction principle is *None*. With this option, the demands from sales orders and demand forecasts will be added together by master planning logic, so that demand forecasts must be manually adjusted to reflect forecast consumption. This option does not involve any related information for an item. Case 7.1 illustrates the use of manual adjustments to demand forecasts.

Forecast Consumption and Sales Orders with Past Due or Invalid Ship Dates A key aspect of forecast consumption involves the requested ship date on a sales order line, or the confirmed ship date if specified. It is assumed that these are realistic dates, and that you maintain the information to avoid past due or invalid ship dates. It is difficult to correctly interpret forecast consumption when sales orders have past-due or invalid ship dates.

7.4 Additional Considerations about Demand Forecasts

Many of the considerations about demand forecasts have been covered in previous sections. Examples include the typical business process to maintain S&OP game plans for a make-to-stock product, the definition of forecast models and forecast consumption logic, and the use of demand forecasts in the master planning calculations. This section covers several additional suggestions, starting with the time horizon, time increments and due dates for demand forecasts. It provides ideas about demand forecasts for a customer or a group of items, and translating monthly or weekly forecasts into daily increments. It also covers the use of demand forecasts in a multicompany supply chain.

Time Horizon for Demand Forecasts The time horizon for dates assigned to demand forecasts must exceed an item's cumulative manufacturing lead time in order to provide any forward visibility, especially for purchased components. The time horizon should be reflected in several master plan policies -- termed time fences and expressed in calendar days -- for considering forecasts, explosions, and coverage planning.[1] Other time fence policies are typically shorter, such as the time fences for consideration of capacity and action messages.

---

[1] The use of master plan policies provides the simplest approach to these time fence policies. As an alternative, you can define them as part of the coverage group assigned to each item. This alternative approach applies to scenarios with differing time horizons for different products, but it also involves higher levels of data maintenance and complexity.

The time increments for demand forecasts can be different across the time horizon, such as weekly increments over the time horizon reflecting the cumulative manufacturing lead time, and monthly increments thereafter. The next point covers time increments.

Time Increments and Due Dates for Demand Forecasts   The time increments and due dates for demand forecasts depend on the situation. One or more of the following suggestions can be considered.

◆ *Granularity of time increments and period lot sizing logic.* This guideline means that the granularity of demand forecasts can support period lot sizing logic for planned orders. Weekly forecasts provide sufficient granularity for many scenarios, although some scenarios can benefit from daily granularity in the near term. As a general rule, monthly forecasts do not provide sufficient granularity. However, monthly forecasts may apply to items produced once a month, and staggered forecast dates could reflect the anticipated production schedule throughout the month.

◆ *Significance of due dates for demand forecasts.* It is important that production planners can consistently interpret the significance of due dates assigned to planned production orders stemming from demand forecasts. For example, the forecast due dates can reflect a Monday date or Friday date in scenarios involving weekly time increments. Other scenarios may stagger the due dates, or use daily time increments in the near term, so that the planned order due dates will be spread throughout the week.

◆ *Time increments for demand forecasts and the time buckets for forecast consumption.* The time increments for demand forecasts can be different than the time buckets for forecast consumption purposes. As a dominant business practice, you might specify weekly demand forecasts and use monthly time buckets for forecast consumption.

◆ *Time increments and reducing the impact of past-due forecasts.* As time progresses, the demand forecasts for dates previous to today's date will be ignored by master planning logic. This is termed past-due forecast. Past-due forecasts can have a dramatic impact when using an overly-simplified approach to time increments and forecast dates. An example involves monthly forecasts with a due date on the 1st of the month, where the demand forecasts become past due as time progresses. Smaller time increments and staggered dates can lessen the impact of advancing time and the resulting past-due forecasts.

◆ *Reasonable approximation of the item's master schedule.* This guideline means that planned production orders (stemming from the demand forecasts) can be easily firmed with little need for manual adjustments, and that planned orders can provide the basis for making sales order delivery promises based on ATP logic. The guideline does not apply to scenarios with demand seasonality requiring a level-loaded master schedule, as defined by approved planned orders or scheduled production orders. Case 8.1 provides an illustration.

Demand Forecasts for a Group of Items Some scenarios employ demand forecasts for an item group rather than an individual item. This approach employs a user-defined template (termed an *Item Allocation Key*) that spreads out a total quantity across several items based on a mix percentage per item. The synonyms for an item allocation key include a planning bill or planning BOM. With this approach, a forecast entry for the item group would specify the item allocation key and the ship-from site/warehouse. Case 7.2 illustrates demand forecasts for a group of salable items.

Each entry within the item allocation key can optionally define the ship-from site/warehouse. For example, the entries could define the mix percentages for shipping the same item from different sites/warehouses. With this approach, a forecast entry for the item group would simply specify the item allocation key.

Demand Forecasts by Customer Some scenarios involve customer-specific forecasts for salable items, which also involve forecast consumption logic by sales orders from the customer. The correct logic requires an item-specific policy about forecast consumption – labeled "include customer forecasts in the demand forecast" – embedded in the coverage group assigned to the item. The label is slightly misleading because the policy refers to forecast consumption logic; a master plan policy determines whether demand forecasts will be included. Customer-specific forecasts are not consumed by a sales order from other customers.

The correct logic involves the previously described basics of forecast consumption, such as the reduction principle with fixed or implied forecast periods, and the item-specific policy to "reduce forecast by" sales orders. Similar to general demand forecasts with forecast consumption within a forecast period, sales orders will consume the earliest customer-specific forecasts within the period prior to consuming forecasts later in the period.

As an alternative, demand forecasts can be entered for a customer group (rather than for a specific customer), so that forecasts are consumed by a sales order from any customer with the same customer group.

Translating a Monthly or Weekly Demand Forecast into Daily Increments Some scenarios employ daily increments in the near-term demand forecast, thereby providing greater granularity for planned order quantities based on period lot sizing logic. The following examples illustrate how to translate monthly or weekly forecasts into daily increments.

◆ *Translate Monthly Forecasts into Daily Increments.* You can enter a monthly demand forecast (for first day of the month) along with a *Period Allocation Key* that will automatically result in daily increments. For example, you would predefine the period allocation key indicating 30 daily increments and a percentage for each daily increment such as 3.33%. This example means that a monthly forecast of 300 would result in daily increments of 10. The assigned percentage may vary to reflect demand patterns within a month, such as higher sales at the end of the month. Other period allocation keys would be needed for months with a different number of days.

◆ *Translate Weekly Forecasts into Daily Increments.* You can enter a weekly demand forecast (for the date corresponding to the first working day of the week) along with a *Period Allocation Key* that will automatically result in daily increments. For example, you would predefine the period allocation key indicating five daily increments and a percentage for each daily increment such as 20%. This example means that a weekly forecast of 100 would result in daily increments of 20. Other period allocation keys would be needed for weeks with a different number of working days.

Demand Forecasts for a specified BOM Version A few scenarios involve manufactured items with multiple BOM versions (or route versions) that are approved-but-not-active. You can optionally identify one of these versions as part of the demand forecasts for the item, and master planning logic will consider the specified version (rather than the active version). The specified version will also be considered when firming the resulting planned production order.

Demand Forecasts in a Multicompany Supply Chain Some scenarios involve a multicompany supply chain within one instance of the database, where demand forecasts must be entered for the relevant company and ship-from location. There are two basic scenarios for using demand forecasts in a multicompany supply chain.

◆ *Enter demand forecasts for the selling company that actually stocks and sells the item.* These requirements will be communicated across company boundaries as planned intercompany demand for the supplying company. Actual sales orders at the selling company can consume these demand forecasts.

◆ *Enter customer-specific demand forecasts for the supplying company that stocks the item.* In this scenario, demand forecasts are entered for the customer that represents the sister company. In addition, the intercompany sales order must consume the customer-specific demand forecast, as defined by policies within the coverage group assigned to the item.

A subsequent chapter provides further explanation of master planning in a multicompany supply chain (Chapter 17).

Other Purposes of Demand Forecasts The suggestions for using demand forecasts have focused on using one forecast model and one set of master plan data to support S&OP purposes. These demand forecasts typically involve forecast consumption logic and continuous updates. Different forecast models and different sets of master plan data (or forecast plan data) can serve different purposes, as summarized below.

◆ *Original Annual Forecast.* One forecast model can represent the original annual forecast, thereby supporting comparisons against actual results or other sets of forecast data. The original annual forecast typically reflects one aspect of the budgeting process. For example, the identifier (and description) for the forecast model could refer to "Original Annual Forecast for 201X".

◆ *Long-Range Planning.* An additional forecast model can support long-range planning for material or resources. These demand forecasts can be used by the master planning task to generate a separate set of master plan data, or by the forecast scheduling task to generate a set of forecast plan data. For example, the resulting requirements for material can be used in vendor negotiations for purchased items. The requirements for resources, or aggregate requirements for resource groups, can be used to justify equipment investments or anticipate needed head counts.

◆ *S&OP Simulations.* One or more sets of demand forecast data can be used for simulation purposes. One example would be different sets representing the best-case and worst-case scenarios, and the calculation of corresponding requirements. As another example, you can run the master planning task using infinite capacity planning to anticipate overloaded periods. After adjusting available capacity and consideration of alternate routings, you run the master planning task again using finite capacity to highlight unrealistic delivery dates.

◆ *Project-Oriented Operations.* Project budgets are based on forecasted requirements, where a unique forecast model is often defined for each version of the project's budget. In addition, the forecasted requirements for items and production resources can optionally be included in the master planning calculations. As one example using a two-level forecast model, the sub-models identify the relevant forecast models for various projects.

The rationale for using of different sets of master plan data and different forecast models was previously mentioned as part of the basics of master planning.

7.5 Maintain Demand Forecasts using Microsoft Excel

Many manufacturing businesses want to maintain demand forecasts using a spreadsheet. By opening entity data in Microsoft Excel, you can view and edit data, and then update the system by publishing it. You can start from either Excel or Dynamics 365 for Operations to open the entity data.

In the simplest scenario, you can start from the Demand Forecast Lines page to view existing data and then click Open in Microsoft Office so you can edit it. Typical changes include adding new lines and adjusting the existing lines, and then publishing it to update the demand forecasts.

More useful scenarios involve historical data within the spreadsheet, so that user-defined calculations can generate new lines and adjust the existing lines. The nature of extracting this historical information – such as shipments of salable items or usage of stocked components – depends on the situation. A standard extract is not currently available. However, as described in the next section, the statistical forecasting approach displays historical information in a spreadsheet format.

7.6 Calculate Demand Forecasts based on Historical Data

Some scenarios can benefit from the calculation of demand forecasts based on sales history information. One approach is included within the standard software, where demand forecasts are calculated using the Microsoft Azure Machine Learning cloud service.[2] The service performs best match model selection and

---

[2] A different approach for calculating demand forecasts was included in the previous version Dynamics AX 2012 R3, where the forecast models in Microsoft SQL Server Analysis Service were used to create predictions.

offers key performance indicators for calculating forecast accuracy. The Wiki help provides a comprehensive explanation of this functionality, so an extended explanation is not included here. In addition, third-party packages provide different approaches to demand forecasting.

Use of the resulting data generated by a statistical forecasting approach must still adhere to the previously mentioned considerations about demand forecasts and safety stock for managing day-to-day operations. For example, the resulting data often reflects monthly time increments, so that the time granularity (of weekly or daily) and due dates must be considered. Additional considerations include demand forecasts by customer (or customer group) or by item group, demand forecasts for stocked components, demand forecasts for different ship-from sites/warehouses, and forecast consumption logic. The statistical aspects of demand variability should also result in calculated safety stock quantities that meet desired customer service levels.

7.7 Safety Stock Requirements

Safety stock represents a key element in S&OP game plans for those scenarios with stocked end-items or stocked components. An item's safety stock requirement is defined by the minimum quantity field. You can manually enter a value, or calculate a proposed minimum quantity based on an item's historical usage and its lead time.[3] The significance of the minimum quantity differs between two major approaches for solving S&OP scenarios with stocked items. One approach employs the minimum quantity as part of min-max logic, and the second approach employs the minimum quantity to represent an inventory plan in combination with demand forecasts.

◆ *Minimum quantity for min-max purposes.* Min-max quantities provide one approach to S&OP game plans with a stocked item. When using a min-max coverage code, you specify the item's minimum quantity and maximum quantity for each relevant site/warehouse. The minimum quantity represents the average daily usage multiplied by the item's lead time. Alternatively, you can define a pattern (termed a minimum key and a maximum key) to identify different quantities over multiple time periods.

---

[3] The calculation of a safety stock quantity reflects an item's fixed lead time. The assignment of these lead times was previously described for purchased items (Section 6.3), manufactured items (Section 6.5) and transfers (Section 6.8).

◆ *Minimum quantity for inventory plan purposes.* A second approach to S&OP game plans with a stocked item involves demand forecasts, where the minimum quantity represents the inventory plan at a relevant site/warehouse. The inventory plan covers demand variability to meet the desired customer service level in order to reduce stock outs, partial shipments, and delivery lead times. Stated another way, this minimum quantity reflects a percentage of forecast accuracy for a given item; it does not represent a desired inventory position. The minimum quantity is commonly called an inventory plan or safety stock. The second approach applies when using a coverage code of period or requirement.

The definition of an item's minimum quantity provides the starting point for further explanation about calculating proposed minimum quantities to support the two different purposes.

Define an Item's Minimum Quantity You define an item's minimum quantity for a specified site/warehouse on the Item Coverage form, typically with a requirement date reflecting today's date plus the item's lead time. The same form can also be accessed from the Item Coverage Setup form, which identifies items still requiring the setup information. The requirement associated with the item's minimum quantity is identified by pegging information as "Safety Stock" on the Net Requirements inquiry.

Calculate an Item's Minimum Quantity based on Historical Usage You can calculate a proposed minimum quantity based on an item's historical usage, either for min/max purposes or for inventory plan purposes to cover demand variability. An item's historical usage reflects all issue transactions during a specified time period, including sales order shipments, inventory adjustments and other issue transactions. The calculations also identify the impact of the proposed minimum quantity on inventory value, and the change in inventory value relative to the current minimum quantities. A printed report summarizes the impacts on inventory value for all items included in the calculations.

You perform these calculations using the Safety Stock Journal and its related journal lines. The business process for using the Safety Stock Journal to calculate the proposed minimum quantities is summarized in Figure 7.4 and described below. A master scheduler role often performs this business process.

Figure 7.4 Typical Process to Calculate Safety Stock Quantities

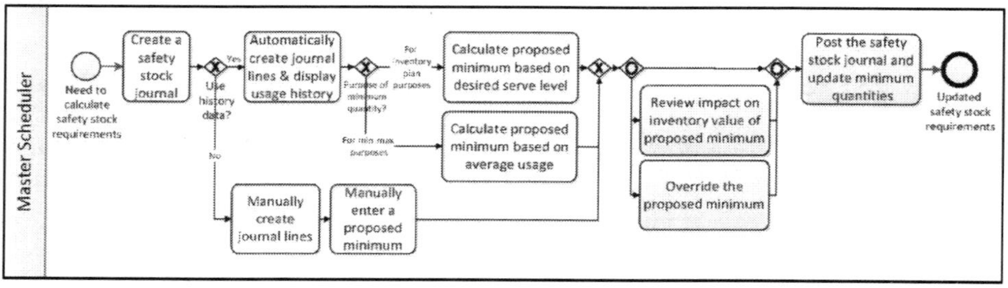

Overview The master scheduler uses a safety stock journal to calculate proposed minimum quantities for selected items based on historical usage during selected periods. For a given safety stock journal, the calculation of proposed minimums can reflect either (1) average usage for min/max purposes or (2) demand variability for inventory plan purposes, but not both. The proposed minimums can be manually overridden if needed, and you can review the potential impact on inventory value of the proposed minimums. Posting the journal automatically updates the associated minimum quantities.

Create a Safety Stock Journal The master scheduler starts from the Safety Stock Journal form to create a new journal. The journal identifier reflects a number sequence defined in the Master Planning Parameters. For each new journal, you should enter a meaningful journal name about its purpose.

Automatically Create Journal Lines and Display Usage History The master scheduler starts from the journal lines in order to access the dialogue to *Create Lines*. As part of the dialogue, you specify the relevant historical periods (expressed as from and to dates) and the selection criteria for items (such as the buyer group or coverage group). You also indicate calculation of the standard deviations in order to support calculation of an inventory plan based on a desired customer service level. This step results in the automatic creation of journal lines, where each line identifies an item and site/warehouse and several calculated quantities about usage history. The calculated quantities include average issues per the item's lead time, average issues per month, and the monthly standard deviation. It should be noted that you can only perform the automatic creation of journal lines when no lines exist.

Calculate Proposed Minimum based on Desired Service Level The master scheduler starts from the journal lines in order to access the dialogue to *Calculate Proposed* minimum quantities. As part of the dialogue, you select the calculation option for Use Service Levels and the desired percentage (such as 95%), and indicate the proposed minimum should also be displayed in the new minimum field. This step results in calculation of a proposed minimum for each journal line and its potential impact on inventory value.

Calculate Proposed Minimum based on Average Usage The master scheduler starts from the journal lines form in order to access the dialogue to *Calculate Proposed* minimum quantities. As part of the dialogue, you select the calculation option for Use Average Issues During Lead Time, and optionally use a multiplying factor and/or lead time margin. A multiplying factor (different than 1) can increase or decrease the proposed minimum. The incremental lead time margin (greater than 0) will be combined with an item's lead time to calculate the proposed minimum. You can also indicate the proposed minimum should be displayed in the new minimum field. This step results in calculation of a proposed minimum for each journal line and its potential impact on inventory value.

Review Impact on Inventory Value of Proposed Minimum The master scheduler selects a journal line and views the potential impact on inventory value of the proposed minimum, and also the potential change in inventory value relative to the currently specified minimum. You can view the total potential impact of all journal lines by printing the report for the journal, or by copying the lines to a spreadsheet.

Override the Proposed Minimum The master scheduler selects a line and manually overrides the value for the new minimum quantity field.

Post the Safety Stock Journal and Update Minimum Quantities The master scheduler posts the journal in order to update the minimum quantity associated with each journal line.

Manually Create Journal Lines and Manually Enter Proposed Minimums The master scheduler can manually create journal lines. This approach prevents calculation of a proposed minimum so that it must be manually entered. However, you can still view the potential impact on inventory value of the proposed minimum, and the potential change in inventory value relative to the currently specified minimum.

Example Screen of the Safety Stock Journal The example of a Safety Stock Journal in Figure 7.5 illustrates the results of calculating minimum quantities for inventory plan purposes, where the journal lines identify manufactured end-items and the relevant site/warehouse.

Figure 7.5 Example Screen of a Safety Stock Journal

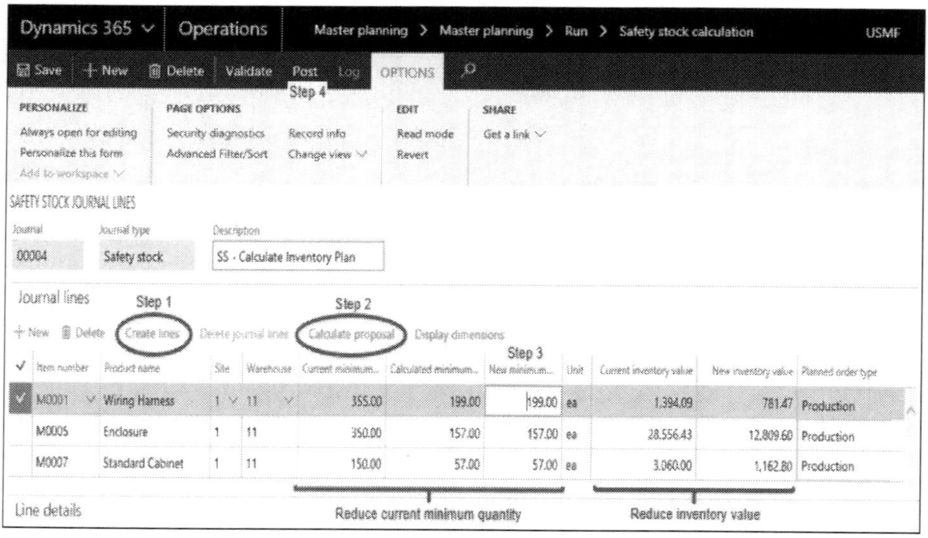

In the example data, replenishment of each end-item is based on coverage planning using period lot-sizing logic and demand forecasts, although this is not shown in the figure. The figure highlights the key steps to (1) create journal lines, (2) calculate proposed minimum quantities, and (3) review and optionally override the new minimum quantities. Based on the calculated results, the current minimum quantities should be reduced, which will also reduce inventory values. As a final step, you can (4) post the journal to automatically update the current values (on the Item Coverage page) with the values from the "new minimum" field.

7.8 Demand Forecasts for Stocked Components

Stocked components can support shorter delivery lead times for make-to-order products. The make-to-order product may have a standard BOM and routing, or it may represent a configured item with a BOM/routing defined by a configuration technology. Demand forecasts for these stocked components provide one approach to drive replenishment, but the approach requires the correct forecast consumption logic to avoid doubled-up requirements.

The entries of demand forecasts for a stocked component are just like demand forecasts for saleable items. The key difference involves forecast consumption logic, so that the demand forecasts will be consumed by any type of demands (also termed issue transactions) within a forecast period. In addition to sales order demand, the demand forecasts for components will be consumed by dependent demands stemming from planned or actual production orders for the make-to-order products. The demand forecasts can also be consumed by transfer requirements to a different warehouse stemming from planned or actual transfer orders. This approach avoids doubled-up requirements when using demand forecasts for stocked components.

To support this forecast consumption logic, the item representing the stocked component must have a "Reduce Forecast By" policy of "All Transactions" rather just "Sales Orders", as defined within the coverage group assigned to the item. This policy works in combination with the selected option for a reduction principle and the use of a reduction key. A previous section described the reduction principle options, and the definition and use of reduction keys (Section 7.3). Case 7.3 illustrates the use of demand forecasts for stocked components, and Case 7.5 illustrates similar forecast consumption logic for stocked end-items at regional distribution centers.

7.9 S&OP Game Plans using Demand Forecasts for Stocked Components

Demand forecasts for stocked components often represent one of several key elements in the business process to maintain S&OP game plans for a make-to-order product. In a common scenario, the combination of demand forecasts and actual demands for a stocked component drive the item's replenishment. Figure 7.6 illustrates a typical process to maintain the S&OP game plans for a make-to-order product with stocked components

Figure 7.6 Typical Process to Maintain S&OP Game Plans for a Make-to-Order Product with Stocked Components

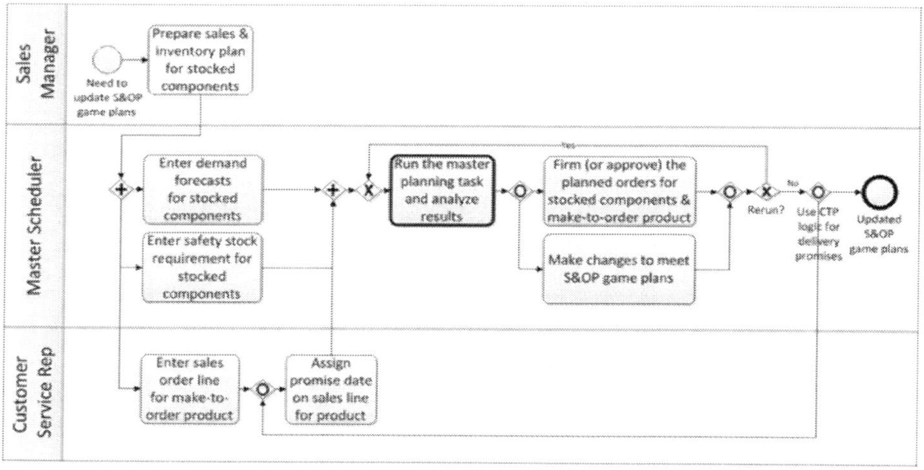

The master scheduler determines which components should be stocked, and works with the sales manager to analyze the projected requirements. These projected requirements must be translated into entries for demand forecasts and safety stock. The master planning task generates planned orders for the stocked components, and the master scheduler can approve (or firm) these planned orders as part of the S&OP business process. After entering a sales order line for a make-to-order product, the associated production order can be created from the sales line, or the production order can be created by firming the planned order generated by master planning calculations. The selected approach determines linkage between orders.

7.10 S&OP Game Plans using Demand Forecasts in a Distribution Network

The S&OP game plans for a stocked product in a distribution network share many similarities to those for a make-to-stock product, such as the use of demand forecasts and safety stock requirement to drive replenishment. However, there are several key differences. First, the primary responsibility for maintaining the S&OP game plans involves a different role (such as a DRP coordinator or inventory manager). Second, the primary focus involves purchase orders and transfer orders rather than production orders. And third, the critical considerations include stocking levels at different locations. A typical business process to maintain the S&OP game plans for a stocked product in a distribution network is illustrated in Figure 7.7.

Figure 7.7 Typical Process to Maintain S&OP Game Plans
using Demand Forecasts in a Distribution Network

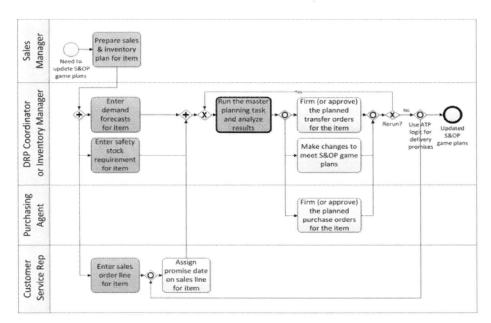

The business process shown in Figure 7.7 shares many similarities to the typical process for make-to-stock products described in a previous section, so that further explanation focuses on the key differences. The figure indicates the common steps with grey shading.

Firm (or approve) the planned transfer orders for the item The use of transfer orders -- both planned and actual - applies to a distribution network. Planned orders can be approved or firmed by a DRP coordinator (or an equivalent role), and the suggested quantities and/or dates may be adjusted.

Firm (or approve) the planned purchase orders for the item A purchasing agent typically firms the planned purchase orders that reflect the S&OP game plans and the model of SCM decision making logic. The suggested quantities and/or dates may be adjusted on planned orders prior to firming.

Make changes to meet the S&OP game plans The DRP coordinator and purchasing agent may need to coordinate several types of changes to meet the S&OP game plans. For example, the changes often involve expediting of existing purchase orders or transfer orders. The changes may also involve working with customer service representatives to delay the promised delivery date on sales orders.

Assign promise date on sales line for the item When the customer service rep creates a sales order line for the item, the earliest possible dates for shipment and delivery can be automatically assigned based on available-to-promise (ATP) logic. In scenarios where the item is stocked at multiple locations, the customer service rep may evaluate the delivery alternatives for different ship-from locations, and then update the sales line based on the selected option.

7.11 Using Supply Forecasts

One confusing aspect of forecast data concerns the difference between a demand forecast and a supply forecast. Demand forecasts typically represent a demand pull strategy, whereas supply forecasts represent a push strategy which applies to certain types of raw materials. Examples include agricultural-related products that must be picked and processed at certain times of the year, and animal-related products (such as poultry, beef and pork) requiring a maturation period before the animals can be sent to market.

A supply forecast typically indicates the intended purchase of these raw materials. Each forecast entry includes the forecast identifier, quantity, delivery date and ship-to location for the item. The actual creation of a purchase order consumes the supply forecast for a purchased item, and the creation of a production order consumes the supply forecast for a manufactured item. This is different than the forecast consumption logic for demand forecasts. However, many of the same considerations about demand forecasts still apply. This includes the reduction principle, such as the use of monthly time buckets or implied forecast periods for forecast consumption purposes. Case 7.4 illustrates one scenario for using supply forecasts.

Two caveats apply to the use of supply forecasts. First, the demands stemming from a supply forecast are not easily visible whereas the demands stemming from demand forecasts are visible. For example, the inquiry about net requirements does not display the supply forecast, and it is not displayed in pegging information about the source of demand. However, the system does display a checkbox (labeled supply forecast) to indicate whether a planned order or actual supply order stems from a supply forecast. The second caveat applies to the action messages for an item with supply forecasts. The action message for decrease should be suppressed so that planning calculations do not generate a message to cancel the item's supply orders for satisfying the supply forecast.

It is particularly important for the S&OP game plans to match demands to the incoming supply associated with supply forecasts. In addition, the determination of size and quality upon receipt of the raw material may impact actual availability.

7.12 Using the Forecast Scheduling Task and Forecast Plan Data

The forecast scheduling task calculates demands and supplies within set of forecast plan data based on several policies such as a time horizon and the relevant forecast identifier. Each set of forecast plan data has a user-defined identifier. Multiple sets of forecast plan data can be calculated based on different forecast identifiers, typically to reflect various scenarios for simulation purposes.

A set of forecast plan data represents gross requirements to support planning of materials and capacity, whereas a set of master plan data represents net requirements to support day-to-day supply chain coordination.

7.13 Additional Case Studies

Case 7.1: Demand Forecasts with No Forecast Consumption Logic A manufacturing company produced standard products based on actual sales orders. The limited forward visibility of these sales orders meant that demand forecasts for end-items were used to drive replenishment of long lead time materials. The master scheduler avoided any confusion in forecast consumption logic by using a reduction principle of none. He maintained the demand forecasts so that they represented the incremental demand that will be added to sales order demands.

Case 7.2: Demand Forecasts by Item Group A manufacturing company had thousands of stocked end-items, and wanted to minimize the effort to maintain forecasts for individual items. Using an Item Allocation Key, the items were grouped together for forecasting purposes, with a mix percentage assigned to each item, so that aggregate forecasts could be entered for each group of items. This approach reduced the number of forecasts to be maintained, from thousands of individual items to a few dozen groups.

Case 7.3: Demand Forecasts using a Planning BOM for Stocked Components A manufacturing company wanted to forecast a group of stocked components that represented the long lead time components for their make-to-order products. The concept of a planning BOM was implemented with an item allocation key, which identified the stocked components and a mix percentage of their typical usage. A demand forecast for an item group specified the item allocation key and a quantity reflecting expected unit sales for their make-to-order products. This demand forecast was entered in weekly increments over a 3-month rolling time horizon, and monthly increments thereafter.

Case 7.4: Supply Forecasts for Food Product Ingredients A food products company produced several types of trail mix containing different tree nuts, such as chestnuts and walnuts. They monitored the expected global availability of these raw materials, and arranged purchase agreements with the suppliers. Supply forecasts identified the expected quantities and delivery dates for each raw material, thereby driving the generation of planned purchase orders. The actual purchase orders consumed the supply forecasts.

Case 7.5: Demand Forecasts for Stocked End-Items in a Distribution Network A manufacturing company had a distribution network consisting of a manufacturing plant, regional distribution centers and selling locations. An end-item's inventory was stocked at a distribution center, and then transferred to a selling location to meet actual sales order demand. In this scenario, they entered the item's demand forecasts for each distribution center, and the transfer order requirements consumed the demand forecasts. This required the correct forecast consumption logic. That is, the coverage group assigned to the item and the warehouse representing a distribution center had a *Reduce Forecast By* policy of "All Transactions" rather just "Sales Orders".

7.14 Executive Summary

Demand forecasts represent a critical element in many S&OP game plans for stocked products. They can also apply to stocked components in the S&OP game plans for make-to-order products. Another critical element consists of safety stock requirements, typically to anticipate variations in actual demand and achieve the desired service levels.

This chapter reviewed the basics of demand forecasts and the related topic of forecast consumption logic. It covered different approaches to maintain demand forecasts, and different approaches to safety stock requirements. It included several typical business processes to maintain the S&OP game plans using demand forecasts and safety stock. The case studies highlighted variations in the use of demand forecasts.

Chapter 8

Sales Order Considerations

Several sales order considerations are especially important for master planning. Many of these have been covered in previous chapters, such as the significance of sales orders in S&OP game plans, the inventory locations related to sales order shipments, and forecast consumption by sales orders. This chapter covers some additional considerations such as delivery promises and reservations.

Realistic promises for sales order shipments and deliveries can help improve customer satisfaction and supply chain coordination. The initial assignment of sales order promises can be supported using several different approaches that reflect a delivery date control policy, and the relevant option depends on the S&OP scenario. This chapter starts with a brief background about the different approaches to creating orders and the sales order dates for shipment and delivery. It explains the basic rules for delivery date control, and summarizes the options for the delivery date control policy. It also covers reservations, delivery alternatives and backorders for sales orders. These considerations are reflected in the following sections within the chapter.

1. Different Ways to Create Sales Orders
2. Sales Order Dates for Shipment and Delivery
3. Basic Rules for Delivery Date Control
4. Delivery Date Control for a Sales Order Line
5. ATP Information for a Sales Order
6. CTP Logic and the assumption about use of On-hand Inventory
7. Analyze Delivery Alternatives for a Sales Order
8. Reserve Material for a Sales Order line
9. Sales Orders for a Configurable Product
10. Identify Sales-Related Backorders
11. Additional Case Studies

8.1 Different Ways to Create Sales Orders

Sales order processing often involves many variations, starting with the different approaches for creating sales orders. Several approaches for creating sales orders are listed below. Each variation builds on a basic business process for sales orders, and typically involves additional steps or considerations. Extended explanations of these variations in business processes fall outside the book's scope, but they have been provided in the 2016 Editions of my books about discrete manufacturing, process manufacturing and warehouse management.

◆ Enter a sales order for standard products
◆ Enter a sales order for configurable products
◆ Enter a sales order using the customer service capabilities for call centers
◆ Create a sales order via release from a blanket sales order
◆ Create a sales order from a sales quotation
◆ Create a sales order for a replacement item related to a Return Material Authorization (RMA)
◆ Enter a sales order, and create a linked production order
◆ Enter a sales order, and automatically create a sales event manufacturing kanban
◆ Enter a sales order, and create a linked purchase order for a direct delivery or a special order
◆ Automatically create an intercompany sales order from an intercompany purchase order

Additional approaches apply to e-commerce scenarios, where the imported information creates sales orders. Additional approaches also apply to project-oriented operations, such as creating a project sales order or item requirement.

8.2 Sales Order Dates for Shipment and Delivery

A sales order header has a requested ship date and a requested delivery date, where the difference represents the transportation time between the ship-from warehouse and the delivery address. It also has a confirmed ship date and confirmed receipt date. A similar set of these four dates applies to each sales order line, and (if applicable) the delivery schedule lines for a sales order line. The dates on a sales order header can be initially inherited by the sales lines, and changes in the header dates can optionally change the dates on sales lines.

These dates typically reflect basic rules about the calendar of working days assigned to the ship-from warehouse, customer receiving point, and mode of delivery. You can view this information on the *Available Ship and Receipt Dates* page (which can be accessed directly or by using the *Simulate delivery dates* function), and optionally select and transfer the desired dates to update the confirmed dates on the sales order. The confirmed dates can also be updated by performing the *Calculate confirmed delivery dates* function for the sales order.

Several basic rules can be enforced for the shipment and delivery dates on a sales order header and for each line item, but only when you assign one of major options for delivery date control. The option for a sales order header is inherited from a companywide value, which typically reflects a value of "Sales Lead Time" to enforce basic rules. The option for each sales line is inherited from an item-specific value, where the option should reflect the S&OP approach for the item.[1]

The example screen shown in Figure 8.1 illustrates a sales order and the key fields about different delivery dates and the options for delivery date control (in the header and line items). The first two lines identify stocked products with delivery dates governed by ATP logic. The third line identifies a make-to-order product with a delivery date governed by CTP logic. A date could can also be calculated by performing an Explosion for the selected line, as highlighted in the figure.

Figure 8.1 Example Screen of a Sales Order

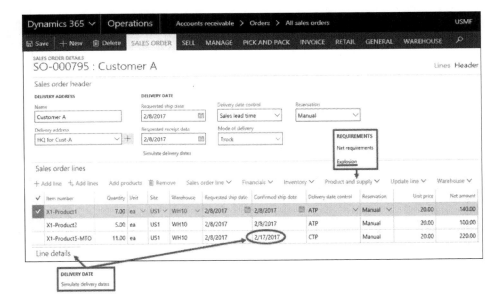

---

[1] You define the item-specific option for delivery date control (inherited by a sales line) as part of the Default Order Settings for a salable item.

8.3 Basic Rules for Delivery Date Control

Several basic rules can be enforced for the shipment and delivery dates on a sales order header and for each line item, but only when you assign one of the three major options for delivery date control. The following basic rules apply when initially entering a sales order header or line item, and when entering changes such as a different date, quantity, or ship-from location.

◆ *Calendar for the ship-from warehouse.* The calendar assigned to the ship-from warehouse determines the working days when items can be shipped.

◆ *Calendar for the customer receiving point.* The calendar assigned to the customer (or the applicable customer address) determines the working days when items can be received.

◆ *Transportation time to customer.* The number of days for transportation time can be specified for the different combinations of the ship-from warehouse, the delivery address characteristics (such as the country, state, county, or ZIP code), and the mode of delivery (such as air or truck).

◆ *Calendar for mode of delivery.* A calendar can be assigned to various modes of delivery for the ship-from warehouse, where the calendar determines the working days when items can be transported. For example, a truck route may only occur on Thursdays.

◆ *Order entry deadlines for taking sales orders.* The concept of an order entry deadline means that orders received after a specified time are treated as if they were received the next day. You define a set of deadlines for each day within a week (termed an order entry deadline group), and then assign the deadline group to each customer and site.

◆ *Sales lead time.* A sales lead time can represent the number of days to prepare a stocked item for shipment (such as a value of 0 or 1 day), or it can represent the quoted lead time for a buy-to-order or make-to-order product. It will be automatically reflected in the shipment date when using any of the three major options. The number of days for sales lead time is specified as a companywide default value, and it can be defined as item-specific overrides.[2]

---

[2] As an alternative approach, the number of days for sales lead time can be defined within sales trade agreements, so that an applicable sales line (for the customer and item) inherits the sales lead time as well as the sales price or discount.

8.4 Delivery Date Control for a Sales Order Line

A delivery date control option applies to each sales line, and it is initially inherited from the option assigned to the item. The four options are summarized in Figure 8.2 along the typical scenario. For example, the option for ATP (Available To Promise) is typically assigned to a stocked item, whereas the option for CTP (Capable To Promise) is typically assigned to a buy-to-order or make-to-order item.

Figure 8.2 Delivery Date Control Options for a Sales Order Line

Delivery Date Control Option	Scenario	Comments
Sales Lead Time	Use Basic Rules *or* Quoted Lead Time	Enforce basic rules for assignment of dates. The number of days for "sales lead time" can reflect prep time or a quoted lead time.
ATP	Stocked End-Item	Enforce basic rules and use ATP logic for dates. Analyze ATP information
CTP	Make-to-Order or Buy-to-Order End-Item	Enforce basic rules and use CTP logic for dates
None	Allow assignment of unrealistic dates	Ignore basic rules for assignment of dates

♦ *Using the Sales Lead Time Option.* This option enforces the basic rules for the assignment of dates. In some scenarios, the number of days for "sales lead time" can represent a quoted lead time for the item.

♦ *Using the ATP Option.* This option typically applies to stocked items, where ATP logic focuses on just the salable item. It enforces the basic rules and employs ATP logic for assignment of dates. The ATP option requires several additional policies about underlying assumptions to correctly calculate an available-to-promise date. You can view the ATP information to answer questions about availability, as described in the next section.

♦ *Using the CTP Option.* This option typically applies to a make-to-order or buy-to-order item. It enforces the basic rules and employs CTP logic for assignment of dates. The CTP option considers available inventory and receipts for the salable item (if applicable), and automatically results in a net change explosion when needed. The use of CTP logic involves a critical assumption about the use of on-hand inventory.

◆ *Using the None Option.* Assigning an option of *None* will disable the rules for delivery date control, thereby allowing assignment of unrealistic dates. As a general guideline, any sales line with this option should be highlighted as an exception requiring follow up.

As an alternative approach, you can perform an explosion for a sales line for calculating a ship date, and it only works when the item's coverage code is other than Manual. You can optionally transfer the calculated date to the confirmed ship date.

Continuous Checking of Sales Order Promise Dates The concept of continuously checking the sales order promise dates is embedded in the calculated delay messages generated by master planning logic. That is, the message indicates when a sales order ship date cannot be met, and identifies the projected ship date.

8.5 ATP Information for a Sales Order

The use of ATP logic for a sales order line typically applies to stocked items, and results in automatic assignment of the ship and delivery dates. Changes to a sales line (such as a change in quantity or ship-from warehouse) result in a message prompt to recalculate these dates. You can also view the ATP information to answer questions about availability, as illustrated in Figure 8.3 and described in Case 8.1. An excellent article by Evert Bos described the effective use of ATP.

Figure 8.3 Example Screen of ATP Information for a Sales Line

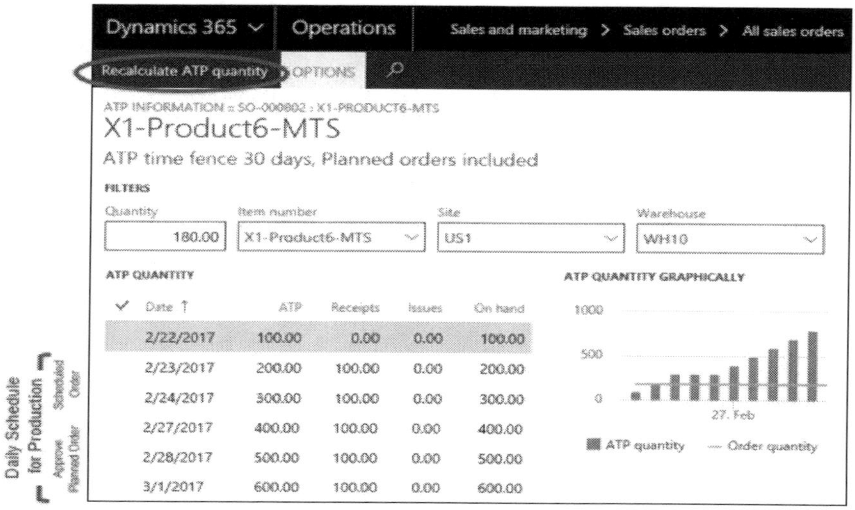

Case 8.1   ATP Information for a Sales Order Line   A manufacturing company produced a family of make-to-stock items based on demand forecasts. The daily production schedule over a rolling 5-day horizon consisted of scheduled orders (for 2 days) and approved planned orders (for the next 3 days). The daily granularity was also reflected in the near-term demand forecasts, which resulted in planned production orders for each day. When entering a sales order for these items, the ship date was automatically calculated based on ATP logic. A customer frequently asked about different availability options, so they analyzed the ATP information for the sales line -- as illustrated in Figure 8.3. In this example data, the sales order quantity of 180 will not be available for shipment until completion of tomorrow's production order, as shown in the ATP quantity information (in tabular and graphical formats). When applicable, the filters were used to simulate a change to the quantity, item or ship-from location, and the *Recalculate ATP Quantity* function updated the displayed information.

8.6 CTP Logic and the assumption about use of On-hand Inventory

The use of CTP logic involves a critical assumption about the use of on-hand inventory. It can differ from master planning logic, which assumes on-hand inventory will be considered for meeting requirements before all other sources of supply. When used for CTP logic, this assumption can lead to situations where existing inventory cannot be considered to fulfill an immediate or near-term order date because of sales orders with future dates (that could be satisfied by scheduled receipts).

You can optionally "override the on-hand" assumption so that CTP logic will consume on-hand inventory "after all other supply". This means scheduled receipts meeting the requirement date will be considered first by CTP logic, as illustrated in Case 8.3. This assumption can be specified as a master plan policy which acts as a companywide default. Alternatively, it can be overridden in the policies within the Coverage Group assigned to an item, or in its Item Coverage policies for a specified site/warehouse.

8.7 Analyze Delivery Alternatives for a Sales Order

The delivery alternatives for meeting a customer's requested delivery date and quantity can reflect product availability at different ship-from warehouses and different modes of delivery. It may also reflect different product variants (such as size or color) in some scenarios. You can evaluate these options for a sales line using the Delivery Alternatives information, and select the desired option for updating the promised dates, the ship-from warehouse, and the mode of delivery on the sales line. You can also choose to ship a smaller quantity than ordered (based on availability) and ship the remainder at a later date, which results in a delivery schedule for the sales line. Case 8.2 illustrates use of the Delivery Alternatives information.

The example screen shown in Figure 8.4 illustrates use of the Delivery Alternatives page, where the figure highlights the two ways for accessing it for a selected sales line. In the example data for a manufactured item, selecting the faster delivery alternative from warehouse WH1 will update the sales order line information to reflect the different ship-from warehouse and expected receipt date.

Figure 8.4 Example Screen of Delivery Alternatives for a Sales Line

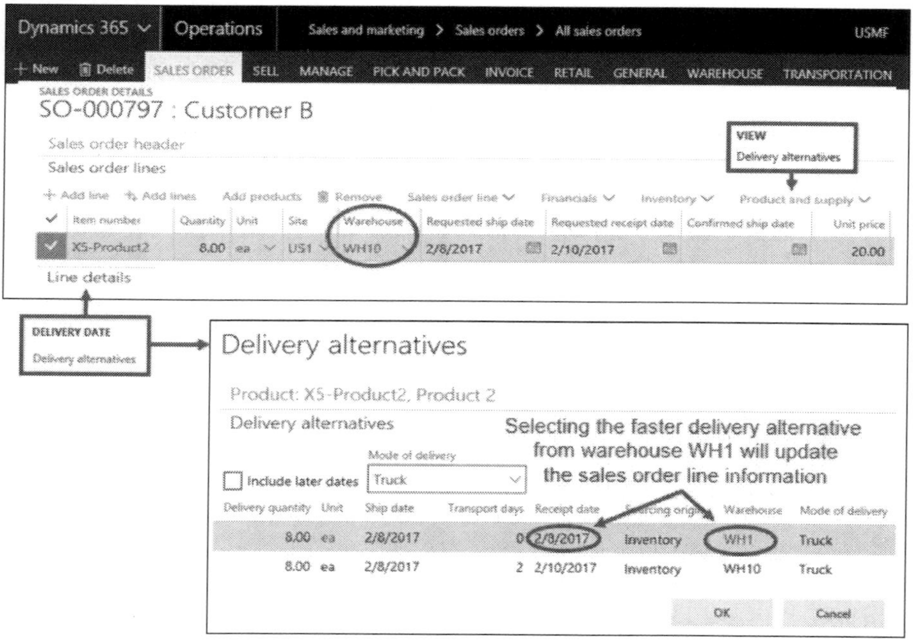

Additional options for the delivery alternatives can be displayed for a purchased item with approved vendors, where you could source the item via a special order or direct delivery order. An additional capability also applies when sourcing from an intercompany vendor, since delivery dates can be calculated based on the item's availability in the sourcing company.

8.8 Reserve Material for a Sales Order Line

Many scenarios employ reservations at the time you release a sales line for picking, and the picking list (or picking work) communicates these reservations. Other scenarios require reservations at the time of order entry, or reservations against an item's scheduled receipts.[3] A few scenarios require reservations of specific batches.

The reservation policy assigned to a sales order line item indicates whether inventory will be reserved automatically or manually. The options for this reservation policy include *Automatic* and *Manual*.[4] When initially adding a line item, its reservation policy can be inherited from the item or from the sales order header.

◆ *Inherit reservation policy from the item.* The item's reservation policy is embedded in the Item Model Group assigned to the item, with a value of *Automatic* or *Manual* (but not *Default*).

◆ *Inherit reservation policy from the sales order header.* The option for the item's reservation policy (embedded in the Item Model Group) should be *Default*. The reservation policy for a sales order header can be inherited from the companywide policy (embedded in the A/R Parameters), and this acts as a default value when adding sales order line items. A change to the reservation policy in the sales order header can update the policy for every line item.

The reservation logic differs between the basic and advanced approaches to warehouse management. The advanced approach requires assignment of an additional item policy for the reservation hierarchy.

8.9 Sales Orders for a Configurable Product

A configurable item provides the starting point for configuring a custom product, typically in the context of a line item on a sales order or sales quotation. The configuration process varies based on the configuration technology. With the constraint-based configuration technology, for example, the process reflects a product configuration model assigned to the configurable item. The configuration process results in creation of a configuration id and its associated BOM and route versions. The configuration process can also calculate a ship date, which can

---

[3] The policy concerning reservations defaults from the sales order header, which defaults from a companywide policy embedded in the A/R parameters. An additional companywide policy determines whether reservations can be made against scheduled receipts.
[4] A third option is termed *Explosion*, which means reservations are made for the components of a manufactured item.

automatically populate the information on the sales line. Alternatively, a net change explosion can calculate a ship date.

The next chapter about item master considerations provides further explanation about the additional information for a configurable item.

8.10 Identify Sales-Related Backorders

A sales-related backorder simply refers to any sales line with a ship date prior to today's date (aka the backorder date). The backorder date can also be specified. The definition of a backorder also applies to a sales line with an unshipped or partially shipped quantity, where the line has not been closed short when reporting actual shipment. This represents the more common interpretation of a sales-related backorder. Some scenarios need to identify the quantity for an unshipped or partially shipped line as "backordered" on sales order documents.[5] A standard inquiry provides information about sales-related backorders.

The customer service representative typically reviews sales-related backorders and then initiates action for a selected backorder. The actions may include updating the promise date, reducing the quantity, or multiple delivery lines. The rep can also request expediting of a supply order for the item.

8.11 Additional Case Studies

Case 8.2: Analyze Delivery Alternatives for a Sales Order Line The customer service reps at a manufacturing/distribution company frequently encountered situations where the customer's requested delivery date could not be met. They needed to quickly assess product availability at different ship-from warehouses, for different product variants (if applicable), and for different modes of delivery to identify the options with the earliest delivery dates. They accessed the Delivery Alternatives information to support these order promising tasks. This approach allowed them to review the available options and select one as the basis for updating the promised ship date and delivery date on the sales line. In some cases, they opted to ship a smaller quantity than ordered (based on availability) and ship the remainder at a later date, which resulted in a delivery schedule for the sales line.

---

[5] You define the treatment of unshipped and partially shipped line items by the Backorder Tracking policy (within the Forms Setup form in the A/R Parameters), where the policy indicates whether backorder information should be included on the printed versions of packing slips and invoices.

Case 8.3: Place a Sales Order on Hold The customer service reps at a company assigned a "hold code" to a sales order to prevent any further processing -- such as a confirmation, picking/shipping or invoicing -- while still allowing changes to the order. Different user-defined hold codes represented variations of an order hold. An additional policy for a hold code determines whether the reservations for a sales order (if any) should be removed after placing it on hold. In either case, master planning logic still recognized the sales order as a demand.

Case 8.4: Capable-to-Promise Logic considers On-Hand Inventory after all other Supply A manufacturing/distribution company frequently took sales orders with future delivery dates for selected products. They wanted the capable-to-promise logic to satisfy these demands by first considering expected receipts of these products (prior to the requirement dates), such as receipts related to purchases, transfers, or production. In this way, the on-hand inventory would then be considered for sales orders with immediate ship dates. This assumption about current inventory was item-specific, and defined by a policy embedded in the Coverage Group assigned to an item.

8.12 Executive Summary

Realistic promise dates for sales order shipments and deliveries can help improve customer satisfaction and supply chain coordination. The initial assignment of the promise dates should align with the item's S&OP game plans, and a sales line with an unrealistic promise date should be highlighted as an exception requiring follow up.

This chapter focused on promise dates for sales orders in traditional manufacturing scenarios, and the use of a delivery date control policy. The three major options for this policy include *ATP, CTP* and *Sales Lead Time*, and the relevant option depends on the S&OP scenario. The chapter also covered the analysis of ATP information, delivery alternatives and backorders, and the use of reservations for sales orders.

Chapter 9

Item Master Considerations

Information about material items provides the foundation for managing supply chain activities in distribution and manufacturing environments. A comprehensive common database about item information must satisfy requirements stemming from multiple stakeholders to avoid the problems associated with multiple nonintegrated files.

This chapter focuses on item master considerations relevant to master planning. These include enterprise- and company-level information for an item, units of measure, the production type, and key aspects of the additional information for purchased items, manufactured items, and salable items. They also include different approaches to item identification and other types of items. These considerations are reflected in the following sections within the chapter.

1. Enterprise- versus Company-Level Information for an Item
2. Unit of Measure Considerations for an Item
3. Significance of Production Type for an Item
4. Additional Information for a Purchased Item
5. Additional Information for a Manufactured Item
6. Additional Information for a Salable Item
7. Additional Information for a Configurable Item
8. Item Identification using an Item Number and Variant Codes
9. Other Types of Items
10. Additional Case Studies

This book primarily focuses on material items identified by an item number. This means you initially define each product by assigning a Product Type of *Item* and a Product Subtype of *Product*, which indicates the item identifier consists of just an item number. In addition, each item must be treated as a stocked product based on a policy within the Item Model Group assigned to the item.

9.1 Enterprise- versus Company-Level Information for an Item

The definition of a material item requires an understanding of enterprise-level versus company-level information whether you manage one or multiple companies within an instance. In summary, the concept of enterprise- versus company-level information has been implemented using two different constructs and their identifiers -- termed the product number and the item number. The product number provides a unique identifier for enterprise-level information about products, whereas the item number provides the unique identifier for company-level information about items. Key aspects of enterprise-level information include the product name and extended description (and their translations if applicable), and unit of measure conversions (if applicable). All other item information is defined at the company level. Two key forms are employed to maintain product and item information: the Products form (for product information) and the Released Products form (for item information).

The conceptual model of enterprise- versus company-level information gives rise to two different approaches for defining items, termed the multi-company approach and the single-company approach.

♦ *Multi-company approach to defining items.* You employ a two-step process to initially define a product and then release the product to a selected company. Releasing the product creates an item number that matches the product number, and you maintain the company-level information for the item number. You can apply a template to partially populate the item information.

As an example, a given item may be manufactured in one company and sold to a sister company that represents a distribution operation, so that the product needs to be released to two different companies. The multi-company approach supports the concept of a centralized engineering function, where centralized engineering may apply to one or more companies.

♦ *Single-company approach to defining items.* You employ a one-step process to simultaneously create product and item information, which automatically releases the product to the company. The one-step process allows you to specify a template (to partially populate the item information) when initially defining the item, or to apply a template later. This one-step approach can also be used in a multi-company environment to initially create a product and auto-release it to one company.

The identifiers for a product number and item number are typically assigned the same value. For example, releasing a product to a selected company automatically creates an item number that matches the product number. The one-step process also supports the assignment of the same identifier. If needed, you can optionally override the item number for a company, thereby supporting a company-specific identifier. [1] Deleting an item number from a company simply removes its authorization for the company; it does not delete the product number.

Additional considerations apply to companywide information versus site- and warehouse-specific information for an item, as described in a previous chapter about modeling inventory locations (Section 5.5).

9.2 Unit of Measure Considerations for an Item

Master planning logic calculates the quantities for demands and supplies in terms of an item's inventory unit of measure (aka UM or UOM for short). However, additional units of measure can be important for different purposes, including purchasing, sales, engineering, production, and warehousing. For example, a different UM may be used for sales orders, demand forecasts or purchase orders, and these must be authorized for the item along with UM conversion factors. The unit of measure codes and the assignment of an item's authorized UM represent enterprise-level information, whereas other UM considerations (such as the item's inventory UM) represent company-level information.

Definition of Unit of Measure Codes The unit of measure codes (or UM codes for short) represent enterprise-level information that is language specific. The UM codes for two different systems of units – metric units and US standard units – are automatically loaded into the system, along with the unit conversion factors (such as grams per kilogram). Additional UM codes must be defined (such as box, case or pallet), and the UM conversion factors are often item specific (such as the number of items per box).

Inventory UM for an Item Each item requires one UM for costing and inventory purposes. This is termed the inventory UM for the item. An item's inventory UM is reflected in its inventory balances, master planning calculations, product costs, and many of the inventory transactions. It is also reflected in the definition of BOM and routing information for a manufactured item, where component quantities and time requirements are typically expressed per the inventory UM for the manufactured item. The inventory UM for an item cannot

---

[1] You can override a different value for the item number (after it has been released to a company) using the rename capability, or when creating an item number and product number using the single-company approach.

be changed after you report inventory transactions, so the assignment of an inventory UM requires careful consideration.

Authorized UM for an Item The item's inventory UM represents an authorized UM for the item. Any other UM must be authorized before it can be used for the item. An authorized UM means it has a UM conversion factor that ties it back to the item's inventory UM. Standard UM conversions apply to UM codes representing US or metric standard units, such as conversions between kilograms, grams, and milligrams. Additional UM codes such as box and case may need to be defined, along with their UM conversion factors for an item. When entering transactions for an item, you can view an item's authorized UM in the drop-down list for the UM field.

9.3 Significance of the Production Type for an Item

The assignment of a *Production Type* to a material item impacts how the item can be used. The production type indicates whether an item is manufactured or purchased, and whether a manufactured item employs the BOM or formula approach to product structure information. The BOM approach generally applies to discrete manufacturing scenarios whereas the formula approach generally applies to process manufacturing scenarios, but many scenarios employ both approaches. This section focuses on the significance of production type when using the BOM approach to product structure, and a subsequent chapter about process manufacturing covers its significance when using the formula approach (Section 18.1).

The following two values for a production type apply when using the BOM approach to product structure.

◆ *None.* A production type of *None* indicates the item represents purchased material. You cannot define BOM or routing information for the item, or create production orders for the item.

◆ *BOM.* A production type of *BOM* indicates a manufactured item, and you can define bill of material and routing information for the item. The item can also be purchased.

The production type of an item can be changed from *None* to *BOM*. However, changing it from *BOM* to *None* has an additional impact because the item can no longer have BOM information, so that the Master BOMs assigned to the item (if any) will be automatically removed.

The production type provides one indicator of whether an item is manufactured or purchased. However, the actual make/buy indicator is embedded in the *planned order type* for the item. For example, the planned order type indicates whether master planning logic should generate planned production orders or planned purchase orders. The planned order type of production also indicates that cost calculations should consider an item's BOM/routing information.

9.4 Additional Information for Purchased Items

A purchased item is typically indicated by its primary source of supply of planned purchase orders (as part of the item's coverage planning data). However, purchase orders can be created for any material item.

The definition of information for a purchased item involves several activities performed by different roles, such as the purchasing agent, cost accountant and quality manager. Various aspects of defining a purchased item are especially relevant to master planning, as summarized below. For example, an item's preferred vendor for planned purchases should reflect an approved vendor, the purchase trade agreements can support a special case of planning data for purchased items, blanket purchase orders provide one grouping basis when firming planned purchase orders, and consignment replenishment orders provide visibility of expected receipts of consigned inventory.

◆ Define planning data for a purchased item (Section 6.3)
◆ Define and enforce approved vendors for a purchased item
◆ Define purchase trade agreements for a purchased item
◆ Define blanket purchase orders for a purchased item
◆ Manage consigned inventory of purchased components (Section 13.6)
◆ Define batch tracking policies for a purchased item (Section 15.1)

9.5 Additional Information for Manufactured Items

A manufactured item is typically indicated by its primary source of supply of planned production orders (as part of the item's coverage planning data). However, production orders can be created for any material item with an approved BOM.

The definition of information for a manufactured item involves several activities performed by different roles, such as the product designer, process engineer, production planner, cost accountant and quality manager.   Various aspects of defining a manufactured item are especially relevant to master planning, as summarized below.

◆   Define planning data for a manufactured item (Section 6.5)
◆   Significance of a single production order (Section 6.6)
◆   Define the bill of material for a manufactured item (Chapter 10)
◆   Define the routing for a manufactured item (Chapter 11)
◆   Define the BOM/routing for a subcontract manufactured item (Section 12.7)
◆   Define batch tracking policies for a manufactured item (Section 15.1)

With the current system design, a product must be released to a company before you can define its BOM and routing information as part of the company-level information.

9.6 Additional Information for a Salable Item

The definition of information for a salable item involves several activities performed by different roles.   Various aspects of defining a salable item are especially relevant to master planning, as summarized below.

◆   Define forecast consumption policies for a salable item (Section 7.3)
◆   Assign a delivery date control policy to a salable item (Section 8.4)
◆   Assign start dates for selling and shipping a new product

9.7 Additional Information for a Configurable Item

The definition of a configurable item typically applies to a salable end-item and its configurable components if any.   The additional information for a configurable item depends on the configuration technology being used.   When using the constraint-based configuration technology within the standard software, for example, the configurable item must be designated as a product master with a product dimension group that includes the configuration variant code.   You also define a product configuration model corresponding to a configurable item, and then approve and activate the model for the item.   A model is also required for each configurable component in a multi-level custom product.

The product configuration model specifies the mapping between prompts/responses (in the configuration process) and the needed components and operations. The configuration process results in the automatic creation of a configuration ID, and the mapping results in an automatically-created BOM version and route version for the item and configuration ID. These three outputs are also created for each configurable component in a multi-level custom product. You can manually maintain these BOM and route versions, which is especially helpful when the configuration process results in partially defined information.

9.8 Item Identification using an Item Number and Variant Codes

Some scenarios can benefit from item identification based on the combined identifiers of an item number and one or more additional fields, where each additional field is termed a variant code. This means you initially define a product by assigning a Product Type of *Item,* a Product Subtype of *Product Master*, and a Configuration Technology of *Predefined Variant*. You also assign a Product Dimension Group to indicate the applicable variant code(s).

Standard functionality includes four possible variant codes named size, color, style and configuration. You define the possible values of a variant code for a given item, such the values for an item's color or size. The use of multiple variant codes for a given item also requires definition of the valid combinations of these values. The use of a variant code (and its possible values) represents enterprise-level information of an item.

Several aspects of item information can only be defined for an item number, so that they apply to all of its variants. Examples include the item's inventory UM, item group, and the policies for batch tracking and batch attributes. Other aspects of item information can be defined for each combination of values for applicable variant codes. Examples include the BOM and routing information for manufactured items as well as product costs, sales prices and purchase prices.

9.9 Other Types of Items

The book focuses on items representing material, but many manufacturing and distribution environments also require other types of items. Examples include service items and non-stock material.

Item Identification of a Service An item number can represent a service, where you designate a product type of *Service* when initially creating a new product. For the item number, you also assign an Item Model Group with a "not stocked product" policy and an actual cost valuation method, and a separate Item Group that represents the services.

Some scenarios involve subcontract manufacturing. The approach to subcontract manufacturing employs a separate item number to represent the subcontracted service, where you also define the item as a component within the parent item's BOM.

Item Identification of Non-Stock Material Item numbers can identify non-stock items, typically representing indirect material used for maintenance, repair, and operations (MRO) purposes. The inventory of non-stock material is not tracked, and standard costs do not apply. You typically define a unique Item Model Group with a "not stocked product" policy and a FIFO valuation method, and assign it to non-stock material.[2] In addition, you typically define a separate Item Group for non-stock material. Trade agreements can be defined for the non-stock material, such as purchase price trade agreements.

9.10 Additional Case Studies

Case 9.1: Enterprise-Level Policies for Items in a Multicompany Supply Chain A manufacturing/distribution business modeled their multicompany operation using multiple companies within a single instance, and goods flowed between different sites/warehouses in the different companies. As part of the enterprise-level policies for items, they standardized their item identification and product names, the UM conversion factors and NMFC code for each item, and enforcement of batch number tracking and the use of storage dimensions. Other company-level policies and data about each item were considered the responsibility of each company.

Case 9.2: Customer Supplied Material An item representing customer supplied material was used as a component in a manufactured product. The item was treated just like any other purchased material, except that its site-specific standard costs were assigned a zero value. This approach supported BOM information about the component, visibility of requirements, coordination via purchase orders, and tracking of receipts, inventory and material usage.

---

[2] One implication of a "not stocked product" is that the item cannot be specified as a component in a BOM.

Case 9.3: Variant Codes for Hardware A hardware manufacturer of screws, bolts and nuts was considering the use of variant codes to replace their current item numbering scheme. The current scheme used significant digits in the item number to represent a product, its characteristics, and its pack sizes. For example, the characteristics of a bolt included length, diameter, finish, and head type, and the pack sizes included 10, 100, and 500 counts. The existing item master had thousands of item numbers reflecting different combinations of these attribute values. The number of new items was growing to meet customer-specific demand for additional variations. The proposed scheme consisted of an item number to represent the product (such as a type of bolt) and several variant codes to represent the product characteristics and pack sizes. The proposed scheme would simply data maintenance about item identification, such as simply adding new values for relevant variant codes and automatically creating new combinations of the values.

Case 9.4: Configurable Item for a Customized Overhead Crane One product line at an equipment company involved a customized overhead crane for moving heavy material around a factory floor. A configurable item and its product configuration model were defined for the overhead crane. The user dialogue in the product configuration model identified usage characteristics, such as maximum load weight, mounting height, and the factory floor dimensions. The model translated the usage characteristics into the required materials and operations to produce the customized overhead crane.

9.11 Executive Summary

This chapter covered item master considerations relevant to master planning. These included enterprise- and company-level information for an item, units of measure, and key aspects of purchased items, manufactured items, salable items and configurable items. It also covered different approaches to item identification and other types of items. Several case studies described enterprise-level policies for an item, customer supplied material, and the use of variant codes.

Bill of Material Information

A key aspect of manufactured items consists of product structure information. The product structure is typically modeled by a bill of material (BOM) in discrete manufacturing scenarios. The BOM information defines the product design and provides the basis for product costing, material planning, material usage reporting, batch and serial number tracking, and tracking progress through stages of manufacturing. It often reflects considerations about the routing information, such as the material requirements for specific operations.

This chapter covers bill of material information relevant to master planning. These include the definition of Master BOMs and BOM versions, and the BOM version policies for an item. They also include key aspects of BOM line information, especially the related operation number and the options for defining the warehouse source of components. Other key aspects involve the production BOM for a production order. These considerations are reflected in the following sections within the chapter.

1. Master BOMs and BOM Versions
2. BOM Version Policies for an Item
3. BOM Lines for Components
4. Options for Defining the Warehouse Source of Components
5. Production BOM for a Production Order
6. Additional Case Studies

A second approach for modeling product structure information involves formulas rather than bills of material, as described in a subsequent chapter about process manufacturing. The formula approach supports several unique capabilities in master planning logic, such as production sequencing and substitute components for planned batch orders, and the coordination of co-products.

10.1 Master BOMs and BOM Versions

A master BOM has a unique identifier (termed the *BOM Number*) which can be manually or automatically defined. Manual definition should be used when the identifier needs to be meaningful, such as a revision level. This book employs the term "Master BOM" whereas the actual term is simply *BOM*. The creation of a master BOM typically occurs in the context of creating an item's BOM version, where it is automatically assigned to the item. A master BOM can also be created independently and then assigned to an item. Each assignment of a master BOM to an item is termed a *BOM Version*, and multiple BOM versions may be needed.

Approving and Activating a BOM Version A Master BOM and a BOM versions are initially treated as unapproved, and they have separate approval steps. require approval. Only an approved BOM version can be marked as active. The active BOM version for an item will normally be used in planning and cost calculations. There are several scenarios requiring multiple active route versions for an item, and even multiple approved-but-not active route versions, as described in the next topic.

Rationale for Multiple BOM Versions for an Item Multiple BOM versions can be defined for an item, typically to support the following situations.

◆ Variations between sites producing the same manufactured item

◆ Planned changes with effectivity dates

◆ Variations that reflect larger production quantities

◆ Alternate bills of material. An alternate bill of material is typically an approved-but-not-active BOM version that can be specified for a manually-created production order or rework order. It can also be specified for a sales order line item (for a make-to-order product) or for a BOM line about a manufactured component, so that master planning logic employs the specified BOM version rather than the active version.

◆ Revision levels of a manufactured item, as illustrated in Case 10.1

◆ Engineering versus production BOMs, as illustrated in Case 10.5

◆ Prototypes or production ramp-up

A manufactured item can have multiple active BOM versions that reflect different sites, non-overlapping validity periods, and/or different quantity breakpoints. An item can also have approved-but-not-active BOM versions. These variations are identified in the route version policies for an item.

BOM Versions represent Non-interchangeable Inventory of a Manufactured Item

In some scenarios, the production of different BOM versions represents non-interchangeable inventory of a manufactured item. This is sometimes termed significant revision levels, and it often applies to make-to-order or configure-to-order products. For example, you may specify an approved-but-not active BOM version in the sub-BOM field for a sales order line, or as part of the BOM line information for a manufactured component. To satisfy demand, master planning calculations will ignore available inventory and generate planned production orders for the specified BOM version. This approach requires an item-specific policy (embedded in the Coverage Group assigned to the item) labeled "Use specified BOM version". A similar policy labeled "Use specified route version" can also be used, as described in the chapter about routing information (Section 11.6).

BOM Versions for each Configuration ID of a Configurable Item

A configure-to-order product can employ different configuration technologies to define its BOM and routing information. When using the constraint-based configuration technology within the standard software, for example, you define a configurable item and its product configuration model. The model defines a mapping between prompts/responses and the information for creating BOM lines. Use of the model in the configuration process automatically generates a configuration ID for the configurable item as well as its BOM version and route version. The previous chapter covered the definition of a configurable item (Section 9.7).

Enforce Rules about BOM Information

Several companywide rules can be optionally enforced about BOM information, as defined in the Inventory and Warehouse Management Parameters and summarized below.

◆ *Mandatory quantity and dates.* This policy requires that a validity period must be entered for a BOM version, and that a quantity must be entered for a BOM line.

◆ *Block removal of approval.* This policy prevents a change in status when a master BOM or BOM version has been approved.

◆ *Block editing.* This policy prevents changes to BOMs once they have been approved.

An additional policy indicates when BOM circularity should be checked. As a general guideline, it should be checked when entering a BOM line thereby providing immediate feedback.

10.2 BOM Version Policies for an Item

The BOM version policies for an item are used to support multiple BOM versions. A BOM version can be site-specific or companywide, and it can have effectivity dates (and a quantity breakpoint if applicable). The BOM version policies also indicate whether it is approved and active. The following explanation covers two key fields in the BOM version policies for an item.

Site-Specific versus Companywide BOM Versions Specifying a blank site for an item's BOM version indicates a companywide bill of material, whereas a specified site indicates a site-specific bill. The primary difference is that master planning logic will use a site-specific BOM version (if it exists) that matches the site of the item's requirements. If a site-specific BOM version does not exist, the master planning logic will use the companywide BOM version for the manufactured item. Master planning calculations will generate an error message if an appropriate BOM version does not exist.

A secondary difference concerns the options for defining the warehouse source of a component. For example, the warehouse source can be manually specified for a site-specific BOM version, but not for a companywide BOM version. A subsequent section provides further explanation about the various options for designating the warehouse source of component inventory.

Effectivity Dates for an Item's BOM Version The effectivity dates for an item's BOM version can represent planned changes in the item's product structure. For example, a manufactured item may have two BOM versions -- one valid to date X and the other valid from date X+1 -- to indicate planned changes. A blank value for the starting and/or ending date indicates no limitation. An item can have multiple active BOM versions with non-overlapping dates.

Example Screen of the BOM Versions for an Item The example screen shown in Figure 10.1 illustrates several key points about the BOM versions for an item, and the BOM lines for components. In this example data, the manufactured item "X3-Product1" has three approved and active BOM versions with non-overlapping validity dates, where they represent site-specific bills of material for site "US1". Each BOM version involves the assignment of a master BOM such as "BOM-0000138" shown in the example.

One of the breakout boxes at the top of the figure illustrates the ability to create a new BOM version (by assigning an existing master BOM), or to create both a new master BOM and a new BOM version. The second breakout box illustrates the ability to approve and activate a BOM version.

The bottom part of Figure 10.1 illustrates the BOM lines for components. In this example data, the first two components are needed for Operation 10 and the third components is needed for Operation 20. The warehouse "WH10" identifies the warehouse source of these components. Another option for defining the warehouse source of a component involves the "resource consumption" policy, as described in a subsequent section (Section 10.4).

Figure 10.1 Example Screen of the BOM Versions for an Item

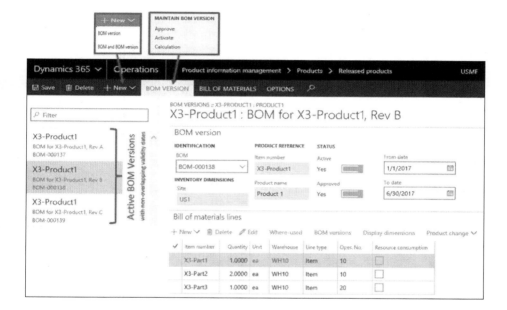

10.3 BOM Lines for Components

A BOM line is used to define each component of a manufactured item. In addition to the item identifier for a component, key aspects of a BOM line include the required quantity and UM, the BOM line type, the associated operation number, and information about the warehouse source of the component. These key aspects of a BOM line were illustrated in Figure 10.1, and this section provides further explanation.

Define Component Requirements as a Quantity The component's required quantity reflects the variable amount needed to produce the parent item. The required quantity also reflects the specified UM for the component. This quantity can be entered as a fraction or decimal. A component's required quantity is normally expressed per a quantity of one parent item, but it can be expressed for a different quantity of the parent item (using the per series field).

A special case of a component's required quantity involves a calculation formula and measurement information, such as height, width, depth, and density. This approach often applies to cut-to-size components, such as a cut-to-length component where the component quantity depends on the length measurement of its parent item. In this way, a single master BOM can be assigned to multiple manufactured items and each parent item will have a different measurement for length. Case 10.6 provides an illustrative example.

Impact of the Operation Number assigned to a Component When routing data exists, the operation number assigned to a component provides the key link between the BOM information and the associated operation within the routing. There are several impacts of assigning an operation number to a component. For example, the operation's scrap percentage affects component requirements, and the resource assigned to the operation can determine the relevant warehouse source for picking the component for a production order. These impacts are summarized below.

◆ Align the due date of a component with the start of its associated operation. Components with a blank operation number are required at the start of the production order.

◆ Align the due date of a component with the end of its associated operation, which typically applies to a component representing a subcontracted service.

◆ Calculate component requirements to reflect the scrap percentage of the operation, and its cumulative scrap percentage in a multi-step routing.

◆ Populate the picking list based on the started quantity for a specified operation number (or a range of operation numbers).

◆ Segment the picking list by operation number. A picking list can be generated for all components with the same operation number.

◆ Determine the resource that requires the component in order to support resource consumption logic about the warehouse source of component inventory.

The operation number assigned to a component should correspond to the operation number in the associated route version for the manufactured item. However, the operation number in the routing may not exist in some cases. For example, you can specify a different route version when manually creating a production order, or override the operations in the production routing.

Warehouse Source of a Component   A component's warehouse source indicates where to pick the item for a production order.   There are several options for defining a component's warehouse source.   The selected option impacts master planning logic about material requirements at the component's warehouse, and the related information will be inherited by the Production BOM and ultimately by the picking list journal for a production order.

As one of the simplest options, you can specify the component's warehouse source as part of the BOM line when using site-specific BOMs.   Other options employ the "resource consumption" policy for each BOM line, which defers assignment of a warehouse source until a resource (or resource group) has been scheduled for each routing operation.   This requires routing information and operation numbers linking BOM lines to specific operations.   The next section provides further explanation about the various options for a component's warehouse source (Section 3.5).

Impact of the BOM Line Type   The BOM line type represents a key policy impacting master planning logic and supply chain management.   In most cases, it simply designates whether a manufactured component will be treated as a normal item or a phantom item, as described below.   However, it can also designate a make-to-order or buy-to-order component.

◆   *Item (or Normal).*   Master planning logic will suggest a planned order to satisfy requirements.   These orders are not directly linked to the production order for the parent item.

◆   *Phantom.*   A phantom only applies to a manufactured item.   The requirements for a phantom component are passed (or blow-through) to its components and routing operations.   The impact of blow-through logic becomes obvious in the production BOM and routing for a production order.   The netting logic within master planning ignores the phantom's on-hand inventory and scheduled receipts (if applicable), and suggests planned orders for the phantom's components to satisfy requirements.   Case 10.4 illustrates the use of phantoms.

BOM Line Type for a Make-to-Order or Buy-to-Order Component   The BOM line types of *Pegged Supply* and *Vendor* support make-to-order and buy-to-order components, as described below and illustrated in Case 10.2.

◆   *Make-to-order component.*   A BOM line type of *pegged supply* applies to a manufactured item, and represents a make-to-order production strategy with direct linkage between production orders.   That is, a production order for the parent automatically generates a linked order (termed a *sub-production* or *reference order*) for each manufactured component with a line type of pegged supply.[1] The system indicates linkage via the reference fields in each production order, and linked orders can be scheduled separately or synchronized.

The netting logic within master planning ignores the component's on-hand inventory and scheduled receipts, since the system assumes the component is being produced just for the parent item's production order. The master planning calculations will generate planned production orders to provide visibility of requirements, but these planned orders cannot be firmed.

A make-to-order component was previously mentioned in terms of its impact on coverage planning data for a manufactured item (Section 6.7) and its use in S&OP scenarios for make-to-order products (Section 2.3).

◆ *Buy-to-order component.* A BOM line type of *Vendor* applies to a purchased item or service, and it represents a buy-to-order component. That is, a production order for the parent automatically generates a linked purchase order (also termed a reference order) for each purchased component with a line type of vendor.[2] Similar to make-to-order components, the system assumes the component is being purchased just for the parent item's production order, and master planning logic ignores the component's on-hand inventory and scheduled receipts. Master planning calculations will generate planned purchase orders to provide visibility of requirements, but these planned orders cannot be firmed.

A buy-to-order component has one other unique feature, since a preferred vendor can be defined for the component as an override to the preferred vendor for the item. When automatically generating a linked purchase order, the system assigns the component's preferred vendor (if defined) or the item's preferred vendor to the purchase order. This line type is commonly used to support purchases of a component that represents a subcontracted service, and a subsequent chapter about production orders provides further explanation of subcontracted production (Section 12.8).

A line type of vendor can also be assigned to a manufactured component, and it works just like the line type of pegged supply. As a minor difference, it results in a production order type labeled *vendor* rather than *standard*. For example, a production order type of vendor could indicate that a subcontractor will produce the manufactured component.

---

[1] The production order for a make-to-order component is automatically generated when the status of the parent item's production order has been changed from created to estimated, or to a higher status such as scheduled.
[2] The purchase order for a buy-to-order component is automatically generated when the status of the parent item's production order has been changed from created to estimated, or to a higher status such as scheduled.

A buy-to-order component was previously mentioned in terms of its impact on coverage planning data for a purchased item (Section 6.4).

Considerations about Planned Scrap The planned scrap for a component can be expressed as a percentage or a fixed quantity or both. When using routing data, the planned scrap percentage for an operation can also affect the requirements of components associated with the operation. An accumulated scrap percentage may also apply in a multistep routing because of scrap percentages for previous operations. Each production BOM and routing (for a production order) inherit the scrap factors from the item's BOM version and route version, and these can be overridden. These scrap factors are included in planning and cost roll-up calculations.

Effectivity Dates of an Component The effectivity dates provide one approach for managing planned changes to BOM information.

10.4 Options for Defining the Warehouse Source of Components

A component's warehouse source indicates where to pick the item for a production order. There are several options for defining a component's warehouse source. The selected option impacts master planning logic about material requirements at the component's warehouse, and the related information will be inherited by the production BOM and ultimately by the picking list journal for a production order. This inherited information can be optionally overridden.

Four basic options are summarized in Figure 10.2 and described below. The first three options reflect the use of a picking list journal for reporting the picked material, which also indicates actual material usage for the production order. Each option involves considerations about BOM and routing information, and the requirements for additional information vary by option.

The fourth option displayed in the figure represents a slightly different purpose for the picking list journal, and it is typically employed when using the advanced approach to warehouse management. It assumes components will be picked and delivered to a production input location based on work orders for Raw Material Picking, so that the picking list journal is only used for reporting actual material usage from the production input location.

Figure 10.2 Options for Defining the Warehouse Source of Components

Purpose of Picking List Journal		Pick from Locations in Suggested Warehouse Source of Components			Pick from Production Input Location
		Option #1	Option #2	Option #3	Option #4
		Use specified warehouse on BOM Line for component	Use default warehouse for item	Assign input warehouse based on production unit and scheduled resource	Assign production input location based on scheduled resource
BOM & Route		Site-Specific BOM	Applies to Site-Specific or Companywide BOM		
		Routing Information not Required	Routing Information Required		
Additional Information		BOM Line has no Resource Consumption Policy		BOM Line has Resource Consumption Policy and an Operation Number linked to Routing	
		None	Item's default inventory warehouse for required site	Resource group has an assigned production unit (with its input warehouse)	Resource group (or resource) has an assigned production input location

Legend: ▢ = Supports the Advanced WMS approach to warehouse management

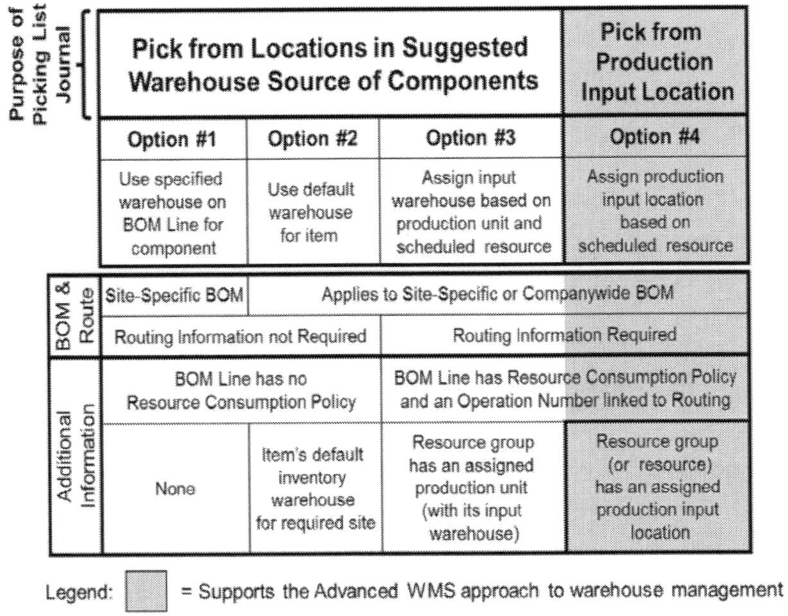

Option #1: Use the specified warehouse on the BOM line for the component The first option only applies to a site-specific BOM version, and the specified warehouse must belong to the site. After creating a production order for the manufactured item, the component in the Production BOM inherits the component's specified warehouse.

Option #2: Use the default warehouse for the item The second option does not specify a component warehouse on the BOM line, and requires additional information about the item's default inventory warehouse for each site (as defined in the item's site-specific order settings). After creating a production order, the component in the Production BOM inherits the component's default inventory warehouse for the required site.

A shown in the figure, the first two options do not require routing information, and they represent the most straight-forward approach. In addition, they do not employ the "resource consumption" policy on a BOM line, even when routing information has been defined.

Option #3: Automatically assign an input warehouse based on the scheduled resource and its related production unit The third option requires routing information and operation numbers linking BOM lines to specific operations. It employs the "resource consumption" policy for each BOM line, which defers assignment of a warehouse source until a resource (or resource group) has been scheduled for each routing operation. A resource group has an assigned production unit, which might be assigned to multiple resource groups with a common warehouse source of components. This is termed the input warehouse for a production unit. After scheduling a production order, the component in the Production BOM inherits the input warehouse associated with the resource group performing the operation.

Option #4: Automatically assign a production input location based on the scheduled resource The fourth option represents a different purpose for the picking list journal, as mentioned earlier. It assumes components will be delivered to a production input location which will be identified on the picking list journal for reporting actual material usage from the location.　Delivering components to a production input location involves work orders for Raw Material Picking when using the Advanced WMS approach to warehouse management. It involves transfer journals or withdrawal kanbans when using the basic approach to warehouse management.

The fourth option requires routing information and operation numbers linking BOM lines to specific operations, and it also employs the "resource consumption" policy for each BOM line, just like the third option.

You define a location representing each production input location within a warehouse, so that it can be assigned to a resource group or to individual resources within the group.　After scheduling a production order, the component in the Production BOM inherits the production input location associated with the resource group (or resource) performing the operation.

It is feasible to assign both a production input location and a production unit to a resource group, but scheduling logic will use the former for assigning the location to components in the Production BOM.

10.5 Production BOM for a Production Order

A production BOM (aka the order-dependent BOM) refers to the BOM lines attached to a production order. It initially contains the BOM lines inherited from the BOM version used to create the production order. Changes to the production BOM do not affect the Master BOM. Creation and maintenance of the production BOM reflect several rules.

◆ Creation of a production order for a manufactured item also creates a production BOM.

◆ The production BOM initially reflects the item's BOM version that was used to create the production order. In most cases, this will be inherited from the active BOM version for the delivery date and site on the production order. However, you can manually specify a different BOM version for the item when creating the production order, where the BOM version can be approved-but-not-active.

◆ The production BOM contains components of a phantom.

◆ You can modify the components in a production BOM at any time prior to ending the production order. For example, you can manually maintain the information, or copy BOM lines from another production order or Master BOM.

◆ A material item can be issued to a started production order even when the component does not exist on the production BOM. The issued component will be automatically added to the production BOM with a required quantity of zero.

10.6 Additional Case Studies

Case 10.1: Revision Levels for a Manufactured Item   A manufacturer employed the BOM versions to represent the revision levels for a manufactured item, such as revision A, B and C. The inventory resulting from production of different revision levels was treated as interchangeable by master planning logic. For reference purposes, the identifier assigned to each Master BOM represented a combination of the item number and revision level. The item's BOM version policies identified the effectivity dates for phasing out (and phasing in) these BOM versions. A different item number identified a complete change in a product, since this represented the maxim about changing form/fit/function.

Case 10.2: Make-to-Order Production Strategy   A basic variation in manufacturing involves the choice of production strategies as part of the S&OP game plans for an item. The two classic production strategies are termed make-to-stock (MTS) and make-to-order (MTO). In many cases, a make-to-order strategy does not require a link between the production order and the sales order for the item. In other cases, a make-to-order strategy requires this linkage. You can establish linked orders by first creating a production order for a sales order line for the end-item, and then scheduling this production order to automatically create the linked production orders for components (termed reference orders). The reference orders reflect BOM information about components, where a BOM line type of *pegged supply* indicates a make-to-order component and a BOM line type of *vendor* indicates a buy-to-order component. Figure 10.3 illustrates how to create linkage between a sales order line item and a production order, and the impact of the BOM line type on creating linked production orders and linked purchase orders for components.

Figure 10.3 Make-to-Order Product with Linked Orders

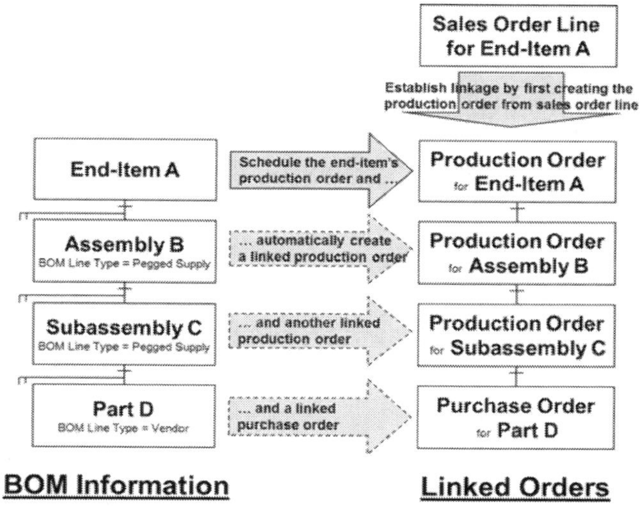

Case 10.3: Kit Items   A manufacturing company sold kits of material, where a separate item (and associated BOM version) defined each kit's components. Several types of kits could be sold. One type of kit was priced and sold as a single item, and posting the sales invoice resulted in backflushing of the item's components. Another type of kit was priced and sold as separate component items. Each sales order line for a kit item was exploded into its components, thereby creating multiple line items with separate prices that were shipped and invoiced separately. Other scenarios involved the selection of kit components from a

predefined list, pricing based on the sum of sales prices for kit components, returns of an entire kit or selected components, and selective printing of kit information on sales-related documents.[3]

Case 10.4: Phantoms for Intermediate BOM Levels A toy company produced and sold cases of toys to retailers, where each case included boxes of the individual toy. Each box represented the consumer unit and an intermediate level of packaging. Each case and box of the toy had separate item numbers, with different UPC codes, measurements, and weights. The box with an individual toy was treated as a phantom in the product structure because the packaging line could insert the toy into a box and pack them immediately into cases. It was sometimes stocked or sold separately.

Case 10.5: Engineering versus Production BOMs The engineering department wanted to define a separate engineering BOM and then convert it into a BOM for production purposes. They defined a separate BOM version for a manufactured item that represented the engineering BOM. At the appropriate time, it was copied into a different BOM version for production purposes, and it was subsequently approved and activated for production. The starting effectivity date for the BOM version considered current inventories and other factors.

Case 10.6: Cut-To-Size Materials A fabricated products company needed to express BOM requirements in terms of the number of pieces of cut-to-size materials, such as steel rod and sheet metal, but did not want to create item numbers for each unique size. They solved the problem using the calculation formula and measurements for a component's required quantity. One example involved sheet metal purchased in pounds, costed and stocked in 5x10 sheets, and with component requirements expressed in square feet. Each parent item produced from the sheet metal required different height and width measurements, but only one master BOM to calculate the required square footage in sheet-size increments (50 square feet). This approach also identified purchasing and stockroom picking requirements for the raw materials, and provided cut-to-size instructions for production.

10.7 Executive Summary

Discrete manufacturers typically employ bills of material to model their product structure. This chapter described the key information about BOM version policies and BOM lines, and the options for defining the warehouse source of components. Several case studies illustrated the use of BOM information, such as linked orders, kit items and cut-to-size material.

---

[3] See www.AXtension.com for additional information about their kitting add-on module.

Chapter 11

Routing Information

Routing information provides a model of the processing steps for a manufactured item, expressed as operations that identify the production resource requirements. The routing information provides the basis for calculating value-added costs, capacity planning and production scheduling of resources, reporting of actual labor and resource usage, and tracking progress through the processing steps. In addition, the bill of material often reflects considerations about an item's routing information, such as the material requirements for specific operations.

This chapter focuses on routing information relevant to master planning in manufacturing scenarios. This information includes the definition of production resources and resource groups, resource capabilities, and the use of master routings and route versions. It also includes the definition of master operations and their use in routings. Other key aspects involve the different scheduling methods for production orders based on routing data, and the production route for a production order. These considerations are reflected in the following sections within the chapter.

1. Production Resources and Resource Groups
2. Resource Capacity and Finite Capacity Considerations
3. Master Planning with Finite Capacity
4. Using Resource Capabilities
5. Using Employee Competencies
6. Master Routings and Route Versions
7. Route Version Policies for an Item
8. Master Operations
9. Define an Internal Operation in a Routing
10. Comparison of Scheduling Methods: Job versus Operation Scheduling
11. Production Route for a Production Order
12. Additional Case Studies

Routing data provides the basis for suggested production schedules. Production scheduling often requires consideration of many factors that are difficult to model, especially with dynamic changes to priorities and/or available capacity. In this case, the suggested schedules provide a rough approximation and a starting point for manual scheduling that reflects more complex considerations.

To simplify the explanations, this chapter does not cover project manufacturing scenarios involving forecasted hours for production resources, or the use of resources to represent project personnel (which involves additional scheduling and costing considerations).

11.1 Production Resources and Resource Groups

The definition of production resources and resource groups provides the foundation for modeling routing information. Their significance primarily reflects the assignment of a Resource Type. The resource type indicates whether a production resource represents a machine, an individual employee, a type of production worker, a tool, or some other type of capacity constraint or manufacturing cost. It may also represent a tightly linked group of machines or a manufacturing cell that can be treated as single resource. Each resource must belong to a resource group. A resource group typically represents similar resources located in close proximity within the same site. You can specify a resource or a resource group as the resource requirement for a routing operation.

Identification of Production Resources and Resource Groups   A production resource has a unique identifier and description, and a resource group also has a unique identifier and description. Each resource must be assigned to a resource group, and changes in this assignment can be indicated by validity dates. A resource group is assigned to a site, and the site applies to all resources within the resource group.

Example Screen for Production Resources   The example screen shown in Figure 11.1 illustrates the definition of production resources for a machine and for an employee. In the example data, the resource "X1-Machine1" represents a machine within the resource group "X1-MachGrp", and the resource "000021" represents an employee (with an assigned worker of 000021) within the resource group "X1-TeamA". Both resources have an assigned calendar of "1Shift5Day", which consists of 8-hour days for a 5-day week.

Figure 11.1   Example Screen for Production Resources

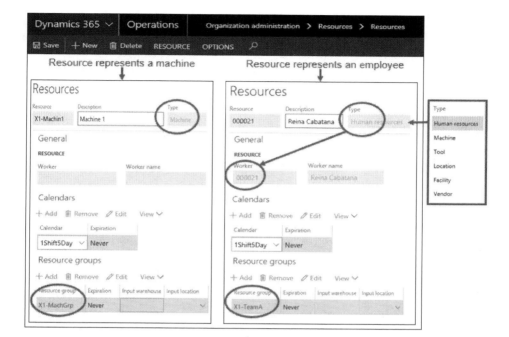

Types of Production Resources and what they Represent   The assignment of a resource type to a resource (and resource group) provides the primary indicator of what it represents, which then influences the definition of related information. The most commonly used resource types consist of a machine or human resource. Some suggested guidelines for identifying resources and their resource group are provided below.

◆ *Resource represents a Machine.* A resource type of machine often represents a single machine, but it may also represent a tightly linked group of machines that acts as a single entity for capacity planning and scheduling purposes. The resource capacity for a single machine is typically expressed as one, and its calendar reflects the relevant shift pattern.

When defining a resource group related to machines (and then assigning machines to the group), the grouping typically represents machines in close physical proximity with similar characteristics in terms of capabilities and operating costs.

◆ *Resource represents a Miscellaneous Area.* A resource type of machine is sometimes used to model a miscellaneous area comprised of a mixture of personnel and equipment performing various operations. This provides the basis for defining routing operations, and an approximation of costing, capacity planning, and scheduling considerations. The resource capacity provides an approximation of how many operations can be concurrently processed within the miscellaneous area, and the calendar reflects the relevant shift pattern.

◆ *Resource represents a specific Employee.* A resource type of human resource can represent a specific employee by assigning the worker ID, as illustrated in Figure 11.1. When defining the related resource group, the grouping typically represents a labor pool or a team of people in close physical proximity with similar characteristics in terms of capabilities and labor rates. In this way, you can model crew size requirements in a routing operation by specifying the resource group and the number of required resources within the group. The calendar assigned to the resource reflects the relevant shift pattern for the employee.

You can change the assignment of an employee to a different shift by specifying the validity dates of the assigned calendars. You can also change the employee's assignment to a different resource group by specifying the validity dates of the assignment.

When the resource represents a specific employee, you have an additional option for using employee competencies as the basis for the resource requirements for an operation, as described in a subsequent section.

◆ *Resource represents a type of Production Worker.* A resource type of human resource can represent a type of production worker by not assigning a worker ID. Example identifiers for these resources could be Prod-Worker-1, Prod-Worker-2, and so forth. The above-mentioned considerations about the related resource group and calendar also apply.

◆ *Resource represents a Vendor.* A resource type of vendor typically represents a specific subcontractor (with optional assignment of the vendor number) that performs subcontracted production using supplied material.

◆ *Resource represents a Tool.* A tool resource is rarely specified unless it represents a critical scheduling constraint. Examples of a tool include a serialized die, mold or re-useable fixture. A tool is typically specified as a secondary resource for performing an operation. A resource group for tooling generally represents several serial numbers of the exact same tool. A tool resource does not support tool inventory management or the tracking of tool cycle usage (e.g., for triggering replacement or rebuild). A serialized tool must be identified as an item to support these purposes.

◆ *Resource represents a Location or Facility.* A resource type of location or facility is conceptually similar to a tool resource, and is rarely specified unless it represents a critical scheduling constraint. One example would a clean room. The clean room would typically be specified as a secondary resource for performing an operation. A resource group could represent several similar clean rooms. Modeling a location as a resource simply provides a scheduling constraint. Actual inventory locations must be defined in terms of the site, warehouse, and bin location.

Guidelines for Specifying a Resource or Resource Group in a Routing Operation Several factors should be considered in choosing whether to designate a resource or a resource group as the resource requirements for performing an operation. The following guidelines focus on machines and human resources.

◆ *Specify a Resource for the Operation.* This approach assumes the operation can only be performed at the specified machine, where the operation identifies the machine-specific times and costs. A similar assumption applies to a specified human resource, where the resource represents a specific employee.

◆ *Specify a Resource Group for the Operation* With machines, this approach assumes the operation can be performed on any machine within the group, and the machines have similar run times and cost structures. As part of defining a routing operation, you can optionally specify which machine will provide the default values for cost information and time requirements. Master planning logic with the job scheduling method will assign a specific machine (within the group) to an operation in order to meet the due date.

With human resources, the resource group typically represents a group of employees or production workers with interchangeable skills and similar hourly rates. When defining an operation for the resource group, you can specify the required number of people (aka crew size) for the operation. You can optionally specify which human resource will provide the default values for cost information. Master planning logic with the job scheduling method will assign specific human resources (within the group) to an operation in order to meet the due date and crew size requirements.

Aggregate Capacity and Loads for a Resource Group The aggregate capacity for a resource group is based on the sum of available capacity for the related resources. The aggregate load for the resource group includes the time requirements for its related resources. An analysis of aggregate load versus capacity can help anticipate overloaded periods.

Changing the Assignment of a Resource to a Resource Group In a static environment, you assign a resource to a single resource group. In a dynamic environment with changing assignments, you indicate the expiration date for the current assignment, and also indicate the new assignment. For example, a piece of equipment or a person may be moved to a different site, which would be modeled by assigning the resource to a different resource group.

Production Unit for a Resource Group A user-defined production unit provides one approach for identifying an input warehouse and output warehouse related to production orders at the resources within a resource group. You assign a production unit to a resource group. The use of a production unit to define a component's warehouse source was described in the previous chapter (Section 10.4).

Production Input and Output Locations for a Resource Group The assignment of a production input location to a resource group (or to individual resources within the group) is typically used to support the advanced warehousing approach to production order picking, where a work order for raw material picking delivers components to the relevant production input location. The use of a production input location to define a component's warehouse source was described in the previous chapter (Section 10.4). In addition, the assignment of a production output location to a resource group indicates where to place the finished quantities of a production order.

11.2 Resource Capacity and Finite Capacity Considerations

Key aspects of defining a production resource include the available capacity and the designation of finite capacity. These key aspects and several others are illustrated in Figure 11.2 and described below.

Figure 11.2 Example Screen of a Resource and the key policies about Capacity

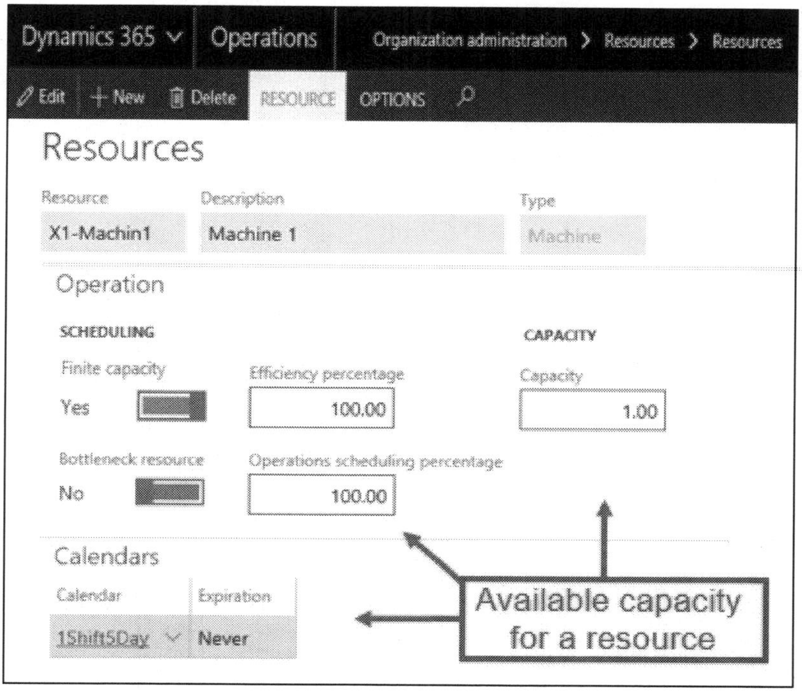

Available Capacity for a Resource A resource's available capacity is defined by two basic factors: the calendar defining the hours of operation and the capacity per hour.

◆ *Hours of Operation.* The calendar assigned to a resource defines the hours of operation for each calendar day. It often reflects the relevant shift patterns. For example, the calendar may represent a single shift (for the time period of 7:00 am to 3:00 pm) over a 5 day week. Exceptions to these working hours -- such as downtime or overtime -- can be identified in a different calendar, and you assign the different calendar to a given date. These are termed calendar deviations.

◆ *Capacity per Hour.* A single resource that can perform one task at a time has a capacity of 1.00 during working hours. However, a resource sometimes represents several people or machines, where more than one task can be performed at the same time. The average number of concurrent tasks is termed the *resource capacity*. With a capacity of 5, for example, up to 5 different operations can be scheduled concurrently for each hour of operation.

A third factor -- termed the *operations scheduling percentage* for a resource -- affects how master planning logic views the resource's available capacity. A scheduling percentage of 80%, for example, means that master planning logic will only consider 80% of the available capacity when assigning loads to the resource. This approach provides flexibility for handling unexpected time requirements.

Designation of Infinite versus Finite Available Capacity The available capacity for a resource (or resource group) can be designated as finite or infinite. An infinite capacity viewpoint means that master planning logic ignores existing loads for the resource, but still considers constraints about available capacity. A finite capacity viewpoint means that master planning logic considers current loads as well as the constraints of available capacity. A resource (and resource group) must be designated with finite capacity to support master planning with finite capacity. This designation also supports scheduling of production orders with consideration of finite capacity.

Designating Bottleneck Resources for Finite Capacity Planning Purposes The optional designation of a bottleneck resource can improve performance of master planning calculations. Additional master plan policies must be defined for consideration of bottleneck resources within the time horizon defined by the bottleneck capacity time fence.

Efficiency and the Impact on Time Requirements for a Resource Efficiency does not impact available capacity but still represents a key consideration in the calendar assigned to a resource. The time requirements expressed in routing operations can be factored up or down based on the efficiency percentage assigned to the resource. The resource's efficiency percentage acts as a default in the resource's assigned calendar. The efficiency for selected working times (such as a lower efficiency for late night hours) can then be manually overridden in the calendar.

11.3 Master Planning with Finite Capacity

A master plan policy indicates whether planned production orders will be scheduled with finite capacity assumptions, and several related policies identify the assumptions. These master plan policies are illustrated in the example screen shown in Figure 11.3 and described below. The example data within the figure illustrates system usage for Case 11.1, which will be described shortly.

Figure 11.3 Example Screen of Master Plan Policies about Finite Capacity

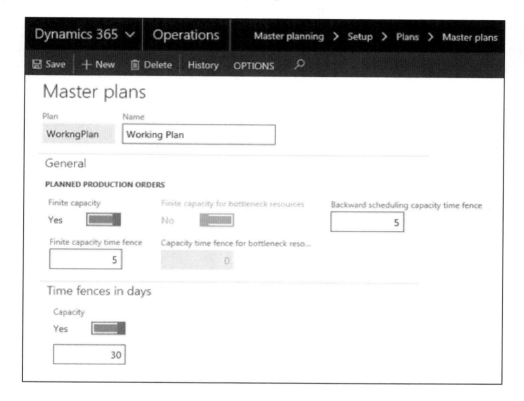

◆ *Finite capacity.* This policy indicates whether master planning calculations will consider finite capacity for planned production orders. The calculations only apply to resources (and resource groups) that have been designated for finite capacity.

◆ *Finite capacity time fence.* This policy represents one assumption about the relevant time horizon for considering finite capacity. It typically reflects a near-term horizon, such as the 5-day horizon shown in the example data.

◆ *Finite capacity for bottleneck resources* and the *capacity time fence for bottleneck resource.* These considerations only apply to resources (and resource groups) that have been designated as a bottleneck for finite capacity. It primarily serves to improve performance of the master planning calculations. The example data indicates it is not being considered.

◆ *Backward scheduling capacity time fence.* This policy ensures that master planning logic will consider available capacity prior to the requirement date for planned production orders.

◆ *Capacity time fence.* This policy indicates the time horizon for calculating capacity requirements stemming from planned and actual production orders, such as the 30-day horizon shown in the example data. This time fence can be defined as one of the policies within the Coverage Group assigned to an item, or as a master plan policy (which overrides the item-specific time fences).

Case 11.1: Master Planning with Finite Capacity   One product line at a manufacturing company consisted of multiple end-items with a multi-level product structure (and the same resource requirements) and a 30-day cumulative manufacturing time. Several key resources had limited capacity, and capacity requirements were calculated over a 30-day time horizon. The suggested production schedules for these key resources were reviewed and adjusted daily, and included consideration of planned orders over a 5-day time horizon.

The key resources were designated as having finite capacity, and master planning calculations employed a 5-day time fence in considering finite capacity when generating planned production orders. These planned orders reflected the scheduling logic embedded in the routing data, and provided a first-cut of production schedules that were subsequently adjusted manually. A time fence of 30-days was also used to calculate capacity requirements (with infinite capacity assumptions) for planned production orders, thereby helping to anticipate overloaded periods.

11.4 Using Resource Capabilities

Capabilities provide one approach for modeling the resource requirements of a routing operation, and they apply to any type of resource. You assign a capability to one or more resources, and a resource can have more than one capability assigned to it. Based on this information, you can then specify the required capability for performing a routing operation.

Each capability has a user-defined identifier and description, and you specify a list of which resources can provide the capability. Conversely, you can assign a capability to resource. The following guidelines apply to the definition and use of resource capabilities.

Specify Date Effectivities of the Resource Capability   Each resource assigned to a capability can be assigned a starting and ending effectivity date. A resource can be listed more than once with different effectivity dates, typically to represent a capability that cannot be performed for a given time period. When a requirement date for the capability falls outside of the effective period, the resource will not be scheduled.

Assign Priorities to Support Alternate Resource Logic   Each resource assigned to a capability can be assigned a numeric priority, where a value of 0 (or 1) represents the highest priority. The priority provides the basis for alternate resource logic in scheduling calculations.[1] That is, the resource with the highest priority will be considered first by master planning logic with the job scheduling method. The resource with the next-highest priority will only be considered when the requirement date cannot be met. Case 11.2 illustrates this use of priorities to model the preferred equipment for a capability.

Specify the Level of Capability to Support Alternate Resource Logic
The level of capability provides an additional basis for determining whether a resource can satisfy the capability. You specify the capability level as numeric value. In a similar fashion, you specify a value for the minimum level needed as part of the resource requirements in a routing operation. Master planning logic with the job scheduling method will only consider resources in the list with an equal or higher value than the minimum level needed. Cases 11.3 and 11.4 illustrate how to indicate preferred equipment based on requirements for a minimum capability.

Specify the Capability as the Resource Requirement for a Routing Operation   One or more capabilities can be specified as the resource requirements for a routing operation. Since the required capability may be satisfied by different resources, you should specify the approximate costs for performing the operation. These hourly rates can be manually specified using the cost category fields, or the cost categories can be initially populated by specifying a "costing resource" for the operation.

Case 11.2: Preferred Equipment for a Capability   The production supervisor wanted to schedule production using the optimal packaging line (out of the three possible packaging lines). When the optimal packaging line was fully booked, the production could be scheduled on another line. To support this logic, the operation's resource requirements (in the route version for each manufactured item) were defined for a "packaging line" capability, and the capability was assigned to the three packaging lines along with a priority sequence. In this way, the master planning logic assigns the optimal line to meet the production due date.

---

[1] A policy - termed *primary resource selection* - determines whether master planning logic assigns resources based on *duration* or *priority*. Selecting a policy value of *priority* supports alternate resource logic based on priorities. The policy can be company-wide or site-specific, as defined on the Scheduling Parameters or Scheduling Parameters by Site form within the Master Planning setup information.

If the due date cannot be met, the master planning logic assigns a different line based on the prioritized list.

Case 11.3: Preferred Equipment based on Minimum Capability The production supervisor wanted to schedule production using the optimal packaging line (out of the three possible packaging lines). One packaging line could only handle small packages, another line could handle small or medium packages (but not large packages), and the third line could handle any package size. To support this logic, the operation's resource requirements (in the route version for each manufactured item) were defined for a "packaging line" capability and a minimum capability level of 1, 2 or 3 (that represented the three package sizes). The capability and a capability level were also assigned to the three packaging lines. In this way, the master planning logic would only assign production to a packaging line that could meet the minimum required capability. For example, large packages were only assigned to the packaging line that could handle them.

Case 11.4: Preferred Machine based on Minimum Capability The production supervisor wanted to schedule production using the optimal machine, where the three machine resources consist of a 20-ton press, a 50-ton press, and a 100-ton press. The setup information involved a capability termed Press, and the three machines were assigned this capability along with a capability level of 20, 50 and 100 respectively. In addition, the press capability was identified as the resource requirement for routing operations along with the minimum level needed. For example, with a minimum level of 40, master planning logic will schedule the operation on the 50-ton or 100-ton press.

11.5 Using Employee Competencies

Some production scenarios require scheduling of highly-skilled employees with specific competencies, such as a certification, course or skill level. After defining a competency, you maintain the related information about each employee's competencies as part of the employee master information. You also define the competency as one of the resource requirements for a routing operation. This approach to resource requirements only applies to human resources representing individual employees where the employee number has been specified. The following guidelines apply to the definition and use of employee competencies.

Employee Skills A skill has a user-defined identifier and description, and also a rating model consisting of a rating and skill level. You assign an actual skill (and a starting date for the skill) to an employee, and an employee can have more than one skill. In addition, you can specify the skill as a resource requirement for performing a routing operation.

Employee Certifications A certification type has a user-defined identifier and description.   You assign a certification type (and a starting date for the certification) to an employee, and an employee can have more than one certification. In addition, you can specify the certificate as a resource requirement for performing a routing operation.

Employee Course A course has a user-defined identifier and description. You assign a course (and a completion date for the course) to an employee, and an employee can have more than one course. In addition, you can specify the course as a resource requirement for performing a routing operation.

Employee Self-Service Workspace for Updating an Employee Competency This workspace enables an employee to add information about a skill (and skill level) or a certificate type (and the start and end dates), and to view their registered courses.

11.6 Master Routings and Route Versions

The concept of a master routing enables you to define it once, and then assign it to multiple items with the same production process. This book employs the term "master routing" whereas the actual term is simply *Route*. A master routing has a unique identifier (termed the *Route Number*) which can be manually or automatically defined. Manual definition should be used when the identifier needs to be meaningful, such as the process specification for a common routing or the item number for an item-specific routing.

A master routing can be created independently and then assigned to an item. It can also occur in the context of creating an item's route version where it is automatically assigned to the item. Each assignment of a master routing to an item is termed a *Route Version*, and a manufactured item can have multiple route versions.

Approving and Activating a Route Version A master routing and a route version are initially treated as unapproved, and they have separate approval steps. Only an approved route version for a manufactured item can be marked as active, and the active route version will normally be used in master planning and cost calculations. There are several scenarios requiring multiple active route versions for an item, and even multiple approved-but-not active route versions, as described in the next topic.

Rationale for Multiple Route Versions for a Manufactured Item Multiple route versions can be defined for a manufactured item, typically to support the following variations.

◆ Variations between sites producing the same manufactured item

◆ Planned changes with effectivity dates

◆ Variations that reflect larger production quantities. A production quantity will reflect the significance of a single production order for a manufactured item (Section 6.6), and Case 11.5 illustrates how to model preferred equipment based on the production quantity.

◆ Alternate routings. An alternate routing is typically an approved-but-not-active route version that can be specified for a manually-created production order or rework order. It can also be specified for a sales order line item (for a make-to-order product) or for a BOM line about a manufactured component, so that master planning logic employs the specified route version rather than the active route version.

◆ Prototypes or production ramp-up

A manufactured item can have multiple active route versions that reflect different sites, non-overlapping validity periods, and/or different quantity breakpoints. An item can also have approved-but-not-active route versions. These variations are identified in the route version policies for an item.

Route Versions represent Non-interchangeable Inventory of a Manufactured Item In some scenarios, the production of different route versions represents non-interchangeable inventory of a manufactured item. For example, you may specify an approved-but-not active route version in the sub-Route field for a sales order line, or as part of the BOM line information for a manufactured component. To satisfy demand, master planning calculations will ignore available inventory and generate planned production orders for the specified route version. This approach requires an item-specific policy (embedded in the Coverage Group assigned to the item) labeled "Use specified route version". A similar policy labeled "Use specified BOM version" can also be used, as described in the chapter about bill of material information (Section 10.1).

Route Versions for each Configuration ID of a Configurable Item A configure-to-order product can employ different configuration technologies to define its BOM and routing information. When using the constraint-based configuration technology within the standard software, for example, you define a configurable item and its product configuration model. The model defines a mapping between prompts/responses and the information for creating route operations. Use of the model in the configuration process automatically generates a configuration ID for the configurable item as well as its BOM version and route version. A previous chapter described the definition of configurable item (Section 9.7).

11.7 Route Version Policies for an Item

The route version policies for an item are used to support multiple route versions. Similar policies were previously described for the BOM version policies for an item, so they are simply summarized here. A route version must be site-specific, and it can have effectivity dates and a quantity breakpoint. The route version policies also indicate whether it is approved and active.

The example screen shown in Figure 11.4 illustrates several key points about the route versions for an item, and the operations within a route version. In this example data, the manufactured item "X3-Product1" has two approved and active route versions with non-overlapping validity dates, where they represent site-specific routes for site "US1". Each route version involves the assignment of a master routing such as "RTE-000100" shown in the example.

Figure 11.4 Example Screen of Route Versions for an Item

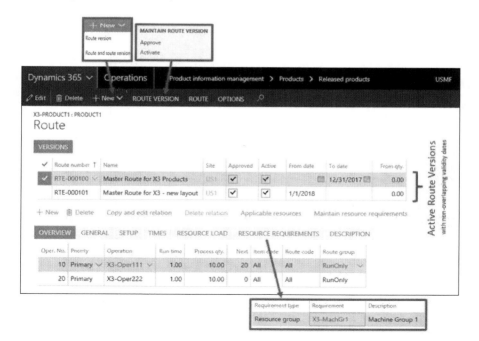

One of the breakout boxes at the top of Figure 11.4 illustrates the ability to create a new route version by assigning an existing master routing, or to create both a new master routing and a new route version. The second breakout box illustrates the ability to approve and activate a route version. The bottom part of Figure 11.4 illustrates the operations within a master routing. In this example data, the first line identifies the master operation "X3-Oper111" for operation number 10, and displays the time requirements (of 10 units per hour) inherited from the master operation. The inherited resource requirements are displayed in a breakout box. A subsequent figure illustrates the definition of this master operation (Figure 11.5). The second line identifies the master operation "X3-Oper222" for operation number 20, and similarly displays the inherited information.

Case 11.5: Preferred Equipment based on Production Quantity The production supervisor at a manufacturing firm wanted to schedule production using the optimal equipment for small and large order quantities. The large order quantities (over 1,000) were produced on larger faster equipment. To support this logic, two different route versions were defined for the relevant manufactured items, where the quantity breakpoint for one route version reflected 1,000 units. This route version contained an operation with resource requirements for handling a large quantity, and the other route version contained an operation with resource requirements for handling the small quantity. In this way, master planning logic will assign the optimal route version to a planned production order based on the required quantity.

Feasibility of a Route Version You can analyze route feasibility to determine whether applicable resources exist to satisfy the resource requirements of operations in an item's route version. For example, an operation's resource requirements may be infeasible due to lack of an assigned resource group (for a resource), or the lack of capabilities with valid dates. Attempts to activate an infeasible route version result in a soft warning message, and an option to review route feasibility. As a supplemental approach, you can also analyze availability of applicable resources when defining a master operation or g specific operation within a routing.

11.8 Master Operations

The concept of a master operation is central to the definition of routing operations. This book employs the term "Master Operation" whereas the actual term is simply *Operation*. A master operation has a unique user-defined identifier and a description, and you define master operations on the Operations form. The identifier typically has some meaning so that its significance is easily understood, such as an abbreviation for an operation or a process specification number. An identifier for a master operation must be specified for each routing operation. The master operation provides default values for the operation's information such as the required resource and associated time. Changing the values for a master operation will automatically update the information on the associated routing operations, subject to applicability rules.

The applicability rules for a master operation represent a key related concept. In defining a master operation, you can specify one or more sets of data that will serve as default values for a given routing operation. Each set has an applicability rule. For example, a set of data could apply to a specified group of items, and an additional set of data could apply to another group of items. The combination of an applicability rule and a set of data is termed an *Operation Relation.*

The example screen shown in Figure 11.5 illustrates the information for a master operation and its applicability rules. In this example, the master operation "X3-OPER111" represents a machining operation and it currently applies to all items and routes. The resource requirements are specified for the resource group "X1-MachGrp" with time requirements of 10 units per hour. The load quantity of "1" indicates a requirement for one machine within the resource group. In the context of a resource group of workers, the load quantity can indicate the crew size requirements.

Figure 11.5 Example Screen of an Operation Relation for a Master Operation

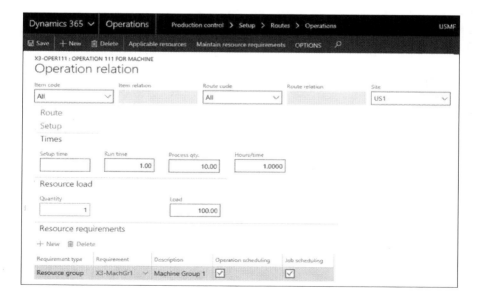

The applicability rule can reflect a specific item, a group of items (based on the Item Group) or all items. In addition, the applicability rule can reflect a specific master routing or all master routings. These applicability rules reflect decreasing levels of specificity. When multiple applicability rules have been defined, the most specific level will be used to inherit values from a master operation.

The applicability rule and set of data (aka the Operation Relation) can be specified when you initially define a master operation. The set of data provides default values when the master operation is specified for a routing operation, as illustrated in a previous figure (Figure 11.4).

Manually overriding the values on a routing operation will automatically create an additional applicability rule for the master operation, and the set of data reflects the manually-overridden values. The new applicability rule indicates the item and master routing in which you performed the manual override. In this way, subsequent changes to the master operation will only affect the one routing operation.

The use of master operations varies from company to company. Many companies already employ the concept of master operations, and they can replicate their current conceptual model. If the concept of master operations does not apply, you can simply create a master operation without any applicability rules or data. When you specify the master operation in a routing operation, no values will be inherited and you must define them. This will automatically create an Operation Relation for the master operation.

11.9 Define an Internal Operation in a Routing

The critical information for an internal operation consists of an operation number, a master operation identifier, the resource requirement, and the time requirements. Previous sections described the various methods for defining a resource requirement and the concept of a master operation. This section explains the other aspects of defining an internal operation.

Operation Number The operation number provides a unique numeric identifier for each operation within a routing, and the basis for scheduling a serial routing. The system automatically assigns new operation numbers in increments of 10 but this operation number can be overridden. The use of operation numbers has several implications as described below.

◆ *Sequence the operations in a multistep routing.* The operation number itself does not provide sequencing logic. For sequencing purposes, each operation requires additional information about the next operation number, whether you are modeling a serial or parallel sequence.

◆ *Identify the last operation within a routing.* You must identify which operation represents the last operation in a routing (with a value of zero "0" in the Next Operation field). This information is helpful when reporting actual production activity for the last operation, so that reporting the units completed at the last operation can automatically update the finished quantity for the production order.

◆ *Identify the material components required for an operation.* Assigning the operation number to the required material (in the BOM line information) allows master planning logic to synchronize material due dates with the operation start date. It provides the basis for calculating the impact of operation scrap percentages on the associated material requirements. It also provides the basis for populating the picking list for a production order based on the started quantity for the operation number.

◆ *Provide an identifier to report actual production activity.* You report actual time and/or unit completions against an order number and operation number.

◆ *Indicate when tests should be performed during production of an item.* The required tests for an item (via the automatic creation of a quality order) can reflect a specified operation number within the routing.

Primary Versus Secondary Resources (Operation Priority) Each operation requires a primary resource, and most production scenarios can be modeled using operations with just a primary resource. Some scenarios have operations requiring one or more secondary resources, such as the people and tools for running a machine. The operation's primary resource represents the pacing resource that determines operation duration. The same operation number must be assigned to each secondary resource, and the same time requirements apply because it is not the pacing resource. Operations with the same operation number are termed *simultaneous operations.* Case 11.6 illustrates the simultaneous requirements for a machine, operator, and tool.

The type of linkage between a primary and secondary resource affects master planning logic, where the link type can be hard or soft. That is, you can indicate that the secondary resources for an operation must start at the same time as the primary resource (a link type of hard). The alternative allows a time gap (a link type of soft or blank).

Case 11.6: Simultaneous Requirements for a Machine, Operator and Tool
One production process at an equipment company required a dedicated machine, a skilled operator, and a specialized mold. To model these simultaneous resource requirements for the operation, the route version for each manufactured item contained three lines with the same operation number. The first line identified the primary resource requirement of the machine, since this acted as the pacing resource. The next two lines identified the secondary resource requirements for the skilled operator and the mold tool.

Resource Requirement Each operation must include at least one resource requirement. The resource requirement can be expressed for a resource, a resource group, a resource capability or an employee competency, as previously described.

Resource Quantity (Crew Size) The resource quantity indicates the number of resources required to perform the operation. An illustrative example involves a resource group with resources representing individual people. For example, a run time requirement of 3 hours and a resource quantity of 2 people would be interpreted as a total load of 6 hours (for the resource group). Master planning logic with the job scheduling method would schedule a load of 3 hours for 2 different resources (people).

Time Requirements Time requirements are normally expressed as hours per unit or units per hour. They can also be expressed in minutes or days (which applies to all time elements for the operation), but cost and planning calculations will convert these time requirements back into hours.[3] This approach to defining time requirements is termed a "standard" resource consumption policy, and you assign the policy to an operation. The next subsection describes some alternate approaches to defining time requirements, whereas this section focuses on the standard approach.

The time requirements are typically defined for run time and optional setup time, but some scenarios employ additional time elements to model the production process. The following considerations apply to the definition of time requirements for various time elements.

◆ *Run Time per Unit* The run time is typically expressed per 1 unit. It can be expressed for a different quantity, such as the run time per 100 units (as defined by the process quantity field). Alternatively, you can define a run rate, such

---

[3] Time requirements expressed in hours reflects an "hours per time unit" value of 1. This "hours per time unit" field can also be used to define time requirements in minutes (a value of 1/60 or .0167) or days (a value of 24) or some other user-specified interval.

as specifying a time requirement of 1 hour and a process quantity that represents the run rate per hour.

♦ *Setup Time*. Setup time represents a fixed requirement before starting the run time for production. Short setup times are typically not defined.

♦ *Changeover Time*. Changeover time represents a fixed requirement after completing the run time for production. It is typically modeled by the "queue after" time element, as described in the next point.

♦ *Other Time Elements for Scheduling and Capacity Planning Purposes*. Other time elements include the number of hours for queue time before and after the operation, and the transit time to the next operation. Many scenarios employ different names for these time elements, such as a changeover time or cooling time rather than a queue time after the operation. Several policies (embedded in the Route Group assigned to the operation) determine the impact of time requirements for these time elements, since they can optionally consume capacity. The impact of route group policies are described in a following subsection.

♦ *Overlapping Operations*. An operation can have a specified overlap quantity (also termed the transfer batch quantity) so that the next operation can start before operation completion.

Alternative Approaches to Defining Time Requirements An alternative approach to defining time requirements may apply to a machine and its machine cycles. The capacity of the machine is expressed as the number of cycles per hour, and the resource requirement identifies the number of required cycles to produce an item. This approach to defining time requirements is termed a "capacity" resource consumption policy, and you assign the policy to an operation. A slight variation builds on the use of machine cycles, and typically applies to a machine using a mold or die to produce a "batch quantity" of an item. This approach to defining time requirements is termed a "resource batch" resource consumption policy, and you assign the policy to an operation.

Time Requirements and the Impact of Route Group Policies A route group defines a set of policies that determine how an operation's time requirements will be treated. With run time and setup time, for example, the associated costs are normally included in cost calculations, and the associated times are normally included in scheduling and capacity planning. In many cases, multiple route groups are defined with different policies about the treatment of each time element, so that the route group can be assigned to relevant operations.

Yield Percentage for an Operation The planned yield percentage for an operation affects the required runtime and the materials tied to the operation. The system automatically calculates and displays an accumulated yield percentage for each operation in a routing with multiple operations.

11.10 Comparison of Scheduling Methods: Job versus Operation Scheduling

The master planning logic is slightly different for the two scheduling methods, which are termed *operation scheduling* and *job scheduling*. The term *job scheduling* may be confusing to those people that think of a job as synonymous with a production order or project, but in this context job refers to the individual time elements within an operation. These time elements can include setup, process and queue times. The scheduling significance of these time elements is defined within the Route Group assigned to an operation.

The ability to handle detailed time elements represents a primary difference between the two scheduling methods. A second key difference concerns the additional functionality supported by job scheduling, such as supporting resource requirements for a capability or employee competency, and supporting the use of Gantt charts. The differentiating factors between the scheduling methods are summarized in Figure 11.6 and explained below.

Figure 11.6 Comparison of Scheduling Methods

<table>
<tr><td colspan="2" rowspan="2"></td><td colspan="2" align="center">Scheduling Method</td></tr>
<tr><td align="center">Operations Scheduling</td><td align="center">Job Scheduling</td></tr>
<tr><td rowspan="8" align="center">Differentiating Factors</td><td>Scheduling Focus</td><td align="center">Resource Group</td><td align="center">Resource</td></tr>
<tr><td>Capacity Planning</td><td align="center">Detailed (by Resource) and Aggregate (by Group)</td><td align="center">Detailed (by Resource) and Aggregate (by Group)</td></tr>
<tr><td>Additional Functionality</td><td></td><td align="center">Schedule detailed time elements (aka jobs)
Lock a job and synchronize related time elements
Assign a resource based on capabilities or employee competencies
Support alternative approaches to the definition of time requirements (e.g. via machine cycles)
Perform block scheduling via properties
Use of Gantt Chart to display production schedule</td></tr>
<tr><td>Time Granularity</td><td align="center">Schedule by Date</td><td align="center">Schedule by Date and Time</td></tr>
<tr><td>Printed Shop Traveler</td><td align="center">Route Card</td><td align="center">Job Card</td></tr>
<tr><td>Reporting Operation Time and Unit Completions</td><td align="center">Use Route Card Journal</td><td align="center">Use Job Card Journal or Route Card Journal</td></tr>
<tr><td>Computer Processing Time</td><td align="center">Faster</td><td align="center">Slower</td></tr>
</table>

♦ *Job Scheduling Method.* This method supports (1) scheduling the time elements for an operation, (2) assigning resources based on a requirement for capabilities or employee competencies, (3) block scheduling based on a property, and (4) use of a Gantt Chart to display production schedule information. Minor differences include the printed shop traveler, the approach for reporting operation time and unit completions, and computer processing time.

♦ *Operation Scheduling Method.* This method does not support the additional functionality described above.

Master planning logic will schedule production and calculate lead times based on routing data – but only within the time horizon defined by a capacity time fence (expressed in days). Otherwise it uses the fixed lead time for a manufactured item. You define the capacity time fence as one of the policies within the coverage group assigned to an item, or as one of the policies for a master plan. In most cases, the capacity time fence reflects near-term scheduling requirements (such as a 30 day horizon), although a longer horizon (such as 365 days) would be used to calculate long-term capacity requirements.

11.11 Production Route for a Production Order

A production route refers to the routing operations attached to a production order. It is also termed the order-dependent routing. Changes to a production route do not affect the master routing. Creation and maintenance of the production route reflect the following rules, which parallel the rules for maintaining a production BOM.

♦ Creation of a production order can also create a production route.

♦ The production route initially reflects the item's route version that was used to create the production order. In most cases, this will be inherited from the active route version for the site and start date on the production order. However, you can manually specify a different route version for the item when manually creating the production order, where the route version can be approved-but-not-active.

♦ The production route contains the routing operations of a phantom.

♦ You can modify the operations in a production route at any time prior to ending a production order.

◆ You can copy operations to a production route -- such as copying from another production order or a Master Routing -- prior to reporting a production order as scheduled.

◆ Time can only be reported when the operation sequence number exists in the production route.

11.12 Additional Case Studies

Case 11.7: Feasibility of a Routing with New Equipment A company was implementing a change in equipment that also required skilled operators with the relevant equipment certification. As part of the new route versions for manufactured items produced by the equipment, an operation specified the resource requirements for the new equipment (as a primary resource) and for the employee certification (as a secondary resource). One concern was the match-up between the equipment availability date (defined by the effectivity date for its resource group) and the availability of certified operators (defined by their certification date). This date could be analyzed by reviewing the feasibility of the resource requirements for an item's route version.

Case 11.8: Burn-In Period after Completing Production The production process for a manufactured item involved a burn-in period after completing assembly at a final assembly work center. The number of burn-in hours was specified using the "queue after" time element. This approach requires the definition of a Route Group in which "queue after" time is designated as working time (but does not consume resource capacity), and the assignment of this Route Group to the operation performed by the final assembly work center.

11.13 Executive Summary

A master routing represents a model of production activities for a manufactured item. Assignment of multiple master routings to an item (termed route versions) can support site-specific variations, planned changes, preferred equipment based on production quantity, and alternate equipment. Each operation within a route version defines the resource requirements and associated time requirements. The case studies illustrated variations in the use of routing data, such as different options for designating preferred equipment.

Chapter 12

Production Order Considerations

Production orders provide a key coordination tool for scheduling and reporting production activities in most discrete manufacturers. Some mixed mode scenarios also use batch orders and/or kanban orders to coordinate production, but this chapter focuses on the terminology and use of production orders.

Several production order considerations are especially important for master planning. Many of these have been covered in previous chapters, such as the S&OP game plans for different manufacturing scenarios, the planning data for manufactured items, the use of BOM and routing information, and the master planning results to coordinate production. This chapter covers some additional considerations such as production order status, reference orders, scheduling logic, production lead time, reservations for components, and subcontracted production. These considerations are reflected in the following sections within the chapter.

1. Different Ways to Create Production Orders
2. Significance of Production Order Status
3. Reference Orders for a Production Order
4. Scheduling a Production Order
5. Scheduling a Production Order with Finite Capacity and Material
6. Significance of Production Lead Time
7. Reservations for Production Components
8. Subcontracted Production
9. Workspaces related to Production Orders
10. Additional Case Studies

Many aspects of production orders are not directly related to master planning, and are not included within the chapter. Extended explanations of these topics are provided in the 2016 Edition of my book about supply chain management for discrete manufacturing.

12.1 Different Ways to Create Production Orders

Production order processing often involves many variations, starting with the different approaches for creating orders listed below. Each variation builds on a basic business process for production orders, and typically involves additional steps or considerations. Extended explanations of these variations in business processes fall outside the book's scope, but they have been provided in the 2016 Editions of my books about discrete manufacturing, process manufacturing and warehouse management.

◆ Manually create a production order
◆ Firm a planned production order to create a production order
◆ Create a production order from a sales order line
◆ Automatically create a production order for a make-to-order component of a production order (aka a reference order)

The example screen shown in Figure 12.1 illustrates the dialogue to manually create a new production order. Key information within the dialogue includes the item, quantity, delivery date, and the deliver-to site and warehouse. Based on this information, the active BOM version and route version will be used (by responding to a prompt), or you can optionally specify an approved-but-not-active version. The bottom of the figure displays the resulting order with a Created status.

Figure 12.1   Example Screen to Create a Production Order

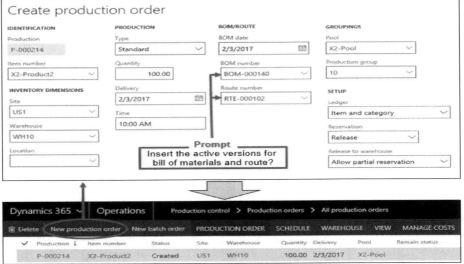

Additional approaches to creating a production order apply to project-oriented operations, such as creation of a project production order. A subsequent chapter covers project manufacturing scenarios.

12.2 Significance of Production Order Status

The life cycle of a production order consists of several steps that update an order status. The order status represents a linear progression that affects order behavior, such as the ability to report actual production activities. The actual reporting of steps in the linear progression can be skipped. Steps can also be reversed by resetting order status.

Each step involves a user-initiated update task (and an associated dialogue) and the update task can change the order status. The update tasks provide a context for understanding the order status of a production order, but an extended explanation of the update tasks falls outside the book's scope. The production order status affects several aspects of system behavior. These are summarized in Figure 12.2 and described below.

Figure 12.2 Significance of Production Order Status

	Impact of Current Order Status	Created	Estimated	Scheduled	Released	Started	Reported as Finished	Ended
1	Master planning recognizes Expected Parent Receipt	Yes	Yes	Yes	Yes	Yes	No	No
1	Master planning recognizes Component Requirements	No	Yes	Yes	Yes	Yes	No	No
1	Master planning recognizes Resource Requirements	No	No	Yes	Yes	Yes	No	No
2	Status Option for Firming a Planned Order	No	No	Yes	Yes	Yes	No	No
3	Timing Option for Automatic Reservations	No	Yes	Yes	Yes	Yes	No	No
4	Generate Reference Order for Component	No	Yes	No	No	No	No	No
4	Ability to Synchronize Reference Order(s)	No	No	Yes	Yes	Yes	No	No
5	Ability to Modify Production BOM or Production Route	Yes	Yes	Yes	Yes	Yes	No	No
6	Ability to Report Actual Production Activities	No	No	No	No	Yes	Yes	No
7	Ability to Split Order Quantity	Yes	Yes	Yes	Yes	Yes	No	No
8	Ability to Delete Order	Yes	No	No	No	No	No	Yes
9	Ability to Reset Order Status	N/A	Yes	Yes	Yes	Yes	Yes	No

As highlighted in the top of the figure, the order status determines whether master planning logic recognizes expected parent receipts, and the expected requirements for components and operations.

Master planning logic will also recognize or ignore remaining requirements based on the reporting of production activities. For example, the remaining component requirements will be ignored when a specific component has been flagged as completely picked, when picking for all components has been flagged as complete, and when an operation linked to the material has been flagged as complete. The remaining time requirements for a routing operation will be ignored when the operation has been flagged as complete, or when the entire routing has been flagged as complete.

Several other aspects of order status related to the use of master planning are listed in the bottom of Figure 12.2 and described below.

◆ *Status option for firming a planned order.* When firming a planned order, an item-specific policy (embedded in the coverage group assigned to the item) determines the order status of the resulting production order. In most cases, you should employ the option for a Scheduled status.

◆ *Timing option for automatic reservations.* The reservation policy for a production order determines when the reservations will be performed automatically. The possible options for automatic reservations include an order status of Scheduled, Released or Started. A subsequent section provides further explanation of reservations for production components.

◆ *Generate and synchronize reference orders.* A reference order reflects a buy-to-order or make-to-order component, where the BOM Line Type is "Vendor" or "Pegged Supply" respectively. Updating the order status to Estimated (or higher) will automatically generate reference orders, and include them in cost calculations for the order. In addition, the reference orders can be included and even synchronized (based on dialogue policies) when updating order status to Scheduled, Released and Started. A subsequent section provides further explanation of reference orders.

◆ *Ability to modify the Production BOM and Production Route.* You can optionally modify information in the production BOM or the production route, as described in previous chapters (Sections 10.5 and 11.11).

◆ *Ability to report actual production activities.* Actual production activities can only be reported for orders with a status of Started or Reported as Finished. These activities include actual material consumption, actual operation time and unit completions for an operation, and receipt of the parent item (and co-products). In addition, releasing a production order generates work orders for reporting raw material picking work when using advanced warehousing. Changing the order status to Ended prevents any further transactions

◆ *Ability to split order quantity.* Production orders can be split any time prior to the Reported as Finished status. Splitting a production order results in a new order for the specified quantity and delivery date. However, a Started production order can only be split for a quantity that has not yet been reported as started. This limitation avoids the complications associated with allocations of issued components and reported operation times to the split orders.

◆ *Ability to delete order.* An order can only be deleted when it has an order status of Created or Ended.

◆ *Ability to reset order status.* You can reset order status to a previous step at any time prior to the Ended status, and relevant transactions will be reversed. For example, resetting the status from Started to Created can reverse the posted transactions for picking lists, route cards and finished quantities (but not the raw material picking work). This can be helpful for backing out transactions to make corrections, to completely start over, or to delete an order. The detailed impacts of reversing the order status differ when going from Started to Released, Released to Scheduled, Scheduled to Estimated, and Estimated to Created, as described in the user documentation.

12.3 Reference Orders for a Production Order

A reference order reflects a buy-to-order or make-to-order component, and updating the order status to Estimated (or higher) generates the reference orders for a production order. Several update tasks for a production order have an option to include reference orders when scheduling, releasing, and starting a production order. For example, the schedule order task can optionally include reference orders and even synchronize them. Resetting order status can apply to reference orders. Deleting an order can optionally delete the reference orders. The update tasks can also be performed for a production order that represents a reference order.

The nature of reference orders has been covered in previous chapters about common S&OP scenarios requiring linkage between orders (Section 2.3), the definition of buy-to-order and make-to-order components in BOM line information (Section 10.3), and the special cases of coverage planning data for purchasing (Section 6.4) and production (Section 6.7).

12.4 Scheduling a Production Order

Scheduling a production order involves a choice of two scheduling methods termed operations scheduling and job scheduling. The scheduling method is only relevant when using routing data, and the choice depends on how you assign resource requirements to an operation (described in Sections 11.8 and 11.9). Job scheduling must be used when resource requirements are defined in terms of resource capabilities or employee competencies, or when you perform detailed scheduling of individual resources via dispatching or Gantt charts. A previous chapter about routing information provided a comparison of the two scheduling methods (Section 11.10)

Example Screens for the Scheduling Dialogue   When scheduling an order using either scheduling method, you specify the critical information in a scheduling dialogue, such as the scheduling direction and several scheduling policies. The example screens shown in Figure 12.3 illustrate the two variations of the dialogue, and the common set of scheduling policies for both.

Figure 12.3 Example Screens of the Scheduling Dialogue for a Production Order

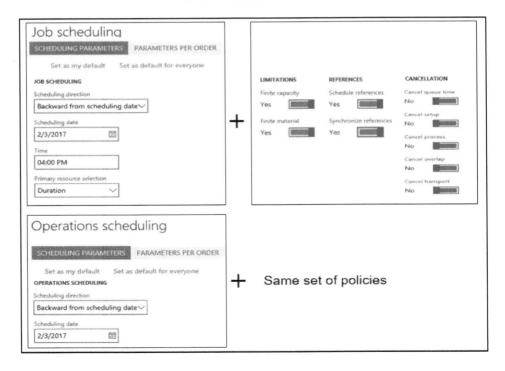

The scheduling direction, for example, could be forward from today's date or backward from a specified scheduling date. The subsequent Figure 12.4 summarizes the options for scheduling direction. Unique aspects of the job scheduling dialogue include the primary basis for resource selection and a specified time.

Each method involves the same set of scheduling policies shown on the right side of the figure. For example, you can optionally include consideration of finite capacity and material. Selected time elements can be excluded, such as queue and transit time, to calculate the fastest possible production throughput. If applicable, you can also schedule and synchronize reference orders.

Special Cases for Policies within the Scheduling Dialogue   The example screens for the scheduling dialogue (shown in Figure 12.3) did not include all possible scheduling policies to keep the figure simple. Several additional scheduling policies represent special cases, as described below.

◆ *Finite Property.* The finite property approach represents a form of block scheduling for grouping similar operations to minimize setup time, and performing them during a predefined block of time in the calendar assigned to a resource. The approach is not generally used, and is not explained further.

◆ *Keep Production Unit* or *Keep Warehouse from Resource*. These policies will limit the consideration of resources based on existing assignments of input warehouses. The existing assignment of an input warehouse for a resource should be considered by scheduling logic to avoid the problem of scheduling on a resource with a different input warehouse. This problem impacts the calculation of component requirements by warehouse, and may create unnecessary complexities. The limitation is normally identified by the "Keep input warehouse from resource" flag. It can also be identified by the "Keep production unit" flag, since a production unit has a specified input warehouse.

Scheduling Direction   Both scheduling methods support different scheduling directions. The basic scheduling directions are forward and backward as of a given date, such as the requirement date. Figure 12.4 summarizes the variations in scheduling directions for both scheduling methods. Planned production orders can also be rescheduled, and the right-hand column displays the available options for scheduling direction.

Figure 12.4 Variations in Scheduling Direction

		Other Parameter	Applicability		
			Operations Scheduling	Job Scheduling	Reschedule Planned Order*
Variations in Scheduling Direction	Forward from today		Yes	Yes	No
	Forward from tomorrow				No
	Forward from the planned start date				
	Forward from a specified scheduling date	Specify a Scheduling Date & Time			Yes
	Backward from a specified scheduling date				
	Backward from the delivery date				No
	Backward from the planned end date				Yes
	Backward from the calculated action date				Yes
	Backward from the calculated delay date				
	Use information from last scheduling				
	Forward from a specified job	Specify a Job Identifier			No
	Backward from a specified job				
	Backward from requirement date		No		Yes
	Forward from order date				

* = Planned orders are initially scheduled using backward scheduling from the requirement date.

Lock a Production Order to Prevent Rescheduling A production order can be flagged as locked to prevent rescheduling, and then unlocked when desired.

12.5 Scheduling a Production Order with Finite Capacity and Material

The scheduling of a production order can optionally include consideration of finite capacity or finite material or both. It ensures that resources are not overbooked and manufacturing doesn't start before materials are available. You specify these considerations as part of the policies within the scheduling dialogue, as mentioned in the previous section and illustrated in Figure 12.3.

◆ *Scheduling with Finite Capacity.* The consideration of finite capacity only applies to resources (and resource groups) within the production route that have been designated as finite for scheduling purposes, just like the master planning calculations. As a unique aspect, you can optionally exclude selected time elements -- such as queue and transit time -- to calculate the fastest possible production throughput.

◆ *Scheduling with Finite Material.* The consideration of finite material applies to all components within the Production BOM. This differs from the master planning calculations with finite material, which only considered components that were explicitly designated as finite material (via use of the calculated delays message).

12.6 Significance of Production Lead Time

Scheduling logic can calculate a variable production lead time for planned and actual production orders based on routing data, or use a fixed lead time when no routing data applies. Several factors apply to the calculation of a variable lead time, such as the order quantity, the resource requirements for routing operations, and the available capacity of resources.

The fixed lead time for a manufactured item can be specified as a companywide value and optionally overridden as a site- or warehouse-specific value. It is typically expressed in working days, but it could be expressed in calendar days for some scenarios. The fixed lead time serves several purposes.

◆ *Scheduling without routing data.* The lead time determines the duration of a production order, either by calculating the start date based on the completion date or vice versa.

◆ *Calculation of safety stock.* The lead time affects the calculation of safety stock, which can reflect average daily usage multiplied by the item's lead time.

◆ *Consideration of finite material in scheduling logic.* The scheduling logic requires on-hand inventory on the start date of the production order or the relevant operation (if applicable). When there is insufficient inventory of the component item, the scheduling logic uses the item's lead time to determine when it will be available. The components' availability date determines when the order can be started.

The fixed lead time should reflect the significance of single order and its typical order quantity and production duration. In the context of subcontracted production of an item, the item's production lead time should reflect the relevant variations of subcontracted production described in a subsequent section.

12.7 Reservations for Production Components

Reservations for production components are typically employed to ensure sufficient inventory exists prior to starting actual production. The reservations can also reflect First-Expired-First-Out (FEFO) logic for items with shelf life considerations. An order-related policy determines when the reservations will be performed automatically. This policy is initially inherited from the companywide or site-specific default, and can be overridden on an order. The possible options for when to make automatic reservations include an order status of Scheduled, Released or Started. A Manual option does not result in automatic reservations so that manual reservations would be required.

Most scenarios using advanced warehousing capabilities will employ reservations when the order status changes to Released, thereby ensuring sufficient inventory exists for raw material picking to the production input location. A related reservation policy determines whether components must be fully reserved or partially reserved so that you can release a production order.

Other scenarios often employ reservations when the order status changes to Started, thereby ensuring sufficient inventory exists for production order picking list purposes. This approach supports generation of picking lists containing components with a flushing policy of "Start".

12.8 Subcontracted Production

Subcontracted production and internal production share many similarities in the use of basic constructs like production orders and picking list journals. They both employ BOM and routing information. However, subcontracted production involves significant differences and several variations. One key difference stems from the approach to modeling subcontracted production, which requires a unique item representing the subcontracted service, and a BOM line specifying it as a buy-to-order component for the manufactured item. Based on this information, a production order for the manufactured item automatically creates the associated purchase order for the subcontracted service. The dual constructs of a production order and its associated purchase order involve additional complexity in setup information and business processes in comparison to internal production.

Subcontracted production can have many possible variations. This section covers the major variations and introduces the key constructs, such as the items representing a subcontracted service, the BOM and routing information for subcontracted production, and the use of a single receipt transaction for updating both the purchase order and production order. Book length considerations preclude extended explanations of these key constructs and the typical business processes, but they are provided in the 2016 Edition of my books about discrete and process manufacturing as well as a previous article about how to manage subcontracted production.

Variations of Subcontracted Production There are many possible scenarios of subcontracted production. The different scenarios typically reflect variations of (1) the routing information with an external operation, (2) the supplied material, (3) the handling of finished quantities and (4) modeling the inventory locations involved in subcontracted production. These four major factors provide an organizing focus for further explanation. A key issue concerns the visibility of inventory at the subcontractor site and the in-transit inventory.

♦ *Variations of Routing Information with an External Operation.* The simplest scenario involves just a single operation within the routing for the manufactured item, where the item's BOM identifies the supplied material for the external operation. More complex scenarios involve a multi-step routing, where each additional step may reflect an internal operation or another external operation. Further explanation focuses on the simplest scenario.

♦ *Variations of Supplied Material for Subcontracted Production.* Subcontracted production involves supplied material. The two major delivery options consist of issuing the supplied material to the production order, and stocking the supplied material at the subcontractor site (via purchase order or transfer order deliveries). The applicable delivery option determines how you define the warehouse source of components in BOM/routing information (Section 10.4). For example, you can specify the warehouse source on the BOM line for a supplied component.

♦ *Variations of Reporting Usage of Supplied Material stocked at the Subcontractor.* Actual material usage can be reported via the picking list journal, either via manual entries (before posting) or auto-deduction based on a started or finished quantity of the production order.

♦ *Variations of Receiving a Finished Quantity for Subcontracted Production.* There are two major variations for receiving a finished quantity for subcontracted production. You can (1) receive the purchase order for the subcontracted service or (2) receive the subcontracted production order, either at an internal site or at the subcontractor site. A purchase order receipt of the subcontracted service can automatically update the finished quantity of the associated production order, thereby supporting a single receipt transaction for both constructs. The finished quantity of the production order can be reported using several different approaches. When received at subcontractor site, you can subsequently report transfer order shipments or sales order shipments.

◆ *Variations in Modeling the Inventory Locations involved in Subcontracted Production.* You must identify a subcontractor as a site or warehouse (in addition to identification as a vendor and resource) to track inventory of supplied components and/or finished quantities. The trade-offs between using a site or warehouse were covered in a previous chapter about modeling inventory locations (Chapter 5).

The major variations of subcontracted production are summarized in Figure 12.5. The variations reflect the options for receiving finished quantities and the options for supplied material. The combinations of these options provide different levels of inventory visibility at the subcontractor site, ranging from no visibility to partial and full visibility.

Figure 12.5 Major Variations of Subcontracted Production

Options for Supplied Material	Options for Receiving Finished Quantities for Subcontracted Production		
	1 Receive Purchase Order for the Subcontracted Service		
	2 Receive Subcontracted Production Order		
	At Internal Site	At Subcontractor Site	
Supplied Material issued to Production Order	No Visibility of Subcontractor Inventory	Partial Visibility of Finished Inventory at Subcontractor	Support Sales Order Shipments or Transfer Order Shipments from the Subcontractor Site
Supplied Material Stocked at Subcontractor	Option for Reporting Usage of Supplied Material		
	Partial Visibility of Component Inventory at Subcontractor	Full Visibility of Component and Finished Inventory at Subcontractor	

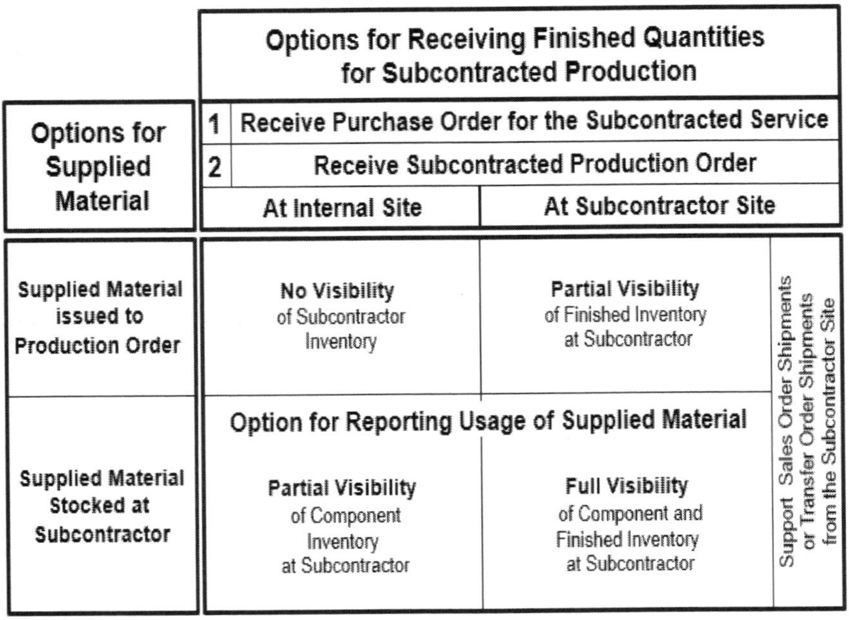

Example Screen of Subcontracted Work The example screen shown in Figure 12.6 illustrates the Subcontracted Work page, which provides a coordination tool for managing subcontracted production. It displays any production order with a linked purchase order for a buy-to-order component, which represents a subcontracted service in this scenario.

The example data within Figure 12.5 consists of three different purchase orders for the item "X4-SubcontractedService" that represents the subcontracted service performed at the subcontractor "Vend-B". The example data also identifies each related production order, and the related operation number and status when using routing data as part of modeling subcontracted production. From this page, you can view additional details about the operation and the BOM line for the subcontracted service. You can also start the related production order or report the finished quantity, as highlighted in the figure. Alternatively, you can access the related production order or purchase order for performing needed actions. For example, you may need to confirm the related purchase order or update the production order.

Figure 12.6 Example Screen for Subcontracted Work

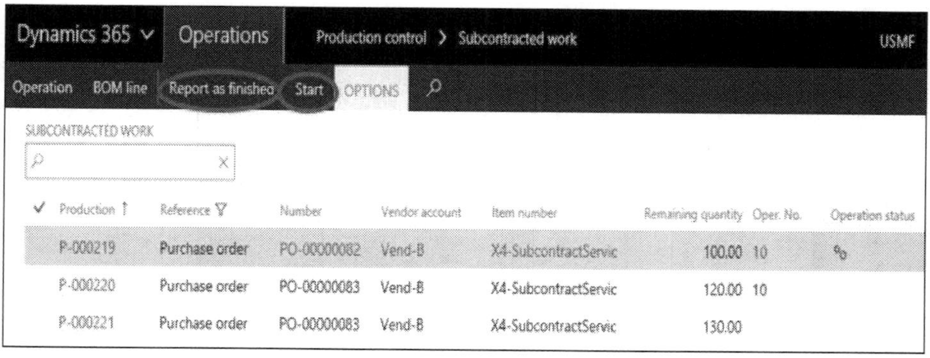

✓	Production ↑	Reference ▽	Number	Vendor account	Item number	Remaining quantity	Oper. No.	Operation status
	P-000219	Purchase order	PO-00000082	Vend-B	X4-SubcontractServic	100.00	10	%₀
	P-000220	Purchase order	PO-00000083	Vend-B	X4-SubcontractServic	120.00	10	
	P-000221	Purchase order	PO-00000083	Vend-B	X4-SubcontractServic	130.00		

Case 12.1: Subcontracted Production with Full Visibility   A manufacturing company produced several products at subcontractors located in other states and countries. The supplied material was transferred and stocked at each subcontractor, and the finished quantities were reported prior to transferring the goods to an internal warehouse. This approach provided full visibility of inventory at the subcontractor site and in transit, and modeled the associated transportation time. The purchase order receipt for the subcontracted service resulted in a finished quantity of the subcontracted production order, which triggered backflushing of the supplied components at the subcontractor warehouse. In this case study, the subcontractor site was identified as a non-WMS warehouse, and the manufacturing plant consisted of WMS-enabled warehouses which involved use of the advanced approach to warehouse management.

Case 12.2: Subcontracted Production without Routing Data   A manufacturing company employed subcontractors to produce several different products, and wanted to model subcontracted production without routing data. The solution approach involved a proposed customization so that the purchase order due date for the subcontracted service automatically aligned with the due date of the production order for the parent item. The lead time for the parent item defined the turnaround time at the subcontractor. In addition, the proposed customization supported a single purchase order receipt transaction that automatically updated the finished quantity for the production order.

Case 12.3: Multiple Subcontractors build same Item   A manufacturing company employed multiple subcontractors to produce the same item, where the supplied components were stocked at each subcontractor. Each subcontractor's location was identified as a unique site, and site-specific BOM versions for a parent item defined the supplied components for each subcontractor. A subcontracted service item was defined for each parent item. Since the company was using standard costs, different site-specific standard costs were assigned to the subcontracted service item and to the supplied components. This approach also entailed the calculation of site-specific standard costs for the parent item.

Case 12.4: Sales Order Shipments from a Subcontractor Warehouse
A manufacturing company stocked an item's finished quantity at the subcontractor site. They entered demand forecasts and sales orders for the site/warehouse representing the subcontractor site. To communicate the need for sales order shipments from the subcontractor site, the DRP coordinator generated the sales order picking lists and e-mailed a copy to the relevant contact person. The contact person sent a return e-mail after completing the requested shipments, and the DRP coordinator simply posted each completed sales order picking list and packing slip.

12.9 Workspaces related to Production Orders

Several predefined workspaces are related to production orders as described in the following summary of each workspace and its applicable functionality.

Production Floor Management Workspace   This workspace primarily supports the production supervisor role. It summarizes several aspects of information about production orders and their related operations (as of a selected date). For example, it identifies the production orders to release and the component availability for each order, and it supports the release of selected orders. It helps prioritize the sequence of jobs for released orders. It identifies the jobs that need to be completed and the jobs with reported deviations (such as a scrap quantity). In addition, it summarizes the number of jobs that are not yet started, stopped, and in progress. By configuring the workspace, you can filter the displayed information for a selected resource, resource group and/or production unit.

Master Planning Workspace   This workspace identifies the planned production orders, and also the action messages and calculated delay messages about production orders.

12.10 Additional Case Studies

Case 12.5: Advanced Planning and Scheduling (APS) Integration   A fabricated products company required APS capabilities to minimize setups and avoid additional equipment purchases for its line of extruded plastic products. Multiple extrusion machines produced plastic pipes of varying diameters and colors. Scheduling considerations included sequence-dependent setup time (based on pipe diameter and color), and machine capabilities for handling different products. Scheduling considerations also included machine-specific run rates, and secondary resources for tooling and skilled operators.   To integrate an APS application, additional attributes were required for resources (e.g., machine capabilities), routing operations (e.g., setup attributes) and calendars (e.g. available crew size by shift).[1]

Case 12.6: Graphical Schedule Board for Production Orders   The production planners at a manufacturing company employed a graphical schedule board to coordinate production orders by viewing the related routing operations at selected work centers, and adjusting them accordingly.[2]   The graphical display could include both actual and planned production orders, and it reflected current information within the system as well as the standard scheduling logic. It did not involve additional APS functionality. Changing the displayed information via drag-and-drop techniques -- such as changing an operation duration, or assigning the operation to a different work center -- automatically updated the current information within the system.   Alternatively, the information could be adjusted in simulation mode to achieve the desired schedule, and then used to update the current information.   Using the graphical schedule board, the planners could perform every function related to a production order, such as firming a planned order, scheduling/releasing/starting an order, or viewing the BOM and route information.

Case 12.7: Splitting a Production Order Quantity   A manufacturing company oftentimes split a production order so that a subset of the order quantity could be produced faster to meet an expedited sales order. This often applied to production orders that had already been started. Due to the limitation within current software functionality, they employed a customization to support

---

[1] See www.Preactor.com for additional information about their Advanced Scheduler module.
[2] See www.DynamicsSoftware.com for additional information about their Graphical Schedule Board.

allocations of issued components and operation times when splitting an order after the entire order quantity had already been reported as started.

Case 12.8: Re-Producing the Same Product An equipment manufacturer sometimes needed to re-produce the exact same product to meet a customer demand. The same Production BOM was necessary because of unique components that were included in the previously-built product (but not in a BOM version for the product). After creating the production order, the Production BOM was replaced by copying it from the previous production order.

12.11 Executive Summary

Production activities can be coordinated and reported using production orders. Several production order considerations are especially important for master planning. Many of these have been covered in previous chapters, such as the S&OP game plans for different manufacturing scenarios, the planning data for manufactured items (including the significance of a single order), the use of BOM and routing information, and the master planning results to coordinate production. This chapter covered some additional considerations such as the significance of production order status, reference orders, scheduling logic, production lead time, and reservations for components. It also covered the variations of subcontracted production, and provided different case studies.

Chapter 13

Purchase Order Considerations

A primary responsibility of procurement is to coordinate and execute the supply chain activities driven by the firm's S&OP game plans. Procurement activities can significantly impact the firm's bottom-line performance in terms of reduced material costs and inventories, improved quality, increased agility, and fewer disruptions stemming from stock-outs or delivery problems.

Several purchase order considerations are especially important for master planning. Many of these have been covered in previous chapters, such as the inventory locations related to purchases, the planning data about purchases, and the master planning results to coordinate purchases. This chapter covers some additional considerations such as the significance of delivery dates and lead times, and identifying problems related to delivery dates. These considerations are reflected in the following sections within the chapter.

1. Different Ways to Create Purchase Orders
2. Significance of Confirmed Delivery Dates
3. Identify Potential Problems in Delivery Dates
4. Significance of Purchasing Lead Time
5. Purchase Order Quantity and Units of Measure
6. Consigned Inventory of Purchased Components

13.1 Different Ways to Create Purchase Orders

Purchase order processing for material often involves many variations, starting with the different approaches for creating purchase orders. Several approaches for creating purchase orders are listed below. Each variation builds on a basic business process for purchase orders, and typically involves additional steps or considerations. Extended explanations of these variations in business processes fall outside the book's scope, but they have been provided in the 2016 Editions of my books about discrete manufacturing, process manufacturing and warehouse management.

◆ Enter a purchase order
◆ Firm a planned purchase order to create a purchase order
◆ Create a purchase order via release from a blanket purchase order
◆ Automatically create a purchase order from an accepted reply to a request for quote (RFQ)
◆ Automatically create a purchase order from an approved purchase requisition
◆ Create a direct delivery purchase order for a sales order
◆ Create a purchase order from a sales order (aka a special order)
◆ Automatically create a purchase order for a buy-to-order component of a production order. This also applies when the component represents a subcontracted service for performing an external operation.
◆ Automatically create an intercompany purchase order from an intercompany sales order
◆ Enter a purchase order for reporting a return to vendor

As a related note, the use of consigned inventory involves automatic creation of a received purchase order (after reporting a change in ownership), as described in a subsequent section.

Additional approaches to creating a purchase order apply to project-oriented operations, such as creation of a project purchase order. A subsequent chapter covers project manufacturing scenarios.

13.2 Significance of Confirmed Delivery Dates

Each purchase order line (and each line within a delivery schedule) has a delivery date and a separate "confirmed" delivery date. The confirmed delivery date is initially blank, and should be updated to reflect actual confirmation from the vendor or the carrier. If specified, the confirmed date will be used for anticipating receipts and by master planning logic -- otherwise the delivery date will be used.

As part of confirming delivery dates for a purchase order, many scenarios send a purchase inquiry to the vendor. A purchase inquiry communicates the contents of a purchase order, thereby providing the basis for external review before confirming the purchase order.

The example screen shown in Figure 13.1 illustrates a purchase order, and highlights the delivery dates. In this example, a purchase inquiry has been sent to the vendor for external review, and the confirmed dates have entered for the purchase order line items. The purchase order has not yet been confirmed.

Figure 13.1   Example Screen of a Purchase Order

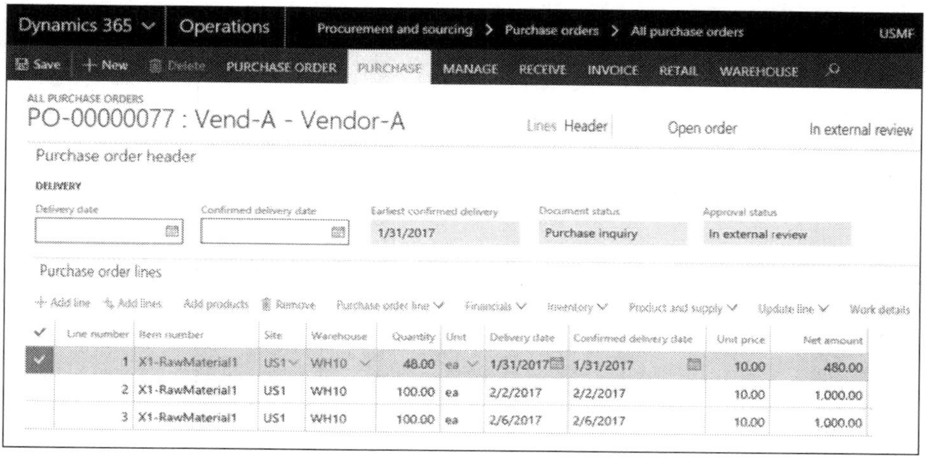

Changing the delivery date within a purchase order header can optionally update the delivery date for every line -- with a prompt or without a prompt, as defined by a companywide policy.

13.3 Identify Potential Problems in Delivery Dates

Several tools can identify potential problems in delivery dates, as listed below. You can access this information directly, or by using the links within purchasing-related workspaces.

◆   Identify purchase order lines without confirmed delivery dates
◆   Identify purchase order lines with past due delivery dates
◆   Identify purchase-related backorders
◆   Identify purchase order lines with an Advance message

The purchasing agent typically reviews the potential delivery problems and then undertakes needed actions. The actions include expediting delivery from the vendor, updating the confirmed delivery date, changing the quantity for the purchase line, and/or creating a delivery schedule to reflect multiple delivery dates and quantities.

13.4 Significance of Purchasing Lead Time

The purchasing lead time for an item can be specified as a companywide value (in working days or calendar days), and optionally overridden as a site- or warehouse-specific lead time, as described in the previous chapter about coverage planning data for purchased items (Section 6.3). This lead time affects the "order date" for planned purchase orders, so that purchase orders can be created in a timely manner.

The actual significance of purchasing lead time has several nuances. It should reflect the vendor's normal ability to supply the item after placing a purchase order, and the normal transportation time. Providing visibility of planned purchases can help improve the vendor's agility and shorten lead times. Longer-than-necessary lead times (and the associated creation of purchase orders by the order date) often result in messages to change the orders. In contrast, shorter lead times mean that planned orders can be automatically adjusted for the changes, thereby reducing the number of messages. Shorter lead times represent greater agility to respond to changes.

Lead Times and the Calendars of Working Days When purchasing lead times are expressed in working days, the calculation of a purchase order start date and/or delivery date can reflect the vendor's calendar as well as the calendar of the ship-to warehouse and the mode of delivery.

Lead Times and the Receipt Safety Margin Some items involve receiving inspection with a significant time requirement of a day or more before inspection results are known. This should be specified as a receipt safety margin so that a purchase receipt occurs before the required date. When using quality orders, you should also specify the expected date for completion of a quality order after it has been automatically generated for a purchase receipt.

Lead Times within Purchase Trade Agreements An item's purchase lead time can be optionally specified within the entry for a purchase price trade agreement, such as specifying a longer lead time for a lower purchase price. However, you must explicitly designate usage of this lead time information as part of the entry. This represents a special case of planning data for purchased items described in a previous chapter (Section 6.4).

13.5 Purchase Order Quantity and Units of Measure

An item's purchase order quantity often reflects order quantity modifiers consisting of a minimum, maximum, and multiple. These modifiers are often expressed in the item's default purchase UM (if specified) otherwise they are expressed in the item's inventory UM. These order quantity modifiers impact planned purchase order quantities. They are also considered when manually creating or maintaining a purchase line for the item, where a soft warning will be displayed when you enter a quantity that does not meet these criteria.

An item's purchase order quantity can reflect any authorized UM for the item. In many cases, the different values for an item's authorized UM will also be reflected in purchase price trade agreements and/or purchase agreements.

13.6 Consigned Inventory of Purchased Components

Some manufacturing companies employ consigned inventory of purchased components. The component inventory is owned by the supplying vendor but stored at the company's site. There is no impact on inventory value until the company takes over the ownership when needed, and the need for payment occurs after the change in ownership. To support consigned inventory of an item, the concept of "owner" has been implemented as an inventory tracking option that must be assigned to the item (much like the tracking option for batch numbers), thereby supporting differentiation of vendor-owned versus company-owned inventory. In addition, a new type of replenishment order provides visibility of incoming vendor-owned inventory, and the vendor-owned inventory can be reserved and moved prior to reporting an ownership change.[1]

The business process for managing an item's consigned inventory starts with identifying the need for replenishment (typically via planned purchase orders), and creation of a Consignment Replenishment Order. The example screen in Figure 13.2 illustrates the key information. The header information identifies the relevant vendor that acts as the owner of the consigned inventory. Each line item identifies the relevant item, the ship-to location, the order quantity and unit of measure, and the delivery dates (consisting of a requested and confirmed date). Master planning logic recognizes the item's scheduled receipts, and the source of supply is identified as a "consignment replenishment order" in the net requirements information. Master planning logic also recognizes the item's consigned inventory after reporting receipt.

---

[1] A previous article provided an extended explanation about how to manage consigned inventory.

Figure 13.2 Example Screen of a Consignment Replenishment Order

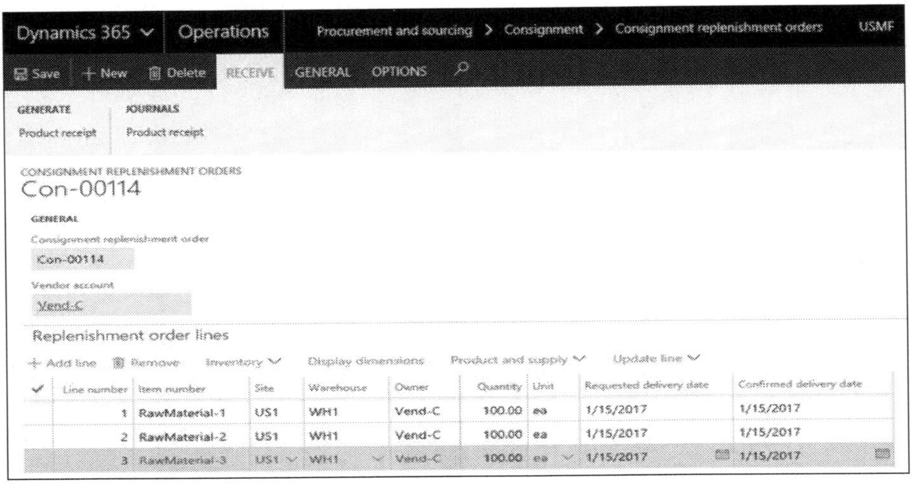

When the consigned inventory needs to be used, an Inventory Ownership Change Journal must be manually created and posted. Each journal line item identifies the relevant item, quantity, from location, and the relevant vendor owner. Two different approaches for creating the journal line items include manually-selected items and automatically-selected production components. Posting an Inventory Ownership Change Journal will automatically create/confirm/receive a purchase order reflecting the change of ownership, and the item's inventory can then be used.

The next chapter includes a case study about consigned inventory, where the material is stocked at an off-site warehouse and must be transferred before reporting actual usage (Case 14.5).

13.7 Executive Summary

Several purchase order considerations are especially important for master planning. Many of these were covered in previous chapters, and this chapter covered some additional considerations. These include the different ways to create purchase orders, the significance of delivery dates and purchasing lead times, and a summary of tools identifying problems related to delivery dates. The use of consigned inventory may apply in some scenarios, which requires visibility of scheduled receipts and automatic creation of a purchase order after reporting a change of ownership.

Chapter 14

Transfer Order Considerations

Transfers between physical sites can be managed using transfers orders or intercompany orders, depending on the grouping of physical sites into companies. This chapter covers transfer orders between sites in a single company and a subsequent chapter covers transfers in a multicompany supply chain.

Several transfer order considerations are especially important for master planning. Many of these have been covered in previous chapters, such as the inventory locations related to transfers, the planning data about transfers, and the master planning results to coordinate transfers. This chapter covers some additional considerations such as delivery dates and reservations.

Realistic dates for transfer orders are critical in master planning logic for coordinating supply chain activities. This chapter provides a summary of shipment and delivery dates, transportation time, and use of delivery date control. It also covers reservations related to transfer orders. These considerations are reflected in the following sections within the chapter.

1. Different Ways to Create Transfer Orders
2. Shipment and Delivery Dates for Transfers
3. Delivery Date Control for Transfer Orders
4. Reserve Material for a Transfer Order Line
5. Additional Case Studies

14.1 Different Ways to Create Transfer Orders

Transfer order processing involves a few variations, starting with the two basic approaches for creating transfer orders. One approach consists of manual creation, and the second consists of firming planned transfers. A slight variation applies to the firming of planned transfers to create transfer journals, as illustrated in Cases 14.1 about transfers between adjacent warehouses.

14.2 Shipment and Delivery Dates for Transfers

A single transfer order usually represents a single shipment and the line items reflect the shipment contents. It sometimes represents a container with a unique identifier, and the transfer order number can be manually assigned to reflect the container identifier.

A transfer order header specifies a shipment date and receipt date, along with the ship-from and ship-to site/warehouses and a mode of delivery such as air or truck. The difference between the two dates reflects the expected transportation time (expressed in days) between the two locations. A shipment date and delivery date also apply to each line item on a transfer order. Changes to the dates or delivery mode within the header information can optionally update the transfer order line items.

Several basic rules can be enforced for the shipment and delivery dates on a transfer order header and for each line item, but only when you assign one of the major options for delivery date control. The option for a transfer order header is inherited from a companywide value, which typically reflects a value of "Sales Lead Time" to enforce basic rules. The option for each line item is inherited from an item-specific value defined as part of the item's Default Order Settings for inventory. The next section provides further explanation of the delivery date control policy.

Transportation Time between Warehouses The transportation time is typically defined for a pair of warehouses. The transportation time is expressed in days, and you can optionally specify a different number of days for different modes of delivery.

In certain special cases, the transportation time between warehouses will vary by item, such as a very large item that requires special transportation arrangements and a longer time for moving the item via large trucks. You can define this transfer time as part of the item's site/warehouse-specific coverage planning data.

Example Screen for a Transfer Order The example screen shown in Figure 14.1 illustrates key information for a transfer order. The header information identifies the relevant warehouses and mode of delivery, the ship/receipt dates (with a one day transportation time between warehouses) and a delivery date control policy (to enforce basic rules). Information about each transfer order line includes the item and quantity, the ship/receipt dates, and the delivery date control policy. In this example, the reservation policy means that inventory will not be reserved when creating the order.

Figure 14.1 Example Screen for a Transfer Order

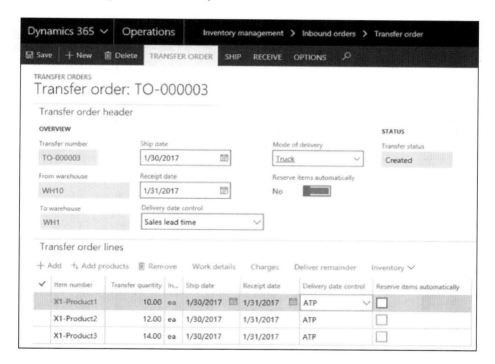

14.3 Delivery Date Control for Transfer Orders

The assignment of a delivery date control policy to the transfer order header and each line item can enforce basic rules such as the working calendar for both warehouses, the calendar for the delivery mode, and the expected transportation time between a pair of warehouses. Figure 14.2 summarizes the delivery date control options for a transfer order line, and the significance of each option.

The ATP option enforces the basic rules and employs Available to Promise logic for the assignment of dates. The ATP option requires several additional policies about underlying assumptions to correctly calculate an available-to-promise date. You can analyze the Available Ship and Receipt Dates form, and optionally transfer a selected set of dates to the transfer order line.

Assigning an option of *None* will disable the rules for delivery date control, thereby allowing assignment of unrealistic dates. As a general guideline, any line item with this option should be highlighted as an exception requiring follow up.

Figure 14.2 Delivery Date Control Options for a Transfer Order Line

Delivery Date Control Option	Scenario	Comments
Sales Lead Time	Use Basic Rules	Auto-assign requested dates based on basic rules Enforce basic rules for manually entered dates*
ATP	Stocked Item	Auto-assign requested dates based on basic rules + ATP logic Enforce basic rules + ATP logic for manually entered dates*
None	Allow assignment of unrealistic dates	Ignore basic rules for manually entered dates

Legend: * = Display exceptions on *Available Ship and Receipt Dates* form, and transfer a selected date to change the ship date

14.4 Reserve Material for a Transfer Order Line

Most scenarios employ reservations at the time you release a transfer order for picking, and the picking list (or picking work) communicates these reservations. Some scenarios require reservations at the time of creating a transfer order, and the reservation policy assigned to a transfer order line item indicates whether inventory will be reserved automatically or manually. When initially adding a line item, this policy – labeled Reserve Items Automatically -- is inherited from the transfer order header, and it can be overridden. The policy for the transfer order header can be inherited from a companywide policy (embedded in the Inventory and Warehouse Management Parameters).

The reservation logic differs between the basic and advanced approaches to warehouse management. The advanced approach requires assignment of an additional item policy termed the reservation hierarchy.

14.5 Additional Case Studies

Case 14.1: Transfers Between Adjacent Warehouses A manufacturing company with two adjacent warehouses (within the same site) employed transfer journals for moving inventory between the warehouses. A transfer journal was initially created and populated with the items and quantities to be moved. The printed version provided a picking list (and turnaround document) for warehouse workers at the originating warehouse, and they entered the actual results for the "from warehouse" on the journal lines. After the material was received, warehouse workers entered the results for the "to warehouse," and posted the transfer journal.

In this scenario, the transfer journals were created by firming planned transfers, which reflects a site-specific policy to "use transfer journals for movements within the site." It also reflects the item's coverage policies about the warehouse source for planned transfers.

Case 14.2: Transportation Constraints about Transfer Orders to/from a Subcontractor An electronics manufacturer located in the United States sent supplied material via truck to its subcontractor in Mexico, and the completed subassembly was sent back via truck to its US location. The weekly truck schedules to and from Mexico were identified as two different modes of delivery, and the associated calendars identified which days the truck departed and an estimated transportation time (expressed in days). The contents of a given truck were identified as line items on a transfer order. Master planning logic used these transportation constraints to suggest appropriate dates and quantities for planned transfer orders and subcontracted production orders, and coordinate the supply chain accordingly. This approach provided full visibility of inventory at the subcontractor location and in transit.

Case 14.3: Updating the Transfer Order Receipt Date for Overseas Deliveries A manufacturing/distribution company purchased many items from suppliers in Asia. The company took ownership when the items were still at the supplier, and then used transfer orders to coordinate deliveries to their U.S. warehouses. Each transfer order represented a container, and the line items represented the container contents. The transfer order receipt date was continually updated to reflect the expected date.

Case 14.4: Reporting "Lost in Transit" for a Transfer Order A transfer order shipment was sometimes "lost in transit," such as an individual line item or a partial quantity of a line item. In these cases, the receiving clerk at the ship-to warehouse identified this as a separate scrap quantity when reporting the total received quantity.

Case 14.5: Transfers from an Offsite Warehouse for Consigned Inventory A manufacturing company identified packaging materials as components of their salable items. The packaging materials represented consignment inventory stocked at a separate off-site warehouse, where the inventory was transferred when needed to a production facility (a different warehouse within the same site). Consignment replenishment orders identified the materials being delivered to the off-site warehouse, and planned transfer orders indicated the need for transfers to the production warehouse. Firming the planned transfer orders created transfer journals (based on a policy for the site). A printed version of the transfer journal provided a picking list (and turnaround document) for warehouse workers at the off-site warehouse, and they entered the actual results for the "from location" on the journal lines. After material was received at the production warehouse, warehouse workers entered the results for the "to location" and posted the transfer journal. An ownership change was posted prior to reporting consumption against production order picking lists.

14.6 Executive Summary

This chapter covered several additional considerations about transfer orders. These included the different ways to create transfer orders, shipment and delivery dates, the use of delivery date control, and reservations for transfer order lines. Several case studies illustrated the use of transfer orders, such as transfers between adjacent warehouses and transfers to/from subcontractor locations.

Chapter 15

Considerations about Batch-Controlled Items

Many manufacturing and distribution scenarios require tracking of batch numbers for a material item. The term *batch number* is used because the software employs the term *lot number* as a system-assigned internal identifier for inventory transactions. Batch numbers only apply to a batch-controlled item. Three key aspects of a batch number - about its shelf life expiration date, batch attributes, and batch disposition code – can impact master planning and reservation logic. The following sections of the chapter reflect these topics, starting with some basics of batch number tracking.

1. Basics of Batch Number Tracking
2. Master Planning and Expiration Dates
3. Reservation Logic and Expiration Dates
4. Reservations and Batch Attributes
5. Batch Disposition Codes
6. Additional Case Studies

The use of batch numbers often involves quality management considerations such as product testing and quality orders. For example, the test results associated with a quality order can apply to a batch number. A subsequent chapter covers several quality management considerations.

15.1 Basics of Batch Number Tracking

The basics of batch number tracking start with the identification of a batch-controlled item. Additional aspects include the assignment of a batch number, merging batches, and the vendor batch information. The basics also include the designation of a shelf life item.

Identify a Batch-Controlled Item A batch-controlled item is identified by a the Tracking Dimension Group assigned to the item, which must include the batch number. The batch number dimension has several policies that enforce batch tracking for issues and receipts, and optionally support unique requirements such as batch-specific costing, pricing and/or coverage planning. The use of advanced warehousing involves an additional consideration, since a batch-controlled item must be assigned an appropriate Reservation Hierarchy that includes the batch number.

Assignment of a Batch Number The assignment of a batch number typically occurs at the time of receipt, such as purchase order receipts, batch order receipts, RMA receipts and inventory adjustments. The assignment of a batch number can be manual or automatic, and several different approaches apply to automatic assignment.

One aspect of batch number assignment involves different batch numbers when reporting multiple partial receipts for the same order. With multiple partial receipts for the same purchase order line, for example, the same vendor batch number may apply but the material needs to be tracked by different internal batch numbers. Another example involves multiple receipts of the same production order (or batch order) where each receipt represents a different physical batch requiring a unique batch number.

You can change the batch number for an inventory quantity by using the Transfer Journal, much like you would change its bin location or combine inventory in a bin location.

Merging Batches Some scenarios involve the merging of two or more existing batches of a batch-controlled item, typically with assignment of a new batch number. There are two different approaches to merging batches, which can be labeled batch merge and transfers to a different batch.

Vendor Batch Information The vendor batch information normally applies to a purchased item, but it can also be used for other items. The information is often recorded upon receipt, but it can be recorded later. The information includes a vendor batch number, a field for the vendor-specified manufacturing date, and two fields for capturing country of origin information.

The vendor batch information includes additional fields related to items with shelf life dates. This includes the vendor-specified dates for manufacturing and expiration, and the options to inherit these vendor-specified dates by the internal batch number. The next point describes how to designate a batch-controlled item with shelf life dates.

Designate a Batch-Controlled Item with Shelf Life Dates The critical policy indicates use of First-Expired-First-Out (FEFO) reservation logic. It is embedded within the Item Model Group assigned to an item, where the policy is labeled *FEFO Date-Controlled* reservations. You can then specify the additional policies about default values for calculating shelf life dates based on the manufacturing date of the item's inventory batches. The three shelf life dates consist of an expiration date, best before date, and shelf advice date.[1] The default values for calculating these dates are expressed in calendar days. Further explanation focuses on use of the expiration date.[2]

15.2 Master Planning and Expiration Dates

The master planning considerations about expiration dates require a brief background about the assignment of an expiration date.

Assignment of a Shelf Life Expiration Date There are several ways to assign an expiration date to a batch number. One approach typically applies to purchased items, where the internal batch number inherits the expiration date based on vendor batch information. A second approach typically applies to manufactured items, where the receipt date of a finished quantity is assumed to be the manufacturing date, and the expiration date can be automatically calculated based on the item-specific default value for an expiration period. As a third approach, you can manually reset the expiration date for a batch number.

A fourth option for assignment of an expiration date applies to manufactured items, but it only applies when using formulas and the related batch orders for the items. It builds on the use of lot inheritance policies to automatically calculate an expiration date based on the ingredients used to produce an item. A subsequent chapter about process manufacturing provides further explanation of lot inheritance policies within the formula line information (Section 18.4).

Expiration Dates in Master Planning Logic Master planning logic considers expiration dates when you specify the policy for *Use shelf life dates* as one of the master plan policies, as previously mentioned (Section 3.1). The logic assumes that a batch's inventory will no longer be available after its expiration date. The logic also assumes that scheduled receipts will have an expiration date reflecting the expected receipt date and item's default value for an expiration period.

---

[1] The best before date means that the material is good through midnight of the day before. The expiry date means that the material is good through midnight of the specified expiration date.
[2] Master planning logic and reservation logic will consider the best before date (rather than the expiration date) when this has been specified as the basis for an item's FEFO logic.

Master planning logic considers the expiration dates in suggesting planned orders to satisfy demands, and the net requirements information identifies expiring inventory. The dates are also considered in net change explosions and capable-to-promise logic, since these generates planned orders that mirror the master planning logic.

15.3 Reservation Logic and Expiration Dates

Expiration dates and FEFO logic are automatically considered in reservations for shelf life items. Previous chapters covered reservations related to sales orders (Section 8.5), production order components (Section 12.6), and transfer orders (Section 14.4). The reservation logic for sales orders entails and additional consideration, as described below.

Sales Order Reservation Logic and Customer Requirements about Remaining Shelf Life The reservation logic for a sales order line considers the requested receipt date at the customer site, so that batches expiring on or before that date will not be reserved. However, a customer may have requirements about remaining shelf life that need to be enforced on sales orders to the customer. For example, the customer may not accept a batch with less than 30 days remaining until its expiration date. A customer's specified time horizon can be defined on the Sellable Days by Customer page (accessed from the Customer page). The horizon can be specified for individual item numbers, a group of items (based on the item group), or all items. Batches will only be reserved when they satisfy the customer requirements about sellable days after the requested receipt date.

If you change a sales order's scheduled receipt date so that it is beyond the expiration date of a reserved batch (per above reservation logic), you will receive a prompt to remove the reservation, keep the reservation and allow you to ship the expired batch, or return the scheduled date to its previous value.

15.4 Reservations and Batch Attributes

One or more batch attributes can be assigned to a batch-controlled item, and actual values recorded against the batch numbers for the item. You can then search for an appropriate batch based on actual values of the item's batch attributes. This is termed a batch attribute search. A batch attribute search may be used in the context of finding an ingredient for production or finding inventory for a transfer order, or in the context of entering a sales order line.

The use of batch attributes requires some setup information, including the definition of batch attributes and the assignment of relevant batch attributes to an item. You can then record actual values of these batch attributes for a specific batch number. Alternatively, you can use the test results from a quality order to update a batch attribute value. An additional option for assignment of batch attribute values applies to manufactured items, but only when using formulas and the related batch orders. It builds on the use of lot inheritance policies to automatically populate the batch attribute values based on the ingredients used to produce the item.

When performing a batch attribute search for a sales order line, the attribute values for the search criteria can be manually entered, or automatically populated based on item-specific values or customer-specific values for the item. Use of the search criteria will result in a displayed list of applicable batches, so that you can reserve the desired batch for the sales order. An additional consideration applies when the inventory quantity of a single batch is insufficient. You can optionally reduce the sales order quantity to reserve the largest available quantity of a single batch, or create a new batch order to produce the requested quantity and reserve the batch for the sales order line.

15.5 Batch Disposition Codes

Batch disposition codes often represent a critical tool for quality management because the policies associated with a code can selectively enforce restricted usage and identify non-nettable inventory. As part of defining the batch disposition codes, one code should reflect available material where the disposition status is designated as available. The number of additional codes will depend on the desired variations in restricted usage, where the disposition status is designated as unavailable. Additional codes (and their policies) can be used to designate whether the inventory is nettable or non-nettable, and whether the inventory can be reserved for sales, production, or transfer purposes.

For codes with an unavailable status, Figure 15.1 summarizes several considerations and the impacts on inventory. The bottom of the figure identifies the possible impacts on master planning logic, where a code can identify whether the inventory is nettable or non-nettable.

An unavailable status provides a form of inventory blocking, and a comparable figure provides a similar analysis of inventory blocking approaches (Section 16.1). Batch disposition codes can be used in conjunction with all three approaches to inventory blocking, but is most commonly used with quality orders for updating the batch disposition code based on pass/fail results of validation.

Figure 15.1 Impacts of Disposition Codes with an Unavailable Status

Considerations	Impacts on Inventory
Create blocking for a specified batch number	Assign a batch disposition code (with an unavailable status) to a batch number
Ability to assign batch disposition code at time of order receipt	Yes
Remove blocking for a batch number	Change the batch disposition code (to one with an available status) for a batch number
Allowable transactions for a batch number that has been assigned a batch disposition code with an unavailable status	Restricted usage for sales orders Restricted usage for production/batch orders Restricted usage for transfer order Move Adjustment out Cycle count Return to vendor Create quality order
Additional considerations	Different ways to change the Batch Disposition Code Split the quantity for a batch number to assign different batch disposition codes
Impact of a batch disposition code with an unavailable status on master planning logic	Nettable or Non-nettable

A batch disposition code with an unavailable status can be assigned to a batch number at any time. The associated blocking can be removed by changing the code to one with an available status. The restricted usage policies do not impact moves, adjustments, cycle counts, and returns to vendor.

The batch disposition code can be changed by a quality order or changed directly. The code can also be changed via a rework order for the item's inventory. When needed, you can split the quantity for a batch number into two or more batch numbers to assign different batch disposition codes. As another option, a subset of a batch number can be blocked via manual assignment of inventory blocking or a blocked value of Inventory Status.

15.6 Additional Case Studies

Case 15.1: Vendor Batch Numbers A manufacturer used several purchased components that were batch-controlled items. At the time of product receipt, the receiving clerks recorded an internal batch number and the vendor's batch number. A bar-coded label with the internal batch number was affixed to the product receipt, and subsequent transactions referred to the internal batch number.

Case 15.2: Sales Order Reservations and Remaining Shelf Life A food products manufacturer used automatic reservations on sales orders to ensure that the shipped products satisfied each customer's requirements for remaining shelf life. The customer's requirements were expressed as the number of sellable days after the product was delivered to the customer, and the automatic reservations reflected First-Expired-First-Out (FEFO) logic.

Case 15.3: Reservations Based on Batch Attributes The customer service reps at a process manufacturer used a profile of customer specifications to find and reserve applicable batches of inventory. The customer specifications were expressed as an allowable value range for selected batch attributes, and batch searching logic was used to find the applicable batches. In some cases, the customer required the same batch, and the service reps were able to identify the largest available batch, or create a new batch order to produce the desired batch attributes.

Case 15.4: Customer-Specific Batch Attributes for a Mining Product The customer contracts for a mining product specified the batch attribute requirements, consisting of a target value and an acceptable range of values for each attribute. A typical contract specified 15 batch attributes for a given product (such as the percentage of molybdenum content and sulphur dioxide), which were defined as customer-specific attributes. The actual values for the product's batch attributes were recorded during production. When entering a sales order for the product, the customer-specific attributes were used as the basis for batch attribute searching, so that applicable batches of inventory could be identified and reserved, and then shipped to the customer.

Case 15.5: Batch Attributes of a Cobalt Product A chemical manufacturer produced batches of various cobalt products to stock, such as cobalt hydrate, cobalt acetate and cobalt chloride. Batch numbers were assigned to the end item and several batch attributes were measured for each batch -- such as the percentage of various trace elements to indicate the level of purity. When customers placed sales orders for the end item, they specified the allowable range of values for these batch attributes, since material purity was a critical factor. The customer specifications for the item were used to identify and reserve the relevant batches within finished goods inventory, which were then shipped to the customer.

15.7 Executive Summary

Batch tracking involves the creation and assignment of batch numbers to an item's inventory. Each batch may also require batch-related information, such as the expiration date for a shelf life item, batch attribute values, or a disposition code to indicate restricted usage. This information serves multiple purposes and can impact master planning logic and reservations. Several case studies illustrated these impacts.

Chapter 16

Quality Management Considerations

The concerns of quality management typically extend across every aspect of supply chain management. A key concern consists of inventory blocking approaches which prevent usage and directly impact master planning logic. Several other considerations indirectly impact master planning, including the impact of holds and stopped flags. These topics are covered in the following sections within the chapter.

1. Summary of Inventory Blocking Approaches
2. Broad Viewpoint of Quality Concerns
3. Impact of Holds and Stopped Flags

16.1 Summary of Inventory Blocking Approaches

Inventory blocking represents a key tool for quality management, such as preventing usage and indicating the need for inspection. There are three basic sources or approaches for inventory blocking -- labeled Inventory Status, Quality Order and Manual. One approach employs a blocked value for Inventory Status. The second approach employs quality orders, and often works in conjunction with the values of Inventory Status. The third approach involves manual assignment of inventory blocking. Each approach results in an entry on the Inventory Blocking page along with information about the source of blocking. The three approaches differ in their impact in how master planning logic treats the blocked inventory, such as identifying the expected date of completion or identifying non-nettable inventory. The three approaches are summarized in Figure 16.1 and described below. The bottom of the figure identifies the impact of blocked inventory on master planning logic. An example screen also illustrates the Inventory Blocking page along with example data about the three approaches (Figure 16.2)

Figure 16.1 Summary of Inventory Blocking Approaches

Considerations about Blocking	Type of Inventory Blocking		
	Inventory Status	Quality Order	Manual
Create blocking for the specified inventory of item	Assign a blocked value for Inventory Status	Create a quality order with full blocking	Manually assign inventory blocking
Ability to assign blocking at time of order receipt	Yes	Yes	No
Remove blocking	Change a blocked value for Inventory Status	Delete or complete the quality order	Delete manual assignment of inventory blocking
Allowable transactions for the blocked inventory	Move, adjustment out Cycle count Return to vendor Create quality order	None	None
Add description of blocking	No	Yes	Yes
Add note or document	No	Yes	Yes
Impact of blocked inventory on master planning logic	Non-nettable	Nettable on expected date	Non-nettable or Nettable on expected date
Additional considerations	Assign to subset of a batch number, or a SN	Block just sample quantity; Destructive testing; Update Inventory Status or Batch Disposition Code after validating test results	Assign to subset of a batch number, or a SN

Inventory Blocking based on a blocked value of Inventory Status This approach reflects a blocked value for Inventory Status which can be assigned at the time of order receipt. The blocking can be viewed on the Inventory Blocking form, and it can only be removed by changing it to a non-blocked value. The inventory is treated as unusable and non-nettable by master planning logic. The blocking prevents most inventory transactions except for moves, adjustments, cycle counts, returns to vendor and creation of a quality order. A blocked value can be changed by a quality order or changed directly (via a client or mobile device transaction). A blocked value can also be assigned to a subset of a batch number or to a specific serial number.

Inventory Blocking based on a Quality Order This approach reflects a quality order with "full blocking" as part of the policies for item sampling. A quality order can be manually created for the specified inventory of an item, including inventory that has already been assigned a blocked value for Inventory Status. Alternatively, an item's quality order can be automatically created based on policies defined on the Quality Association page, such as automatic creation after reporting purchase order arrival or the finished quantity for production.

With full blocking, the inventory associated with a quality order is treated by master planning logic as nettable with an expected availability date. This expected outcome is indicated by the automatically-assigned Expected Receipts checkbox. The expected date inherits the creation date and can be manually changed. However, the blocking prevents all inventory transactions.

Blocking based on a quality order has several additional considerations shown at the bottom of Figure 16.1. For example, blocking can just apply to the sample quantity, and a quality order can be used to update the value of Inventory Status or the Batch Disposition Code.

Inventory Blocking based on Manual Assignment This approach reflects a manual assignment of inventory blocking to existing inventory. It can only be created and deleted on the Inventory Blocking form, and you can optionally define a description and/or notes about the manual blocking. When you create manual blocking, you can indicate the expected outcome as non-nettable or as nettable with an expected availability date. You indicate the expected outcome via an Expected Receipts checkbox. The expected date inherits the creation date and can be manually changed. Manual blocking prevents all inventory transactions. For example, the manual blocking must be removed to report the inventory as scrapped. Manual blocking can also be assigned to a subset of a batch number or to a specific serial number.

Example Screen for Inventory Blocking The example screen shown in Figure 16.2 illustrates the Inventory Blocking page, and employs artistic license to display three examples about the different sources of blocking. The first line for the "X3-Part1" item illustrates blocking based on a blocked value of Inventory Status, where the highlighted field identifies the status as "Blocked". The second line for the "X3-Part2 item illustrates blocking based on a Quality Order, where the highlighted fields include the expected receipt information and the quality order number. The third line for the "X3-Part3" item illustrates blocking based on manual assignment, and the highlighted fields include the expected receipt information.

Additional Blocking Option via Batch Disposition Codes The additional option only applies to batch-controlled items, where you define Batch Disposition Codes and the restricted usage policies for a given code, and then assign the code to a specific batch number. It can be used in conjunction with all three of the above-mentioned approaches, but is most commonly used with quality orders for updating the batch disposition code based on test results. The previous chapter described batch disposition codes and provided a similar figure about their impact on master planning logic.

Figure 16.2   Example Screen of Inventory Blocking

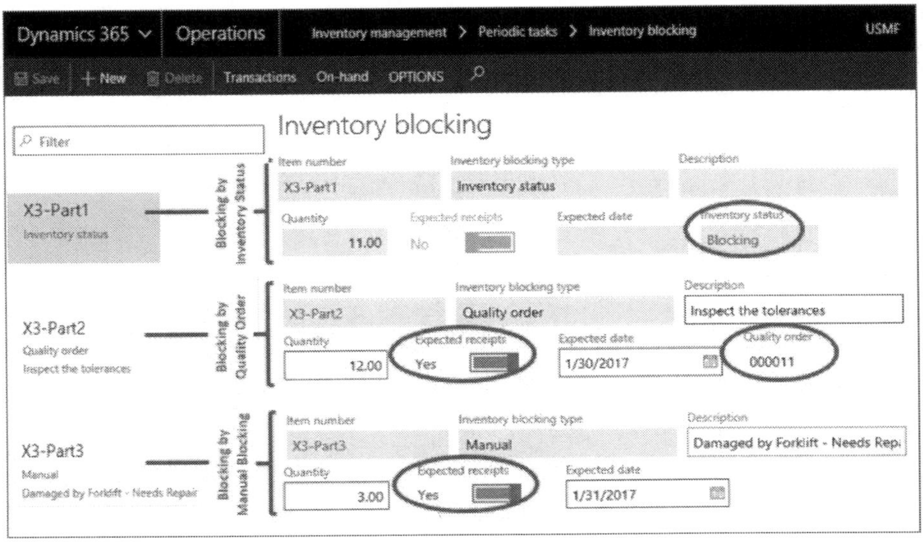

16.2 Broad Viewpoint of Quality Concerns

The concerns of quality management typically extend across every aspect of supply chain management. Several of these concerns indirectly impact master planning, as illustrated by the following.

◆ Approval of authorized BOM and Route versions for a manufactured item

◆ Identify planned changes reflecting continuous improvements in production, such as planned changes to BOM and routing information

◆ Identify planned scrap in production, such as planned component scrap for a BOM line and operation scrap percentages in the routing

◆ Enforce restrictions on sales order processing, such as preventing order entry for stopped items or restricted products

◆ Specify and enforce authorized units of measure for an item, and the UM conversions

◆ Specify and enforce approved vendors for a purchased item or subcontracted service

16.3 Impact of Holds and Stop Flags

Several types of holds and stop flags can impact the processing of sales orders, supply orders and many warehouse transactions. These represent additional restrictions beyond the use of inventory blocking, or the use of batch disposition codes with restricted usage. However, none of them directly impacts master planning logic, and they are included here for completeness sake.

Impact of a Customer Hold on Sales Orders A customer hold status (termed the *Invoicing and Delivery On Hold* policy) can prevent all sales order transactions from being recorded for the customer, or just prevent shipments and invoicing, until it has been removed or changed. It results in a corresponding message when attempting to enter transactions.

Impact of an Order Hold for a Sales Order Assigning a "hold code" to a sales order will prevent any further processing (such as a confirmation, picking/shipping or invoicing) while still allowing order changes until the hold has been cleared. It results in a corresponding message when attempting to enter transactions. An additional policy for a hold code determines whether the reservations for a sales order (if any) should be removed after placing it on hold. In either case, the sales order demand will still be recognized by master scheduling logic. One or more hold codes can be assigned to a sales order, and you can then clear a hold code after it has been resolved.

A hold code can also be assigned to an RMA to prevent further processing, such as receipts or creation of a replacement order.

Impact of Stopped Sales Activities for an Item The sales order transactions for an item can be stopped, either as a companywide or site-specific policy within the item's default order policies. The stopped flag prevents further transactions for an item's existing sales orders (including picking/shipping transactions) until it has been removed. It results in a corresponding message when attempting to enter a transaction. A similar stopped flag can be specified for an item's inventory transactions, which also prevents further transactions.

Impact of a Vendor Hold on Purchase Orders The assignment of a vendor hold for "all" transactions will prevent all purchase order transactions from being recorded for the vendor until it has been removed. It results in a corresponding message when attempting to enter transactions.

Impact of a Stopped Flag for a Purchase Order Line A line item on a purchase order can be flagged as stopped. The stopped flag prevents further transactions for the line item (including registration of arrivals and posting of product receipts) until it has been removed. It results in a corresponding message when attempting to enter transactions.

Impact of Stopped Purchasing Activities for an Item The purchase order transactions for an item can be flagged as stopped, either as a companywide or site-specific policy. The stopped flag prevents further transactions for an item's existing purchase orders (including registration of arrivals and posting of product receipts) until it has been removed. It results in a corresponding message when attempting to enter transactions. A similar stopped flag can be specified for an item's inventory transactions, which also prevents further transactions.

Impact of a Stop Flag for a Production Order The Stop flag primarily serves warehouse management purposes and prevents changes in order status until it has been removed. For example, assigning the Stop flag to a scheduled order prevents a change in order status to Released or Started. By preventing a change to a Started status, it indirectly prevents creation of a picking list journal and reporting of actual picked material. Preventing a change to a Released status impacts the advanced warehousing, since it indirectly prevents creation and reporting of raw material picking work. The Stop flag has no impact when assigned after a production order has been started.

No Impact of a Nonconformance Report You can create a nonconformance report to identify a problem, along with information about the related inventory, purchase order, sales order, or the related vendor or customer. However, a nonconformance report does not prevent any transactions.

16.4 Executive Summary

This chapter summarized several quality management considerations that impact master planning. One consideration involved the different approaches to inventory blocking that directly impact master planning, such as the use of Inventory Status and quality orders. Other considerations indirectly impact master planning, such as the variations of holds and stopped flags.

Chapter 17

Master Planning in a Multicompany Supply Chain

Some manufacturing and distribution businesses have inventory at different physical sites that reflect different companies, and transfers between the sites. The transfers between these sites involve intercompany orders and master planning across the multicompany supply chain. These considerations are reflected in the following sections with the chapter.

1. Master Planning in a Multicompany Scenario
2. Intercompany Orders
3. Variations of Creating Intercompany orders
4. Additional Case Studies

17.1 Master Planning in a Multicompany Scenario

The sequence for performing the master planning task becomes important in a multicompany supply chain involving two or more companies. The calculations apply to a single company, which means the master planning task should first be performed for the top-tier company. This generates planned intercompany demand that communicates requirements to the second-tier company, which represents an up-stream company within the supply chain.[1] The process must be repeated for additional up-stream companies, and this process can be supported by the intercompany master planning task.

---

[1] The term upstream provides a relative reference within a supply chain indicating a source of raw material, whereas the term downstream indicates the direction of the end customer.

Intercompany Master Planning Task A sequence of companies -- termed an intercompany planning group -- can be defined for performing the intercompany master planning task. You also identify the relevant set of master plan data for each company in the sequence. A single intercompany planning group may be sufficient in many scenarios, where the specified sequence often reflects the subset of companies requiring supply chain coordination. You specify the intercompany planning group as part of the dialogue for performing the intercompany master planning task.

Some additional information is specified as part of the dialogue for performing the intercompany master planning task, such as the number of iterations to correctly support more complex scenarios such as bi-directional trade. The additional information typically specifies regeneration calculations for the first iteration and net change calculations for subsequent iterations. The intercompany master planning task can be started in any company, since the sequencing will reflect the specified intercompany planning group.

As part of generating planned purchase orders within one company, the master planning task generates demand for an up-stream company. This demand is labeled *planned intercompany demand*, which differentiates it from other types of demand.

The generation of planned intercompany demand requires some additional setup information within the master plan policies. That is, you designate that downstream planned intercompany demand should be included, and you also specify all possible companies (and their related set of master plan data) that could be considered. These settings only apply when the downstream company is not included in the same master planning run, such as running intercompany master planning where the specified intercompany planning group does not include the downstream company.

Inquiries about Planned Intercompany Demand The planned intercompany demand can be viewed from two perspectives -- incoming and outbound -- that reflect a company's relative position in the supply chain. The outbound perspective identifies planned purchases (to other companies) for a purchasing company, and the incoming perspective identifies planned sales (to other companies) for a selling company.

The example screens shown in Figure 17.1 illustrate the two perspectives. In the example data displayed in the top of the figure, a planned purchase order to the sister company "USMF" is recognized as Outbound Planned Intercompany Demand for the "DEMF" company. You can optionally select a line and then access the Planned Orders page to view (and firm) the planned purchase order.

The bottom of the figure displays the demand from the sister company as Incoming Planned Intercompany Demand.

Figure 17.1 Example Screens for Planned Intercompany Demand

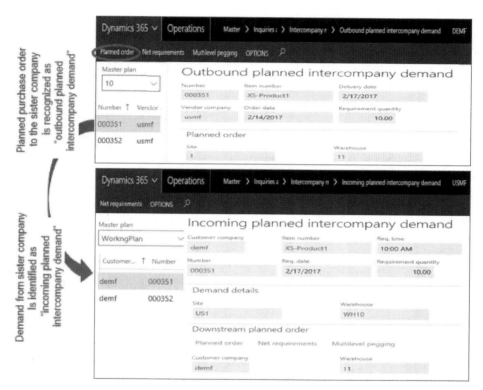

Inquiry about Intercompany Supply and Demand This inquiry shows all orders -- both planned and actual -- that a company has from upstream and downstream companies. The example screen shown in Figure 17.2 illustrates the selling company perspective of sales orders and planned intercompany demands, and the associated information from the buying company's perspective. Starting from a selected line, you can access the Multilevel Pegging page to view all supplies and demands across the multicompany supply chain and a multilevel product structure.

Figure 17.2 Example Screen of Intercompany Supply and Demand

Dynamics 365 ∨	Operations		Master pl >	Inquiries anc >	Intercompany mast >	Intercompany supply and demand				USMF

VIEW OPTIONS 🔎

INTERCOMPANY SUPPLY AND DEMAND

✓	Item number ↑	Site	Warehouse	Requireme...	Require...	Reference	Number	Customer company	Customer reference type	Customer reference	Customer reference status
	X5-Product1	US1	WH10	2/17/2017	-10.00	Sales order	demf000011	demf	Purchase order	000011	Open order
	X5-Product1	US1	WH10	2/24/3017	-22.00	Planned intercompany demand	demf:000352	demf	Planned purchase orders	000352	Unprocessed

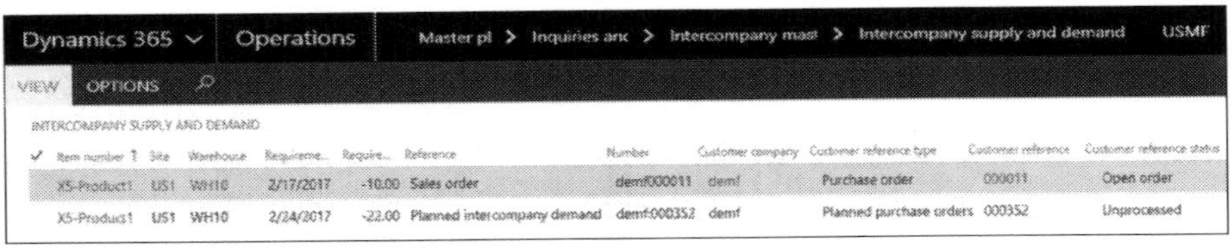

Intercompany Inventory Inquiry The On-Hand Inquiry page contains a Tab for displaying an item's inventory in multiple companies. The inquiry does not display the quantity of in-transit inventory between companies.

Case 17.1: Multicompany Supply Chain for a Global Operation A simplified example of a global manufacturer illustrates a multicompany supply chain. As shown in Figure 17.3, the simplified example consists of two different companies representing a manufacturing company and a distribution company. In the manufacturing company, an intermediate item (produced at one manufacturing site) was transferred to another site for producing the end item. The manufacturing company sold the end-item to domestic customers. The end-item was also transferred to a different company's distribution center for sales to foreign customers, where replenishment was based on demand forecasts for the distribution center. The primary coordination tools across the multicompany supply chain consisted of planned intercompany demand as well as intercompany purchase orders and sales orders.

Figure 17.3 Coordinate a Multicompany Supply Chain

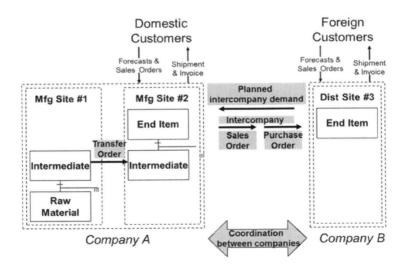

Stocking Levels in a Multicompany Supply Chain   The multicompany scenario described in Case 17.1 (and shown in the figure) included demand forecasts and stocked products at the manufacturing company and at the distribution company. In a slightly different scenario, the products would only be forecasted and stocked at the manufacturing company, and only sent to the distribution company based on actual sales order demand. To stock material in anticipation of the demand from the distribution company, the related demand forecasts at the manufacturing company would be entered as customer-specific forecasts. In addition, the forecast consumption logic must consider intercompany sales orders for these customer-specific forecasts. You indicate this forecast consumption logic as part of the coverage group assigned to the relevant items at the manufacturing company. Case 17.2 provides an illustrative example.

Value of In-Transit Inventory for Intercompany Orders   A separate report about intercompany orders -- termed the Intercompany Goods in Transit Totals report orders -- displays the period beginning balance, period ending balance and net change with a period. This information is grouped by vendor, and it provides the basis for manually-created general ledger entries. An additional report displays the transaction detail about shipments and receipts within a given period.

17.2 Intercompany Orders

Trading between two companies involves a customer-to-vendor relationship. Intercompany orders can be used when both companies exist within the same instance. Placing a purchase order with an intercompany vendor will automatically create a corresponding sales order in the sister company, and vice versa. The origin of an intercompany order identifies whether it was manually or automatically created, as indicated by the origin field in the order header. The origin field can have a value of *source* or *derived* respectively.   The origin field is blank for all other sales orders and purchase orders.

Intercompany orders require setup information about items and also about the vendors and customers representing the sister companies. The setup information will be briefly summarized, and then we'll review several variations of intercompany orders.

Setup Information for Items   A product must be released to both companies to support intercompany trading, and the item's company-level information must be defined in both companies.   In order to support automatic creation of a corresponding order for intercompany orders, several aspects of setup information are critical.

◆ *Default ship-from site/warehouse for an automatically-created sales order.* The default values can be defined for an item or for the customer representing the sister company.

◆ *Default ship-to site/warehouse for an automatically-created purchase order.* The default values can be defined for an item or for the vendor representing the sister company.

◆ *Sales prices and purchase prices.* Item information (at the selling company) should include a standard sales price and/or sales agreements that determine prices on the intercompany sales order and purchase order. Pricing information at the selling company normally dictates the price on the corresponding intercompany purchase order.

Setup Information for an Intercompany Vendor The vendor number must be defined within the buying company so that you can identify the associated sister company. At the same time, you can also identify the corresponding customer number within the selling company. Several policies must be defined about the trading practices between a pair of purchasing and selling companies. For example, the policies determine the ability to change prices and discounts on the derived order.

Setup Information for an Intercompany Customer Just like vendors, the customer information is defined within each company. Hence, a customer number must be defined within the selling company so that you can identify the associated sister company. At the same time, you can also identify the corresponding vendor number within the buying company. You can also maintain the policies about the trading practices between the companies.

17.3 Variations of Creating Intercompany Orders

There are several variations of creating intercompany orders, as illustrated by the following examples. The examples involve a distribution company that purchases products from a manufacturing company. The master planning considerations about sales orders and purchase orders were previously explained, and these same considerations apply to intercompany orders.

Manually Create an Intercompany Purchase Order A basic scenario consists of a manually created purchase order (in the distribution company) to an intercompany vendor (the manufacturing company). This intercompany purchase order automatically creates an intercompany sales order at the manufacturing company. It is termed a two-legged order because it reflects transactions between the two related companies.

The converse situation involving a manually created sales order will automatically generate an intercompany purchase order when the sales order represents a special order or direct delivery order, as discussed in subsequent examples.

Firm a Planned Intercompany Purchase Order Firming a planned purchase order to an intercompany vendor will automatically create an intercompany purchase order and a corresponding intercompany sales order (at the manufacturing company).

Release an Intercompany Purchase Order from a Purchase Agreement A purchase agreement can be defined for an intercompany vendor, where the type of commitment must reflect a purchase quantity commitment. Each line item identifies an item, quantity and the purchase price or discount. You can then generate and view the equivalent sales agreement for the company that represents the intercompany vendor. Releasing an order from the purchase agreement (for a specified line item, quantity and date) creates an intercompany purchase order and a corresponding intercompany sales order at the manufacturing company.

Create an Intercompany Purchase Order from a Sales Order (aka Special Order) A special order can be created for a sales order line, which results in an intercompany purchase order when the vendor is a sister company. This is termed a three-legged order because the sales order shipment to an external customer reflects the third leg. Changes on the originating sales order can automatically update the derived order, such as changes to the quantity, delivery date or delivery address.

Create a Direct Delivery Intercompany Purchase Order from a Sales Order A direct delivery purchase order can be created from a sales order line, which results in an intercompany purchase order (when the vendor is a sister company) that will be directly delivered to the customer. This also creates a sales order in the vendor company, and the sales order shipment can automatically update the related orders. That is, the shipment will automatically update the receipt for the intercompany purchase order and the shipment of the related sales order. Several policies in the setup information only apply to this direct delivery scenario.

Process Intercompany Orders for a Configurable Product Use of the constraint-based configuration technology can generate a configuration ID for a configurable item. This represents enterprise-wide information. In addition, it can create and assign BOM and route versions for producing the configuration ID, which represents company-level information for the producing company. In this way, one company can enter the sales order for a configurable item (and generate the configuration ID) and a different company can produce it. All above-mentioned variations of intercompany orders apply to a configurable product.

17.4 Additional Case Studies

Case 17.2: Stocking Levels in a Multicompany Supply Chain A manufacturing/distribution business consisted of a distribution network of different inventory locations within different companies. For example, the manufacturing companies produced and delivered products to a regional distribution center (via transfer orders). The products were stocked at the regional distribution center based on demand forecasts and safety stock requirements. The products were then delivered to other inventory locations (in different sister companies) within the distribution network based on actual demand expressed as intercompany sales orders. To maintain the correct stocking level at the regional distribution center, the demand forecasts related to each sister company were entered as customer-specific forecasts, and the subsequent intercompany sales orders consumed these forecasts.

Case 17.3: Home Furniture Outlets A company specializing in home furniture had multiple outlets grouped into various companies. Inventory replenishment was based on outlet-specific min/max quantities. As part of sales order processing, inventory could be checked within a given company's outlets or (if necessary) across all outlets. The system automatically created a transfer order for moving items within a company, or an intercompany order for moving items between companies. When inventory was insufficient, the user could generate a purchase order (to the furniture manufacturer) that was directly linked to the sales order.

17.5 Executive Summary

There are many variations of multicompany operations and the use of intercompany orders. Intercompany orders support the coordination of material transfers between two sites in different companies within a single instance. Intercompany orders require setup information in both companies. The chapter described master planning across a multicompany supply chain. It also described several variations for creating and managing intercompany orders, including special orders and direct delivery orders.

Chapter 18

Master Planning in Process Manufacturing Scenarios

Process manufacturing scenarios typically employ formulas and batch orders -- rather than bills of material and production orders -- to model product structure information and coordinate production. Example industries include food products and industrial products. This chapter covers the basics of formulas and batch orders relevant to master planning, whereas previous chapters covered bills of material and production orders. The basics include several considerations about items and formula information. They also include considerations about co-products and by-products, and the use of planning items with co/by-products.

Additional master planning capabilities supported by formula information include the suggested sequencing of planned batch orders, the suggested use of substitute ingredients in planned batch orders, and the coordination of a bulk/pack production process. These considerations are reflected in the following sections within the chapter, which can be segmented into two groups of topics.

Basics of Item and Formula Information
1. Item Master Considerations
2. Master Formulas and Formula Versions
3. Formula Version Policies for an Item
4. Formula Lines for Ingredients
5. Co-Products and By-Products
6. Planning Item with Co/By-Products
7. Production Formula for a Batch Order

Additional Master Planning Capabilities
8. Sequencing of Planned Batch Orders
9. Substitute Ingredients in a Formula
10. Coordinate a Bulk/Pack Production Process

Two aspects of the software capabilities for process manufacturing scenarios -- for catch weight items and potency-based formulas – are not covered due to book length considerations. They are covered in the 2016 Edition of my book about process manufacturing, which also covers the costing aspects of using formulas.

18.1 Item Master Considerations

Information about material items provides the foundation for managing supply chain activities. A previous chapter covered the item master considerations relevant to master planning. These included enterprise- and company-level information for an item, the production type, unit of measure considerations, and key aspects of additional information for purchased items, manufactured items, and salable items. They also included different approaches to item identification.

This section covers some additional considerations that are unique to process manufacturing scenarios. It covers the unique aspects of the production type and units of measure, and provides several case studies about item identification.

Significance of the Production Type for a Material Item The assignment of a Production Type to a material item impacts how the item can be used. The production type indicates whether an item is manufactured or purchased, and whether a manufactured item employs the BOM or formula approach to product structure information. The formula approach is typically used in process manufacturing, and the most common values of the production type are summarized below.

◆ *None.* A production type of None indicates a purchased material. You cannot define formula or routing information for the item, or create batch orders for the item.

◆ *Formula.* A production type of Formula indicates a manufactured item, and you can define formula and routing information for the item. The item is termed a formula item for short. The item can also be purchased, and the item's planned orders for a given site/warehouse can reflect planned production, purchases, or transfers.

Several additional values support manufacturing scenarios involving co/by-products or planning items.

◆ *Co-Product or By-Product.* This production type must be assigned to an item representing a co-product or by-product, so that the item can be specified as such within the formula information for a manufactured item. For co-products, the item's planned replenishment typically reflects planned production of a specified parent item at a given site, but it can also reflect planned purchases or transfers. A subsequent section provides further explanation about co-products and by-products.

◆ *Planning Item.* A production type of Planning Item indicates a special case of a manufactured item, where the production process only results in co-products or by-products or both. The item is termed a Planning Item for short. You can define formula and routing information for the item, and this information can be used to calculate the costs of its co-products. A subsequent section provides further explanation about defining formula information for a planning item.

The production type of an item can be changed from None to Formula. However, changing it from Formula to None has an additional impact because the item can no longer have formula information, so that the Master Formulas assigned to the item (if any) will be automatically removed. Changing the production type from Formula to BOM has a similar impact of automatically removing the Master Formulas assigned to the item, and you would need to define the item's BOM information.

The production type provides one indicator of whether an item is manufactured or purchased. However, the Planned Order Type for an item acts as the make/buy indicator. For example, the planned order type indicates whether master planning logic should generate planned batch orders or planned purchase orders. The planned order type of production also indicates that cost calculations should consider an item's formula/routing information.

Additional Unit of Measure Considerations Master planning logic calculates the quantities for demands and supplies in terms of an item's inventory unit of measure (or UM for short). However, additional units of measure can be important for different purposes, including purchasing, sales, engineering, production, inventory, and warehousing. The additional units of measure for an item are especially important in many process industry scenarios.

An additional UM consideration applies to a bulk/pack production process because it involves a bulk item conversion ratio, which is a different factor than the one you might enter in the standard Unit Conversion form. A subsequent section provides further explanation of coordinating a bulk/pack production process.

Coverage Planning Data for a Manufactured Item with Formula Information A previous chapter covered the key planning data for manufactured items with BOM information (Section 6.3). The same considerations largely apply to a manufactured item with formula information (and a production type of formula), as summarized in Figure 18.1. The figure highlights the unique aspects, where the information about the item's formula version would apply rather than the item's BOM version.

Figure 18.1 Key Planning Data for a Manufactured Item
with Formula Information

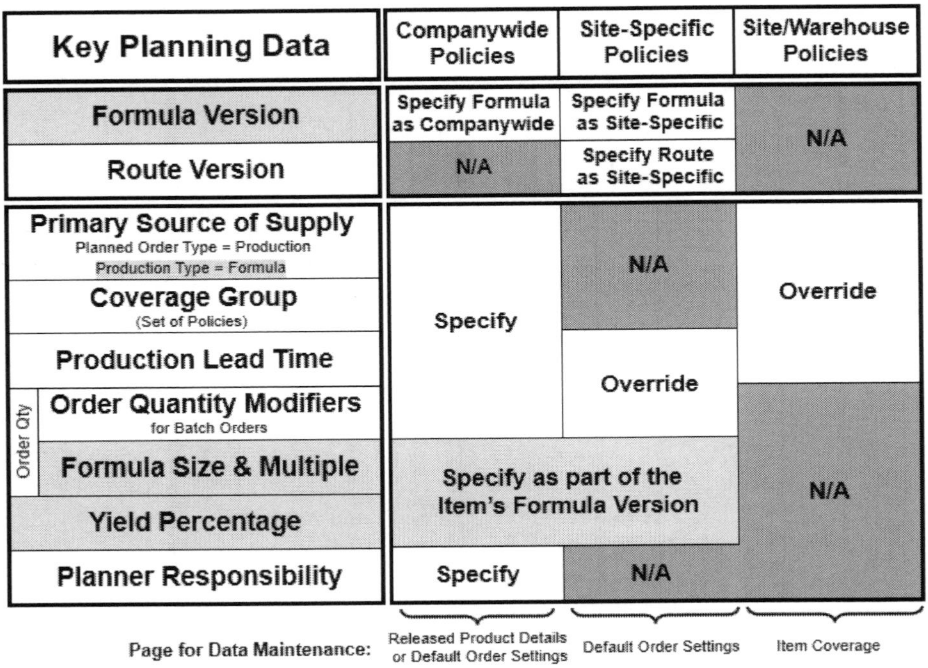

Key Planning Data	Companywide Policies	Site-Specific Policies	Site/Warehouse Policies
Formula Version	Specify Formula as Companywide	Specify Formula as Site-Specific	N/A
Route Version	N/A	Specify Route as Site-Specific	
Primary Source of Supply Planned Order Type = Production Production Type = Formula	Specify	N/A	Override
Coverage Group (Set of Policies)			
Production Lead Time		Override	
Order Quantity Modifiers for Batch Orders			
Formula Size & Multiple	Specify as part of the Item's Formula Version		N/A
Yield Percentage			
Planner Responsibility	Specify	N/A	

Page for Data Maintenance: Released Product Details or Default Order Settings / Default Order Settings / Item Coverage

The unique aspects of an item's formula version include a formula size and multiple, which can act as order quantity modifiers (in conjunction with the item's order quantity modifiers). Another unique aspect includes the expected yield percentage. The other aspects of key planning data are the same, and were previously explained in the chapter about coverage planning data.

A subsequent section provides more detailed explanations about the unique aspects of an item's formula version that relate to planning data (Section 18.3). As already noted, these include companywide versus site-specific formula versions, the formula size/multiple and yield percentage.

Case 18.1: Variant Codes for Stucco A manufacturer of stucco was considering the use of variant codes to replace their current item numbering scheme. One issue concerned the wide variety of customer requirements -- such as different colors, textures, and containers. The proposed scheme consisted of an item number to represent each product line of stucco, and different variant codes to represent a color, texture, sand content, container size, and other factors.

Case 18.2: Significant Item Numbers for Plywood Products A producer of plywood products employed a 34-character item number consisting of several groups of significant digits. For example, these groups indicated the product type, thickness, upper veneer and color, lower veneer and color, glue type and wood type, as well as the length and width of the plywood piece. The significant digits communicated all relevant information for production, sales, and inventory purposes.

18.2 Master Formulas and Formula Versions

A master formula has a unique identifier (termed the *Formula Number*) which can be manually or automatically assigned. Manual assignment should be used when the identifier needs to be meaningful. This book employs the term "Master Formula" whereas the actual term is simply *Formula*. The creation of a master formula typically occurs in the context of creating an item's formula, where it is automatically assigned to the item.[1] Each assignment of a master formula to an item is termed a Formula Version. A formula version has several policies including a specified formula size. This policy is important because a formula line within the formula version defines an ingredient's required quantity in terms of the specified formula size. The policies for a formula version help support multiple formula versions for an item.

Rationale for Multiple Formula Versions Multiple formula versions can be defined for an item, typically to support the following situations.

◆ *Formula variations between sites producing the same manufactured item.* The site-specific formula versions may reflect variations in ingredients or co/by-products, or different formula sizes and yields. In addition, a site-specific formula version may apply to production at one site, and a companywide formula version may apply to production at the other sites.

---

[1] You can separately create a master formula, but the information about formula lines (and possible co/by-products) can only be defined after assigning it to an item and defining the formula version policies.

◆ *Planned changes with effectivity dates.* The multiple formula versions can represent planned changes in the item's formulation, where each formula version has a different validity period. For example, a manufactured item may have two formula versions—one valid to date X and the other valid from date X+1—to indicate planned changes. Planned changes will sometimes reflect seasonality considerations for ingredients, or the availability/costs of alternative ingredients.

◆ *Revision levels for a manufactured item.* The formula versions can represent the revision levels for a manufactured item. The formula version policies indicate the effectivity dates for phasing out (and phasing in) these revision levels. A complete change in a product is typically identified by a different item number.

◆ *Variations due to quantity-sensitive formulations.* The multiple formula versions can represent quantity-sensitive formulations, where each formula version has a different quantity breakpoint. The quantity breakpoints often represent larger formula sizes with higher yield percentages. They may also represent the use of larger or faster equipment to handle the larger quantity, and similar breakpoints can be mirrored in the item's route version.

◆ *Alternate formulas.* Different formula versions may represent alternate formulations for producing the manufactured item, including a version for R&D purposes and a version for trial batches. The most cases, the formula version will be approved (but not active) so that it can be specified for a manually created batch order.

In summary, a manufactured item can have multiple active formula versions that reflect different sites, non-overlapping validity periods, and/or different quantity breakpoints for a batch order quantity. An item can also have approved-but-not-active formula versions.

Approved and Active Formula Versions An item's formula version is initially treated as unapproved, which still allows you to calculate the item's costs. It must be approved to specify it on a manually created batch order. Only an approved formula version can be marked as active. The active formula version will normally be used in planning and cost calculations.

Example Screen of the Formula Versions for an Item The example screen shown in Figure 18.2 illustrates several key points about the formula version policies for an item. In the example data, the manufactured item "X6-BulkProduct1" has two approved and active formula versions with the following significance.

◆ *Formula version for production in a large vessel.* The selected version represents production in a large vessel with a capacity of 2000 pounds and a 99% yield, and it should be used when the required quantity for a planned batch order is 1001 pounds or greater. This is reflected in the formula size and multiple of 2000 pounds, and a "from formula size" of 1001 pounds.

◆ *Formula version for production in a small vessel.* Details of the second version are not shown in the figure, but it represents production in a small vessel with a capacity of 1000 pounds and a 95% yield, and it should be used when the required quantity is 1000 pounds or less. This is reflected in a formula size and multiple of 1000 pounds, and a "from formula size" of 1 pound.

Figure 18.2 Example Screen of the Formula Versions for an Item

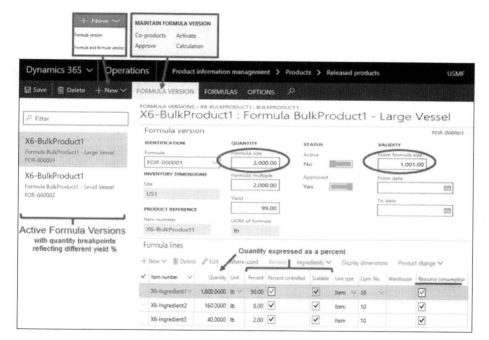

The two formula versions represent site-specific formulas for site "US1", and each version involves the assignment of a master formula (such as "FOR-0000001" shown in the example data). As a related topic, the manufactured item has two different route versions with the same quantity breakpoints and different resource requirements for a large versus small vessel.

One of the breakout boxes at the top of Figure 18.2 illustrates the ability to create a new formula version by assigning an existing master formula, or to simultaneously create both a new master formula and a new formula version. The second breakout box illustrates the ability to approve and activate a formula version, or to maintain co-product information or calculate product costs.

The bottom part of Figure 18.2 illustrates the formula lines for ingredients. In the example data, the requirements for each ingredient have been expressed as percentages, so that the calculated quantity equals the formula size times the percentage. The "resource consumption" policy indicates an option for defining the warehouse source of components (rather than a specified warehouse), as described in a previous chapter about production orders (Section 10.4).

18.3 Formula Version Policies for an Item

The formula version policies serve several different purposes, especially in modeling the characteristics of a batch-oriented production process. For example, the policies enable a manufactured item to have multiple active formula versions that reflect different sites, non-overlapping validity periods, and/or different quantity breakpoints for a batch order quantity. The policies also support batch size considerations in terms of a specified formula size and an associated yield percentage. The following explanation covers the key fields in the formula version for an item.

Site-Specific versus Companywide Formula Versions Specifying a blank site for an item's formula version indicates a companywide formulation, whereas a specified site indicates a site-specific formulation. The primary difference is that master planning logic will use a site-specific formula version (if it exists) that matches the site of the item's requirements. If a site-specific formula version does not exist, the master planning logic will use the companywide formula version for the manufactured item. An error message is generated if an appropriate formula version does not exist. A secondary difference concerns the options for defining the warehouse source of an ingredient, as described in a previous chapter (Section 10.4).

Yield Percentage The expected yield percentage for an item's formula version is oftentimes related to the formula size, and to different formula versions reflecting large quantity breakpoints. A default value can be specified for an item; the system initially assumes a value of 100%. The default value will be inherited (and optionally overridden) for the item's formula version, and this value will be inherited (and optionally overridden) for related batch orders. The yield percentage can be less than or greater than 100%. A yield percentage less than 100% will increase the required quantities of ingredients, since the normal requirements will be divided by the yield percentage. The increased requirements are recognized in planning and costing calculations, and in the order-dependent formula.

A planned yield percentage represents a slightly different concept than planned scrap for a component or a routing operation. Planned manufacturing scrap can be expressed for components and for routing operations. With a component, the planned scrap percentage and/or fixed amount will result in increased requirements. With routing operations, the planned scrap percentage for an individual operation results in increased requirements for its total time and units, and for related material components. In addition, an operation's scrap percentage has a cumulative effect on previous operations in a multi-step routing, and the system automatically calculates an accumulated scrap percentage for each operation. These scrap factors are included in planning and cost roll-up calculations for a manufactured item.

Formula Size and Multiple A batch-oriented manufacturing process is often characterized by the capacity constraints of the equipment, such as a mixing vessel or kettle that handle a batch size of 1000 pounds. In this example, a given batch quantity of a product could be something less than 1000 pounds, or batch sizes of 1000 pounds may be required or preferred. When there is a required or preferred batch size, it can be specified as part of the item's formula version in terms of the formula size and an optional multiple expressed in the product's inventory UM. The formula size must equal the multiple if a multiple has been specified. However, many scenarios do not have a required or preferred batch size, so that a formula multiple of one could be used.

The formula size and multiple assigned to an item's formula version have several implications, as summarized below.

◆ *Defining the required quantity for a component.* A component's required quantity is specified for the formula size, either as a fixed or variable consumption amount.[2] The component requirements can also be expressed as percentages rather than quantities (as described in a subsequent section), so that a required quantity reflects the percentage multiplied by the formula size.

◆ *Suggested quantity for a planned batch order.* The suggested quantity will cover demands and reflect the formula size and multiple associated with the product's active formula version. You can override the suggested quantity.

◆ *Suggested quantity for a manually-created batch order.* As part of the creation dialogue, the quantity will initially default to the corresponding formula size

---

[2] The specified formula size for a formula version is also reflected in the per series quantity for each component, such as a per series quantity of 100 when the formula size equals 100.

for the item's selected formula version. You can manually override this quantity, but a warning message will be displayed if it does not reflect the formula multiple (if specified). The message suggests a rounded-up quantity that reflects the formula multiple, and you can accept or reject the suggested quantity.

The implications become more complex when you specify a minimum quantity or a standard order quantity for a formula item. These can be defined as companywide or site-specific values.

◆ *Suggested quantity for a planned batch order.* The suggested batch quantity will cover demands and reflect the larger of (1) the product's minimum order quantity or (2) the formula size and multiple associated with the product's active formula version.

◆ *Suggested quantity for a manually-created batch order.* The batch quantity will initially default to the larger of (1) the formula size corresponding to the selected formula version for the product, (2) the minimum order quantity, or (3) the standard order quantity. The initial value will also be rounded up to the formula multiple.

Effectivity Dates for an Item's Formula Version The effectivity dates for an item's formula version can represent planned changes in the item's formulation. For example, a manufactured item may have two formula versions – one valid to date X and the other valid from date X+1 – to indicate planned changes. A blank value for the starting and/or ending date indicates no limitation. An item can have multiple active formula versions with non-overlapping dates.

Quantity Breakpoints for an Item's Formula Version A product with a quantity-sensitive formulation or yield percentage can be modeled using multiple formula versions with different quantity breakpoints. For example, one formula version can reflect a small batch size (up to 1000 gallons) with a lower yield, a second formula version can reflect a larger batch size (for more than 1000 gallons) with a higher yield, and both formula versions can be approved and active. A planned batch order will be assigned the relevant formula version based on the required quantity.

The concept of a quantity-sensitive formulation also applies to routing versions, where larger batch sizes are produced on different equipment. Hence, you typically define the same quantity breakpoints in the routing versions and the formula versions.

18.4 Formula Lines for Ingredients

A formula line is used to define each ingredient (aka component) of a manufactured item. Key aspects of a formula line include the item identifier of the ingredient, the required quantity, the associated operation number, and the warehouse source of the ingredient. An ingredient's required quantity reflects the formula size, and the requirement can be expressed as a quantity or percentage. This section summarizes these key aspects of defining an ingredient, starting with the different approaches to defining ingredient requirements.

Define Ingredient Requirements as a Quantity The ingredient's required quantity typically reflects the variable amount needed to produce the specified formula size of the parent item. The required quantity also reflects the specified UM for the ingredient. This quantity can be entered as a fraction or decimal. Some basic variations to the required quantity include a fixed quantity, the rounding up policy, and planned scrap.

Define Ingredient Requirements as a Percentage Component requirements can be expressed as a percentage rather than a quantity, and the component quantity will be automatically calculated based on the specified formula size.[3] The sum of component percentages must equal 100% to approve the formula. If applicable, a mix of percentages and quantities can be used to define component requirements, but the sum of percentages for relevant components must still equal 100%.

Impact of a Scalable Requirement A formula line includes an additional policy – termed the Scalable flag – that automatically applies to requirements expressed as a percentage. With the percentage approach, the Scalable flag simply means that a change in formula size (on a formula version) will automatically change the calculated requirement for quantity.

The Scalable flag can also apply to requirements expressed as a quantity. In this case, changing the formula size will automatically change the ingredient's required quantity, and changing an ingredient's required quantity will proportionally change the formula size (thereby affecting the required quantities of other scalable ingredients).

---

[3] A percentage can be specified for an ingredient when it has been flagged with the Percent Controlled flag, and the relevant quantity will be automatically calculated based on the formula size for the item's formula version. The ingredient percentages are assumed to be scalable for various batch sizes, as indicated by the automatic assignment of the Scalable flag to each component.

Impact of the Operation Number assigned to an Ingredient   When routing data exists, the operation number assigned to an ingredient provides the key link between the formula and the associated operation within the routing. There are several impacts of assigning an operation number to an ingredient, as described in a previous chapter about bills of material (Section 10.3).

Impact of the Formula Line Type   The formula line type indicates whether a manufactured ingredient will be treated as a normal item or a phantom item, or as a buy-to-order or make-to-order ingredient. The related impacts of a line type were described in a previous chapter about bills of material (Section 10.3).

Warehouse Source of an Ingredient   An ingredient's warehouse source indicates where to pick the item for a batch order. There are several options for defining an ingredient's warehouse source using formula and routing information, as described in a previous chapter about bills of material (Section 10.4).

Effectivity Dates of an Ingredient   The effectivity dates provide one approach for managing planned changes to formula information.

Formula Lines with Lot Inheritance Policies   In some scenarios, the shelf life expiration date and/or batch attributes of a manufactured item can be inherited from its ingredients. For example, a manufactured item with multiple ingredients can inherit the earliest expiration date of the ingredient batches. A second example applies to a bulk/pack scenario where a bulk item can be packed into different containers, and the expiration date for a batch of the bulk item can be inherited by the batch for each packed item. A third example involves cutting a steel beam or slitting a rolled good to produce a parent item, and the batch attributes of the parent item can be inherited from its component. These scenarios require lot inheritance policies within the formula line information, and reporting the finished quantity for a batch order results in lot inheritance.

The lot inheritance policies about expiration dates and/or batch attributes only apply to batch-controlled items. A previous chapter covered the impacts of shelf life expiration dates on master planning logic (Section 17.1) and reservation logic (Section 17.2) as well as the impact of batch attributes on reservation logic (Section 17.3). The lot inheritance capabilities require setup information for the applicable formula ingredients, and the capabilities differ for supporting shelf life inheritance versus batch attribute inheritance. However, an extended explanation falls outside the book's scope, although it is provided in the 2016 Edition of my book about process manufacturing.

18.5 Co-Products and By-Products

Some scenarios involve a production process that generates co-products or by-products or both. These two constructs are treated differently within the software. A co-product represents a desirable or reusable output from a production process for a parent item, whereas a by-product typically represents waste. The differences between a co-product and by-product are reflected in different approaches to costing and master planning. For example, a co-product's costs can be calculated (thereby reducing the costs associated with its parent item), and its requirements can result in the generation of planned orders for the parent item. In contrast, you manually specify the costs for a by-product, and the cost calculations will add these costs to the parent item's costs. Master planning logic will ignore a by-product's requirements, and the demands are not displayed as net requirements. Further explanation focuses on co-products.

Item Master Information for a Co-Product   Each item number representing a co-product must be designated with the relevant Production Type. The item number can then be specified as a co-product (or by-product) when defining the formula version for a parent item.

Formula Information for a Co-Product   The co-products for a formula version of a manufactured item are defined separately from the formula lines. A formula version with co-products has several implications for the formula size, master planning, and reporting of co-product outputs for a batch order, as summarized below.

◆ *Implications for the Formula Size and Ingredient Quantities.* The total expected output of a formula version includes the formula size (for the parent item) and the expected quantity of the co-products. The ingredient quantities should be specified for this total expected output rather than just the formula size. Ingredient requirements expressed as a percentage will only reflect the formula size, so that ingredient requirements are typically expressed as a quantity.

◆ *Master Planning Implications of a Co-Product.* Sales forecasts, sales orders and other demands can apply to the parent item and the co-product. Master planning logic will generate planned orders to cover these demands based on the site/warehouse-specific planning data. The planning data for a co-product item determines whether master planning generates planned purchase orders or transfer orders, or planned batch orders for a designated parent item. The next point provides further explanation of the planning data for a co-product item.

◆ *Reporting Co-Product Outputs of a Batch Order.* The output of a batch order includes the parent item and the co/by-products, or just the co/by-products of a planning item. You can only report the finished quantity of an expected co/by-product unless you specify the *Co/By Product Variations* policy for the batch order. The policy is initially inherited from the formula version used to create the batch order.

Planning Data for a Co-Product Item   When unsatisfied demands exist for a co-product item, master planning logic will generate planned orders to cover those demands. The source of a co-product item typically stems from production of its parent item, whether the parent item represents an actual manufactured product or a planning item. In some cases, the source of a co-product item may be a transfer from another warehouse (or even a purchase), as defined by the item's site/warehouse-specific planning data.

When the preferred source is production, an item-specific policy assigned to the co-product item (termed the planning item field) determines which of two options will be used to handle planned replenishment. Most firms use the first option because the second option involves more work for the planner. Only the first option is explained below.

◆ *Option #1: Planned Batch Orders for a Parent Item containing the Co-Product.* This approach means that planned batch orders for one parent item will be generated to cover demands for the co-product item, regardless of how many formulas include the co-product item. You specify the relevant parent item (using the planning item field) as part of the item master information for the co-product item, otherwise a blank value indicates Option #2 should be used. Option #1 works best when production of the co-product primarily stems from batch orders for one parent item.

Planned replenishment of the co-product item will reflect its expected quantity in the formula version of the parent item, and the planning data for the parent item (such as formula size, lead time and lot sizing logic). Planning data for the co-product item will be ignored by master planning logic.

◆ *Option #2: Planned Batch Orders for the Co-Product Item.* This approach means that planned orders communicate the need to produce the co-product item, and the planner must take additional steps. Option #2 should be the exception rather than the normal approach for replenishment of co-product items.

Modeling a Recycled Product   A recycled product has several different synonyms that vary by industry, such as reclaim, regrind, reusable scrap, and recurrent co-product. With a recycled product, the same item can act as both an ingredient and a co-product output for the production process. This normally creates circular logic when you define both uses in a formula version. However, the scenario can be modeled using the solution approach termed "recycled by-products".[4] The term "recycled product" will be used here.

As a starting point, the item representing the recycled product must be identified with a Production Type of a co-product or a by-product, and assigned an Inventory Model of standard cost. You can then identify it as ingredient within the formula version for a manufactured item. You can also identify it as a co-product output, but with a specified Production Type of "by-product" and a burden type of "recycled." This solution approach impacts master planning logic.

Master planning logic recognizes the ingredient requirements for the recycled product. However, the logic ignores the expected output of the recycled product from planned and actual batch orders, thereby ensuring that the ingredient requirements are not pegged against the output of the same batch order. It can only be pegged after reporting the finished quantity of the recycled product.

Case 18.3: Co-Products in Production of Pharmaceutical Products   A pharmaceutical manufacturer produced batches of various products, which were then placed in vials with labels and individual boxes. As shown in Figure 18.3 for the item "Packaged Product-1", the production process starts with a vessel containing a 1000-pound batch of ingredients, which requires a first level fermentation process of 7 days to produce the "Intermediate Product-1A". This intermediate requires three additional fermentation processes (labeled fermentation B, C, and D in the figure) across an 18-day period to produce the desired "Finished Product-1". Each of these additional fermentation processes result in a usable co-product -- labeled Product-2, Product-3 and Product-4 in the figure, along with expected percentages of output. The formula size of 850 pounds applies to Product-1 because the co-products comprise the other 150 pounds of expected output.

An inspection step for the finished Product-1 requires 14 days to obtain the certified test results. Similar inspection steps apply to the co-products, but they are not shown in the figure. The inspected product can then be used to fill vials that are individually labeled and boxed at a packaging line.

---

[4] A detailed explanation of the recycled by-products approach was provided in a blog titled "Support for Recycled Byproducts in AX 2012 R3 CU8."

Batch numbers are assigned each item, the batches of packaged product are assigned shelf life dates based on the test results at the inspection step. For a given sales order, the customer specifications for remaining shelf life are used in reservation logic to ensure relevant batches will be shipped to the customer.

Figure 18.3 Example Formula for a Pharmaceutical Product

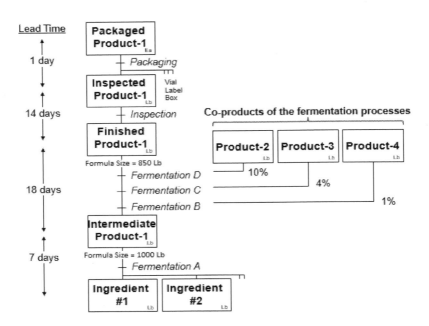

18.6 Planning Item with Co/By-Products

Some scenarios involve a production process that only results in co/by-products, such as a disassembly or grading process. The formula's parent item is simply used for planning purposes and is never received. This is termed a planning item, and there are several implications for item and formula definition as well as master planning.

Item Master Information for a Planning Item A planning item must be explicitly designated on the item master as a planning item using the Production Type field.

Formula Definition for a Planning Item The formula version for a planning item defines the ingredient(s) and the expected co/by-products. An illustrative case study about poultry processing provides a starting point for further explanation. Other illustrative case studies at the end of the chapter include grading/sorting of agricultural products, strip down of used electronic devices, and the use of molds to produce polymer molded products.

Case 18.4: Planning Item for Poultry Processing The example formula in Figure 18.4 illustrates a planning item that represents the cut plan for poultry processing. It has often been called the chicken disassembly scenario.

Figure 18.4 Example Formula for a Planning Item
representing the Cut Plan for Poultry Processing

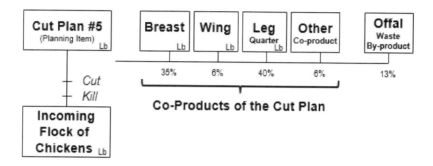

This formula version for the planning item is identified as Cut Plan #5, and it is assigned to the batch order for processing an incoming flock of chickens based on their average size. It defines the single ingredient and the desired output of each co-product (shown here as percentages) as well as the by-product of offal. Additional formula versions identify other cut plans, since the desired co-products vary based on the average size of the incoming flock.

Master Planning Logic for a Planning Item   Master planning calculations can generate planned production orders for the planning item to cover its demand forecasts, as illustrated in Case 18.11 for the strip down of used consumer electronics devices. Planned production orders for a planning item can also be generated based on demands for its co-products, but only when it is designated as part of the co-product's coverage planning data.

18.7 Production Formula for a Batch Order

A production formula refers to the formula lines attached to a batch order. It initially contains the formula lines inherited from the formula version used to create the batch order. Changes to the production formula do not affect the item's formula version. Creation and maintenance of the order-dependent formula reflect several rules. Similar rules applied to the production BOM for a production order.

◆ Creation of a batch order for a formula item (or planning item) also creates a production formula, which includes the ingredients and (if applicable) the co/by-products.

◆ The production formula initially reflects the item's formula version that was used to create the batch order. In most cases, this will be inherited from the active formula version for the delivery date and site (and quantity) on the batch order. However, you can manually specify a different formula version for the item when creating the batch order, where the formula version can be approved-but-not-active.

◆ The production formula contains components of a phantom.

◆ You can modify the ingredients in a production formula at any time prior to updating order status to Ended. For example, you can manually maintain the information, or copy formula lines from another batch order.

◆ A material item can be issued to a batch order even when the ingredient does not exist on the order-dependent formula. The issued ingredient will be automatically added to the order-dependent formula with a required quantity of zero.

◆ You can modify the co/by-products in a production formula at any time prior to updating order status to Ended.

◆ An unexpected co/by-product can be reported as finished, but only when allowed by the co-product variations policy assigned to the order.

18.8 Sequencing of Planned Batch Orders

Production sequencing is typically employed to minimize setup and changeover times at a production resource. Different approaches can be used to support production sequencing, ranging from simple to advanced approaches. More advanced approaches often employ calculations of the minimum setup/changeover times to suggest production sequencing, and even update these times within the routing information for batch orders. These calculations and updates are not typically used in simple approaches.

The standard software functionality supports a simple approach for suggested sequencing, and it only applies to planned batch orders. In terms of setup information, you define one or more item characteristics that impact production sequencing, and you assign a value for each characteristic to relevant manufactured items. You also assign the sequencing logic to the resources and resource groups that require production sequencing. This setup information provides the foundation to support production sequencing within master planning logic. This section starts with a typical process for production sequencing, and further explanation of setup information is provided at the end of the section.

Typical Process for Production Sequencing   A production planner typically starts with the planned batch orders generated by the master planning task, but the planned orders can also be manually entered. The planner can run a separate "sequencing" task to suggest production sequencing for these planned orders. The planner can then accept the suggested production sequencing and ultimately firm the planned orders to create batch orders. These steps within a typical process are illustrated in Figure 18.5 and described below.

Figure 18.5 Typical Process for Production Sequencing

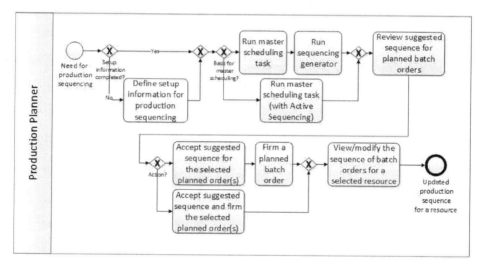

◆ *Run Master Planning Task.* The Master Planning task generates planned batch orders within a set of master plan data, and the scheduled dates/times reflect standard master planning logic. These planned orders can then be considered for production sequencing purposes by running the Sequencing Generator task for the same set of master plan data.

◆ *Run Sequencing Generator Task.* The Sequencing Generator task reviews the planned batch orders (within the time horizon defined by the sequencing time fence) and groups them into campaign cycles, and then calculates suggestions for production sequencing with a campaign cycle. The suggestions include a specific start date/time and completion date/time for a planned batch order, and suggestions are displayed on the Sequenced Planned Orders form.

◆ *Run Master Planning Task (with Active Sequencing and a Regeneration Principle for all items).* The Master Planning task can generate planned batch orders and perform production sequencing (without the need for running a separate Sequencing Generator task), but only when performed with a regeneration principle for all items and with an Active Sequencing policy for the master plan. Otherwise, you must subsequently perform the Sequencing Generator task to suggest production sequencing.

◆ *Review the Suggested Sequence for Planned Batch Orders.* The production planner reviews the suggested production sequence using the Sequenced Planned Orders form. The displayed information reflects a selected set of master plan data, and filtering can help focus on a subset of planned orders. More detailed information can be viewed for a selected planned order, such as viewing the associated routing, the capacity reservations for a resource within the routing, and the pegging information about the source of demand.

The production planner can select one or more planned batch orders to accept the suggested production sequence, or to accept the sequence and firm the planned order.

◆ *Accept Suggested Sequence for the selected Planned Batch Order(s).* Using the Sequenced Planned Orders form, the production planner can select one or more planned batch orders to accept the suggested production sequence. Several actions occur because of acceptance. First, the status of the planned batch order is automatically updated to "approved". Second, the suggested start and completion dates/times are automatically updated to reflect the production sequence. And third, the planned order is no longer displayed on the Sequenced Planned Orders form.

◆ *Accept Suggested Sequence and Firm the selected Planned Batch Order(s).* Using the Sequenced Planned Orders form, the production planner can select one or more planned batch orders to accept the suggested production sequence, and to optionally firm the planned order. Firming a planned order creates a batch order. The suggested start and completion dates/times are automatically updated to reflect the production sequence.

◆ *Firm a Planned Batch Order.* Firming a planned order creates a batch order, typically with a scheduled status (as defined in the Coverage Planning Group assigned to the item).

♦ *View/Modify the Sequence of Batch Orders for a Selected Resource.* The production planner can view the sequence of batch orders for a selected resource by accessing the Dispatch form. An additional step enables the production planner to modify the suggested sequence by moving selected batch orders up or down in the sequence.

Define Setup Information for Production Sequencing Several types of setup information for production sequencing must be defined. These include master plan policies, and the definition of sequence IDs and sequence groups.

♦ *Master plan policies.* The unique aspects of production sequencing are defined by two master plan policies -- for a sequencing time fence and the time bucket for campaign cycles. The sequencing time fence defines the time horizon (expressed in calendar days) used by master planning logic for consideration of planned batch orders and sequencing. The time bucket for campaign cycles is typically defined as a daily or weekly period, or as a specified number of calendar days. When using a weekly time bucket, for example, the suggested sequencing applies to all planned orders within a given week and to each ensuing week until the end of the sequencing time fence. In this example, the first week is identified as campaign cycle 1, the second week as campaign cycle 2, and so forth.

A third master plan policy – termed Active Sequencing – represents another unique aspect of production sequencing. It only applies when running the master planning task with a regeneration principle for all items, and avoids the need for running a separate Sequencing Generator task to suggest production sequencing.

Several other master plan policies must be considered to correctly support production sequencing. This includes the finite capacity policy, and the time fences for coverage planning and capacity must be greater than or equal to the sequencing time fence.

♦ *Define Sequences IDs and Sequence Groups.* The foundation for production sequencing is based on user-defined sequence IDs and sequence groups. A sequence ID reflects a characteristic of the manufactured items that affects production sequencing. For each sequence ID, you define the possible values for the characteristic and assign a numeric ranking to each value for sequencing purposes. Using the Sequence Value form, a manufactured item can then be assigned one or more sequence IDs and the related value for the characteristic. Alternatively, you can assign the sequence ID and value to a group of manufactured items based on the item group. A sequence ID and value can only be assigned to an item number; they cannot be assigned to an item number and variant code.

A sequence group contains one or more sequence IDs, and provides an additional level of ranking when multiple characteristics must be considered for production sequencing. With a sequence group containing two sequence IDs, for example, the planned orders for one characteristic will be sequenced first, and then the planned orders for the second characteristic will be sequenced (within a campaign cycle). You assign a sequence group to the resources and resource groups that require production sequencing. You also assign the finite capacity policy to correctly support production sequencing.

Case 18.5: Production Sequencing for Snack Foods with Peanuts A manufacturer of snack foods produced some products containing peanuts and other products without peanuts. Production sequencing helped minimize the changeover time for equipment cleaning to avoid possible contamination. An example formula for a product containing peanuts is illustrated in Figure 18.6 and described below.

Figure 18.6 Example Formula for Snack Food with Peanuts

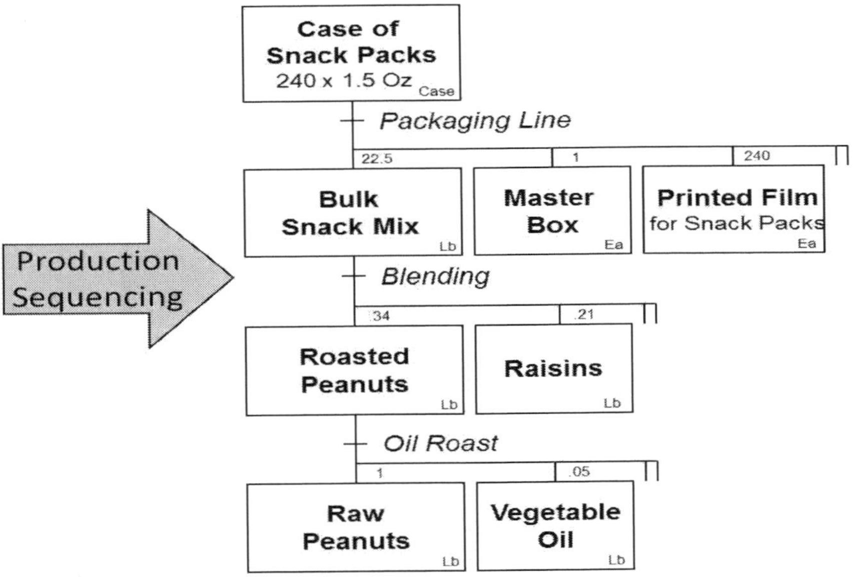

As shown in the figure, a case of the finished good consists of 240 snack packs containing 1.5 ounces of snack food. The multilevel formula reflects the steps within the production process, which include oil roasting of raw peanuts, blending of the roasted peanuts with raisins to produce the bulk snack mix, and then packaging the bulk into snack packs within a case. The production steps occur within different workrooms (identified as resources) comprised of equipment and a team of people. A given production step can be performed by multiple workrooms, and each workroom has different capabilities, so that a routing operation typically specifies the requirement for a resource capability (rather than for a specific resource).

As highlighted by the arrow in the figure, the blending operation (producing the bulk snack mix) required production sequencing to minimize changeover time of the vessels. The sequencing logic was based on an item characteristic, where the snack mixes without peanuts were typically blended first, followed by snack mixes with peanuts and then snack mixes containing peanuts and chocolate. An item characteristic for "blend type" was defined – with possible values of None, Peanuts, and Peanuts/Chocolate – and the relevant value was assigned to items representing each bulk snack mix. In addition, the sequencing logic was assigned to each resource that performed the blending operation. Master planning logic used this information to suggest daily production sequencing for planned production. The production supervisor could manually override the suggestions when needed.

Several additional issues were addressed by the formula and routing information. The routing information provided the basis for scheduling (and rescheduling) all production activities, and generation of daily schedules for each workroom. The improved coordination of material resulted in lower inventories. The formula information included planned yield percentages (and planned scrap percentages for selected ingredients), thereby helping to correctly calculate product costs and avoid material shortages.

Case 18.6: Production Sequencing for Extruded Plastic Pipe A

manufacturer produced extruded plastic pipe with different colors and diameters. Different pipes were typically produced once a week, which reflected a sequencing campaign cycle of one week. To minimize changeover time on the extrusion machines, the production sequence of different pipes reflected light-to-dark colors and small-to-large diameters for a given color. In this context, the production planner defined one sequence ID for pipe color with different values for each color, and a ranking from white to black. A second sequence ID was defined for pipe diameter with different values for each diameter, and a ranking from small to large. The planner also defined a sequence group (labeled "extruded pipe") containing the two sequence ids, where the sequence ID for pipe color was ranked before the one for pipe diameter.

For each item representing an extruded pipe, the production planner assigned the two sequence IDs and the relevant values for pipe color and diameter. In addition, the planner assigned the sequence group "extruded pipe" to each resource representing an extrusion machine, and to the resource group of extrusion machines. The routing operation identified a requirement for the resource group.

Based on this foundation, master planning logic generated planned batch orders with production sequencing that helped minimize changeover time on the extrusion machines.

18.9 Substitute Ingredients in a Formula

Some production scenarios involve the use of substitute ingredients. As one solution approach, you can manually change the production formula for a batch order to identify the desired substitute, or simply issue the substitute rather than the preferred ingredient. Alternatively, you can predefine one or more substitute ingredients in an item's formula information so that master planning logic will consider their use when applicable. Typical examples include the use of more expensive substitutes, or using the substitutes after running out of stock. This approach involves identifying the substitute ingredients in formula lines and several considerations about master planning logic.

Identifying the Preferred and Substitute Ingredients The preferred ingredient (and its quantity) must be defined in a formula line, and each substitute ingredient is also defined as a formula line (with a zero quantity). In addition, each of these ingredients must be assigned a *plan group* and a priority. The assignment of a user-defined plan group provides a grouping of ingredients, and the priority (of 1, 2, and so forth) indicates the desired sequence of substitutes.

Master Planning Logic for Substitute Ingredients Master planning logic will automatically consider the substitute ingredients when there is insufficient inventory of the preferred ingredient, and assign the appropriate substitute(s) to the formula lines for a planned batch order. Based on available inventory, the logic may assign the primary ingredient (up to its available inventory) and then assign the substitute ingredient for the remaining requirements. The assigned ingredients will also be reflected in the formula lines after you firm the planned batch order. This logic does not apply to a manually created batch order. The master planning logic will assign the primary ingredient when there is no available inventory of any substitute.

Case 18.7: Substitute Ingredients for Pet Food A manufacturer of canned pet foods defined the formula information for bulk pet food, which was packaged into different cans with different labels. An ingredient within the bulk item formula often represented the lowest cost filler, and the item number for a higher cost alternative was defined as a substitute ingredient. For example, the cheapest filler may consist of fatty trim whereas the more expensive filler was lean trim. When the available inventory of the low-cost ingredient was insufficient to support production of a planned batch order, master scheduling logic assigned the substitute ingredient (if available) to the formula for a planned batch order.

18.10 Coordinate a Bulk/Pack Production Process

Some manufacturing scenarios involve batch orders for producing a bulk item, and additional batch orders for packaging the bulk into container variations that have unique item numbers. This is termed a bulk/pack production process or containerized packaging. Case studies illustrating a bulk/pack scenario are provided at the end of this section.

A bulk/pack production process often requires synchronization of the batch orders for the bulk item (aka a bulk order) with batch orders for the packaging variations (aka a packed order). Master planning logic will calculate total requirements for a bulk item, and generated planned batch orders to optimize production factors such as the formula size and multiple, the formula maximum, and the quantity-breakpoints for assigning the best formula yield percentage or the best routing version. Master planning logic also synchronizes the planned orders for each packaging variation of the bulk material, so that the bulk can be packaged immediately to meet demand.

An additional construct – termed a consolidated order – also supports synchronization between these batch orders, and provides a single point for managing and reporting production activities. The functionality for consolidated orders requires some simple setup information in the formula information, as described at the end of this section. It builds on the basic model of batch order processing and involves several changes. Changes to the typical business process are illustrated in the top half of Figure 18.7 and summarized below.

Overview The production planner creates a consolidated order that represents a production run consisting of orders for a bulk item and its packaging variations. The production planner typically creates a consolidated order by firming and consolidating planned orders. A consolidated order can also be manually created so that you can assign existing batch orders to it. The consolidated order provides a single point for further coordination and reporting of production.

Using the consolidated order, the production planner can balance the production quantities so that the bulk quantity can be completely packed into the relevant containers. It also provides a graphical planning board, so that the production planner can define the detailed schedule of operation start/stop times for each batch order – for bulk and packed items. The machine operator reports an order as started, which authorizes production activities.

Figure 18.7 Typical Process for Bulk/Pack Production

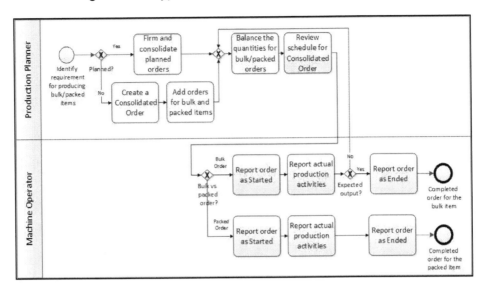

Firm and Consolidate the Planned Orders for Bulk and Packed Items

The production planner analyzes the planned orders that represent a production run for a bulk item and its related packed items.[5] More specifically, you mark the relevant orders on the Planned Orders form, and then perform the "firm and consolidate" function in order to view the selected orders on the Firm Consolidated Orders form. This form consists of three sections – about the consolidated order, the bulk orders, and the packed orders -- and allows you to change information. For example, you can adjust the production quantities of packed items to fully consume the bulk quantity. When finished, you mark and firm the consolidated order, and the information will be displayed on the Consolidated Orders form.

The Consolidated Orders form also consists of the same three sections, so that you can select a consolidated order in the top section and view its related bulk orders and packed orders in the lower two sections. A consolidated order has a separate status that is automatically updated based on the order status of the related batch orders.

Create a Consolidated Order and Add Existing Orders for the Bulk and Packed Items
The production planner manually creates a consolidated order that represents a production run for a bulk item and its related packed items, and then adds existing orders for the bulk and packed items.

---

[5] The discussion assumes the bulk item has a separate batch order. A bulk order is not required when the bulk item is designated as a phantom component, or when filling the packed orders from existing inventory.

Balance the Quantities for Bulk and Packed Orders assigned to a Consolidated Order The production planner employs a consolidated order to analyze differences between a bulk item's production quantity and the quantity required by the orders for its packaging variations. The production planner adjusts the production quantities of packed items to fully consume the bulk quantity. After reporting the actual quantity produced of the bulk item, the production planner may need to re-balance the quantities of the batch orders for the packed items.

Review Schedule of Bulk and Packed Orders assigned to a Consolidated Order The production planner employs a consolidated order for viewing and sequencing the related orders.   When using routing data, the production planner employs a graphical planning board to define the detailed schedule of operation start/stop times for each batch order.

View Consolidated On-Hand Inventory Using the Consolidated On-Hand form, you can view the current inventory balances for the bulk item and the equivalent units for its end-item packaging variations. The equivalent units are expressed in the inventory UM for the bulk item, and reflect the ratios defined on the Bulk Item Conversion form.

Setup Information for Bulk/Pack Production   As part of the setup information for supporting bulk/pack production scenarios, you specify the bulk item as an ingredient of each packed item, and also designate the bulk item in the formula version policies for each packed item. As a prerequisite step, you also define a ratio between these packed items and the item number for the bulk item. The ratio identifies how much of the bulk product is contained within each of the container variations, and the ratio can only be defined between formula items.[6]

The bulk item conversion ratio is a different factor than the one you might enter in the standard Unit Conversion form. For example, the bulk product might consist of a fruit juice with a UM of gallons, so that a .25 ratio applies to the item number for the quart container of juice, and a ratio of 1 applies to the item number for the 1 gallon container. You define these ratios using the Bulk Item Conversion form, which can be accessed directly or from the Released Products form.

Case 18.8: Bulk/Pack Scenario for Refrigerated Cookie Dough A food products company produced several types of refrigerated cookie dough, and also different packaging variations of a given cookie dough. The packaging variations reflected differences in pack size and private labeling. Figure 18.8 shows one

---

[6] The bulk item conversion ratio can be defined for purchased material, where you assign a production type of formula to the item, and also have planned replenishment based on purchase orders.

example of a bulk cookie dough for chocolate chip cookies, where the cookie dough goes through a packaging line to become 1 pound packages within a case. Other packaging variations can also be produced from the same bulk cookie dough.

The production process starts with a mixing vessel containing a 1000-pound batch of ingredients, including flour, sugar, and chocolate chips. Upon completion of the bulk cookie dough, it is immediately sent through a packaging line to produce 1 pound packs placed into a carton containing 36 packs. A given batch of the bulk cookie dough may go into different packages and cartons reflecting different private labels.

The batch orders for the bulk cookie dough (aka the bulk orders) require close synchronization with the batch orders for the packaging variations (aka the packed orders). These multiple orders are grouped together into a consolidated order to support synchronization. Use of the consolidated order, for example, supports batch balancing to optimize the use of a bulk order quantity, and provides a single point for reporting production activities against the bulk orders and packed orders.

Figure 18.8 Example Formula for Refrigerated Cookie Dough

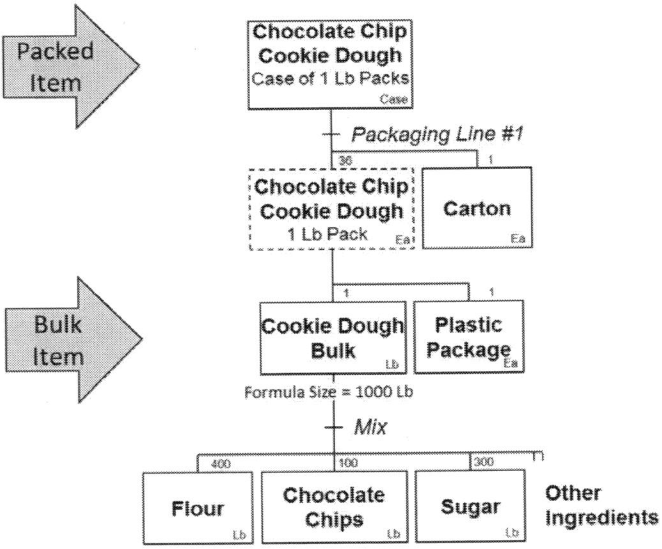

Case 18.9: Bulk/Pack Scenario for Orange Juice   Orange juice with no pulp represents one of the primary products that can be produced from fresh oranges. Figure 18.9 illustrates the multi-level formula for producing a case of no pulp orange juice, where the case consists of four 1-gallon cartons.

The starting point of the production process consists of fresh oranges. The fresh oranges go through a wash/inspection process and an extraction process to produce pure juice. These two processing steps are defined in the routing version for the pure juice. The formula version for pure juice is defined for a typical formula size of 1000 gallons, and identifies the required ingredient quantity of fresh Valencia oranges (8000 pounds) as well as the expected co-products such as pulp (200 pounds) and peel oil (40 pounds). The pure juice acts as the primary ingredient in the end-item's formula, which also includes other ingredients (such as Vitamin A) and packaging (such as the case and the 1 gallon cartons). The end-item's routing defines the resource requirements for the no-pulp packaging line.

Figure 18.9 Example Formula for No-Pulp Orange Juice

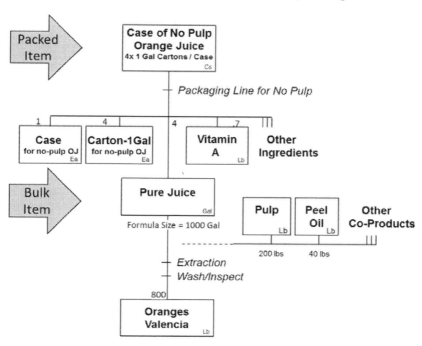

The end-item shown in Figure 18.9 represents one packaging variation for no pulp orange juice. The no-pulp packaging line can also produce other packaging variations, such as a case containing six half-gallon cartons or a case containing four .75 gallon cartons. Figure 18.10 summarizes the formula and routing information for these three packaging variations.

Figure 18.10 Example Formulas for Packaging Variations of No-Pulp Orange Juice

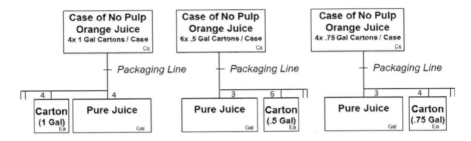

18.11 Additional Case Studies

Case 18.10: Planning Item for Grading/Sorting Cucumbers A food products company produced pickles from incoming cucumbers. As illustrated in Figure 18.11, the formula for the planning item "Grade/Sort Cucumbers" identifies the one ingredient of incoming cucumbers, and the mix percentages for the expected co/by-products. The expected co-products of the grade/sort operation include small, medium, and large cucumbers, and the expected by-product consists of the dirt/rocks gleaned from the incoming cucumbers. The various sizes of cucumbers go through additional processing to produce pickles.

Figure 18.11 Example Formula for Grading/Sorting of Agricultural Products

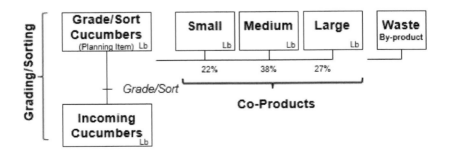

Case 18.11: Planning Item for Strip Down of Used Electronics Products A manufacturing company purchased several types of used consumer electronics devices, and stripped them down to obtain reusable parts that could be sold. Figure 18.12 illustrates the planning item for disassembling one type of used device (Device XYZ), along with its sole component and its multiple co-products of several reusable parts. The expected quantity of each co-product reflected the reusable fraction that could be obtained from used devices. Unusable parts were thrown into a waste container, and the company paid a disposal fee per pound of waste. From an S&OP perspective, the management team defined sales forecasts for the planning items that represented different used devices, and master planning calculations identified the expected receipts of reusable parts.

Figure 18.12 Strip Down of Used Consumer Electronics Devices

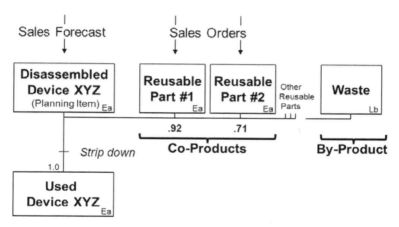

Case 18.12: Planning Item for Polymer Molded Products A process manufacturing firm produced several types of polymer molded products. A simple example consists of a single mold to produce two different parts – a right-hand and a left-hand part -- and the two parts require secondary processing for assembly. The formula and routing for this simple example are shown in the Figure 18.13 and explained below.

The first step involves an injection molding machine and the relevant mold (labeled Mold X in the figure). The ingredients for Formula ABC consist of different pelletized resins that must be melted and combined. In this example, the mold consists of two cavities for producing a right-hand and left-hand part, which are identified as co-products within the formula. In addition, the formula indicates that reclaim is a reusable co-product of the molding process, and the reclaim can be used as an ingredient. The second step involves an assembly operation to assemble the right-hand and left-hand parts.

Figure 18.13 Example Formula for a Polymer Molded Product

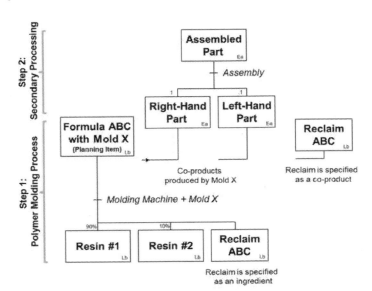

The routing operation for producing the molded parts typically defines the machine cycles that are needed to produce the expected items from a mold. For example, a machine that employs a mold may require 2 cycles to produce a quantity of 10 items. In this case, you define the resource's *batch capacity* as 10. In the operation, you define a *factor* of 2 for the required cycles per batch.

18.12 Executive Summary

This chapter covered the basics of formulas and batch orders relevant to master planning. The basics included several considerations about the item master and multiple considerations about formula information. The basics also included considerations about co-products and by-products, including the use of planning items with co/by-products. Additional aspects of master planning logic supported by formula information included the suggested sequencing of planned batch orders, the suggested use of substitute ingredients in planned batch orders, and the coordination of a bulk/pack production process. Multiple case studies illustrated the use of formula information.

Chapter 19

Master Planning in Project Manufacturing Scenarios

Some manufacturing companies have project-oriented operations. These may be internally focused projects such as new product development, or externally focused projects such as an engineer-to-order (ETO) product where the customer is billed on a fixed price or a time-and-material basis. In any case, a project typically requires a mixture of material, resource time and expenses. It also requires project-specific S&OP game plans to ensure availability of material and production resources to meet the requirements.

This chapter summarizes several common S&OP scenarios in project manufacturing, and employs several case studies to illustrate the coordination of material and production resources via master planning calculations. It does not attempt to explain the broad range of software capabilities related to projects because these topics merit a separate book.   Given this limited focus, the chapter includes the following sections.

1.   Common S&OP Scenarios in Project Manufacturing
2.   Engineer-to-Order Custom Product
3.   New Product Development
4.   Equipment Installation and Maintenance
5.   Additional Case Studies

19.1 Common S&OP Scenarios in Project Manufacturing

Several types of demand often apply to project manufacturing scenarios, and the master planning calculations will generate planned orders to cover these demands. These demands include demand forecasts by project as well as project sales orders and item requirements, as summarized in the top half of Figure 19.1 and described below. The bottom half of the figure illustrates item requirements with a link to the supply order.

Figure 19.1 Common S&OP Scenarios in Project Manufacturing

	Scenario	Key Elements of S&OP Game Plan	Additional Considerations	Basis of Delivery Promises
No Link	Stocked Item or Make-to-Order Item	Demand Forecasts by Project	Coverage Code = Period Forecast consumption by project sales orders and item requirements	ATP
		Project Sales Order or Item Requirement	Coverage Code = Period or Requirement	CTP or Net Change Explosion
Link to Order	Make-to-Order Item	Item Requirement with Project Production Order		
	Buy-to-Order Item	Item Requirement with Project Purchase Order		

Demand Forecasts by Project A demand forecast by project shares many similarities to regular demand forecasts which were previously described (Section 7.2). The differences include the need for additional information when entering a demand forecast, such as the identifier for the project, the relevant activity (if applicable), and a project category. Another difference includes the relevant forecast model because unique forecast models are sometimes used for project budget purposes, and the relevant forecast models need to be included in master planning calculations.

In terms of forecast consumption logic, project sales orders and item requirements can consume the demand forecasts by project, and involve the same considerations about a reduction principle. However, additional aspects of forecast consumption logic must be specified within the Project Management Parameters. At its simplest, the forecast consumption logic applies to a specific project (as well as the item), but it may optionally apply to specific activities, categories and/or parent projects.

Project Sales Order A project sales order only applies when the project has a specified customer (such as an external project), and it shares many similarities to a regular sales order.

Item Requirement for a Project An item requirement for a project is identified as a sales order with an order type of item requirements rather than an order type of sales order. It only applies when the project has a specified customer, and it shares many similarities to a regular sales order. As a unique aspect, item requirements can be created from the demand forecasts for a project. A typical scenario involves project-specific forecasts for budgeting purposes which can be converted to item requirements.

Item Requirement with a Project Production Order You can create a project production order from an item requirement, and this reserves the ordered material for the project. There is a direct link between the production order and the project. After reporting finished quantities for the production order, you can issue the item's inventory to the item requirement via packing slip posting.

One alternative to this approach involves the direct creation of a production order from the project (rather than from the item requirement), or directly entering the order on the Project Production Order page. This approach does not require the additional step of issuing the material to the item requirement.

Item Requirement with a Project Purchase Order You can create a project purchase order from an item requirement, and this reserves the ordered material for the project. There is a direct link between the purchase order and the project, where the purchase order header indicates the project number and a line item indicates the project category. After receiving the purchase order, you can issue the item's inventory to the item requirement via packing slip posting. Alternatively, you can issue the material as part of reporting product receipt when prompted by the message "Consume items for the project immediately".

One alternative to this approach involves the direct creation of a purchase order from the project (rather than from the item requirement), or directly entering the order on the Project Purchase Order page. After posting the product receipt or the vendor invoice, the system automatically issues the material to the project. As a general guideline, the direct creation of project purchase orders should not be used for material items; it should only be used for non-tangible items or services.

19.2 Engineer-to-Order Custom Product

An engineer-to-order product typically requires significant engineering time to design the product, and to define the product structure and new items. These engineering activities can be budgeted and tracked against a project, and even charged to the customer based on a time-and-material or fixed-price basis. The finalized design typically evolves over time, so that the definition of item and BOM information also evolves over time.

The top levels of the product structure for an ETO product can be modeled as subprojects, where the item requirements for the subproject specify the components. Case 19.1 illustrates the use of subprojects for modeling the top levels of the product structure and for managing the engineering time.

Case 19.1: External T&M Project to Design and Build an ETO Product
A manufacturing company produced engineer-to-order machines requiring significant engineering design time prior to building a machine, and installation services after delivery of the machine. For a typical ETO machine, the engineering manager defines an external time-and-materials (T&M) project consisting of three subprojects reflecting engineering design, final assembly of the machine, and installation services. Figure 19.2 illustrates the typical project and subprojects.

Figure 19.2 External Project to Design/Build an ETO Machine

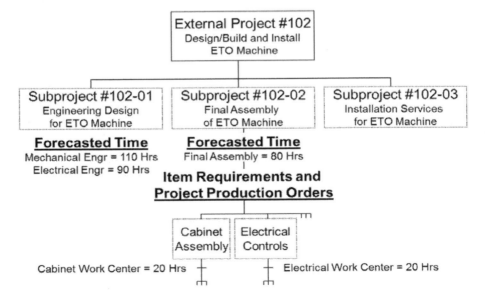

In this example, a subproject is used to model the top level of the product structure, with forecasted time requirements for a production resource (representing the final assembly work center) to perform final assembly of components. An item requirement is defined for each first level component -- such as the cabinet assembly and electrical controls -- and a project production order is generated for each item requirement. This approach provides direct linkage between a project's item requirement and the corresponding project production order.[1]

In this example, the subproject for engineering design has a simple work breakdown structure consisting of several activities (not shown in the figure), and the forecasted time requirements for mechanical engineers and electrical engineers are defined for each activity.

In many cases, a detailed project quotation must be prepared and then accepted by the customer prior to designing and building the ETO machine. The detailed quotation reflects a work breakdown structure of activities, and each activity has forecasted requirements for items and resource hours. After customer acceptance and confirmation of the project quote, the details about item forecasts are transferred to the actual project as item requirements, and the hour forecasts are also transferred.

19.3 New Product Development

New product development is oftentimes undertaken for internal purposes and results in a prototype. Alternatively, the development efforts may be undertaken for a specific customer with requirements for invoicing the customer much like an ETO product. Case 19.2 illustrates the use of an internal project for new product development.

Case 19.2: Internal Project for New Product Development New product development at a discrete manufacturer often entails producing a prototype of the manufactured item, and additional costs associated with engineering time and related expenses. Figure 19.3 illustrates an internal project for developing a prototype. The project's item requirement is specified for just the end-item, which has a multi-level bill of material and routing information. This information is used to calculate the cost of the end-item and its manufactured components, and to coordinate supply chain activities.

---

[1] This example represents one approach for managing production of the top levels an ETO product structure. Another approach employs configurable items for the top levels of the product structure.

The project's forecasted time requirements include engineering time by three major groups of engineers: design engineers, lab technicians and test engineers. The project also has forecasted expenses (such as travel and consulting fees) that will be incurred during prototype development.

Figure 19.3 Internal Project for New Product Development

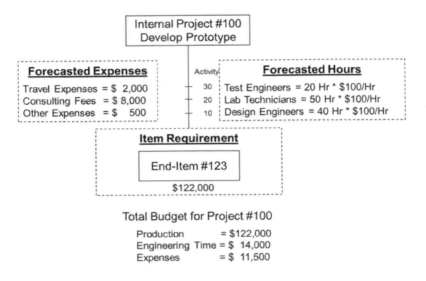

Total Budget for Project #100

Production	= $122,000
Engineering Time	= $ 14,000
Expenses	= $ 11,500

Several project categories provide segmentation of costs related to expenses and resource time. As illustrated in Figure 19.3, the expenses were segmented into three project categories (travel, consulting fees, and other) and the hours were segmented into three categories (design, lab, and test). These project categories help segment budgeted and actual costs for analysis and reporting purposes. The figure also illustrates the use of activities for the forecasted hours, where the activities are simply labeled 10, 20, and 30 in this example.

19.4 Equipment Installation and Maintenance

Many manufacturers and distributors provide value-added services such as installation, repair, and periodic maintenance, where field service personnel or internal service facilities perform the services. The most common examples reflect firms that sell and service equipment, such as computer products, home appliances and industrial equipment. A service order provides the basic tool for defining requirements and reporting actual consumption of material and technician time. Common synonyms include a service work order or service call. Service orders build on the foundation of project information, where you typically create and assign a unique project to each service order.

Different examples of service orders reflect the differences between field service and internal service facilities. Field service examples include equipment installation, upgrades, and preventive maintenance, which typically reflect scheduled activities with predefined requirements for material and labor. These scheduled activities (and their requirements for material and labor) can be defined within a service agreement, which provides the basis for periodic generation of service orders. Ad hoc activities such as equipment repairs or other emergency situations cannot be scheduled in advance, and the material and labor requirements can be difficult to anticipate. Examples for internal service facilities -- such as a repair department -- include equipment repairs on a customer return or service work on a customer-supplied piece of equipment.

When using standard software to support service orders, the material requirements embedded in service agreements (and service orders) are not recognized by master planning calculations. S&OP game plans can anticipate these requirements using min/max quantities or demand forecasts.

19.5 Additional Case Studies

Case 19.3: Configurable Items and the Skeleton BOM for an ETO Product   One product line at an equipment company involved building customized machines to customer specifications. Every customized machine had a unique identifier, and its product structure consisted of the same type of customized subassemblies (such as a power unit, a horizontal table, and a vertical column) with unique item identifiers. Each customized subassembly required several unique components with long purchasing lead times, and subassembly production was initiated prior to receipt of these unique components. Substantial engineering time was required to define the unique item identifiers, initiate purchases of the long lead time components, and ultimately define each machine's product structure (with unique components correctly placed in BOMs). Any delays in these engineering efforts impacted the purchasing and production activities, and the delayed definition of the product structure information made it difficult to coordinate requirements. As a solution approach, the company employed a product configurator to automatically create the unique item numbers and the product structure skeleton, with the unique purchased components correctly placed in the subassembly BOMs. The solution approach resulted in significant reductions in engineering time and the number of delays, and the skeleton BOM provided the correct offsetting of component requirements.

19.6 Executive Summary

This chapter summarized several common S&OP scenarios in project manufacturing, and employed case studies to illustrate the coordination of material and production resources via master planning calculations. One case covered an internally focused project for new product development, and a second case covered an externally focused project for an engineer-to-order (ETO) product where the customer is billed on a fixed price or a time-and-material basis. A third case described the use of a skeleton BOM for ETO products.

Chapter 20

Master Planning in Lean Manufacturing Scenarios

Some manufacturing companies have embraced lean principles and use of the software capabilities to manage kanbans. In comparison to traditional manufacturing, this entails a change in conceptual viewpoints in addition to other changes such as factory layout. One example of a change in conceptual viewpoints involves a production flow, which defines the sequence of activities to produce an item (and replaces the routing information). Another example involves kanban rules, which define how to generate kanban orders for items within the product structure. Other examples involve the tools to coordinate production such as kanban boards. This chapter does not attempt to explain the broad range of software capabilities related to lean manufacturing because these topics merit a separate book.

This chapter focuses on several aspects of lean manufacturing scenarios supported by master planning calculations. This includes scheduled kanbans for a manufactured item, where master planning generates planned kanbans that can be firmed to create the scheduled kanbans. It includes planned purchase orders generated by master planning. And it includes the calculation of fixed kanban quantities based on the demands within a set of master plan data. These considerations are reflected in the following sections with the chapter.

1. Master Planning for Scheduled Kanbans
2. Master Planning for Purchased Components
3. Master Planning and Calculations for the Number of Fixed Kanbans
4. Impacts on the Conceptual Models for Traditional Manufacturing
5. Additional Case Studies

20.1 Master Planning for Scheduled Kanbans

Master planning calculations generate planned kanbans that reflect the planning data for a manufactured item with scheduled kanbans. These planned kanbans are identified in the net requirements for the item, and they can be firmed to create the scheduled kanbans. You can also manually create a scheduled kanban.

Planning Data for a Manufactured Item with Scheduled Kanbans The planning data for generating planned kanbans closely parallels that for planned production orders, which were described in a previous chapter about coverage planning data (Section 6.5). Figure 20.1 summarizes this key planning data and highlights the unique aspects about a production flow and the kanban rule for a manufactured item with scheduled kanbans. The unique aspects are described below.

Figure 20.1 Key Planning Data for a Manufactured Item
with Scheduled Kanbans

Key Planning Data	Companywide Policies	Site-Specific Policies	Site/Warehouse Policies
BOM Version	Specify BOM as Companywide	Specify BOM as Site-Specific	
Production Flow Version with Process Activity at a Work Cell	Define Production Flow and Activities		N/A
Kanban Rule Kanban Type = Manufacturing Replenishment Strategy = Scheduled Kanban	Define Kanban Rule related to Production Flow		
Primary Source of Supply Planned Order Type = Kanban		N/A	Override
Coverage Group (Set of Policies)			
Production Lead Time	Specify	Override	
Order Quantity Modifiers for Production Orders			N/A
Planner Responsibility		N/A	N/A

Page for Data Maintenance: Released Product Details or Default Order Settings   Default Order Settings   Item Coverage

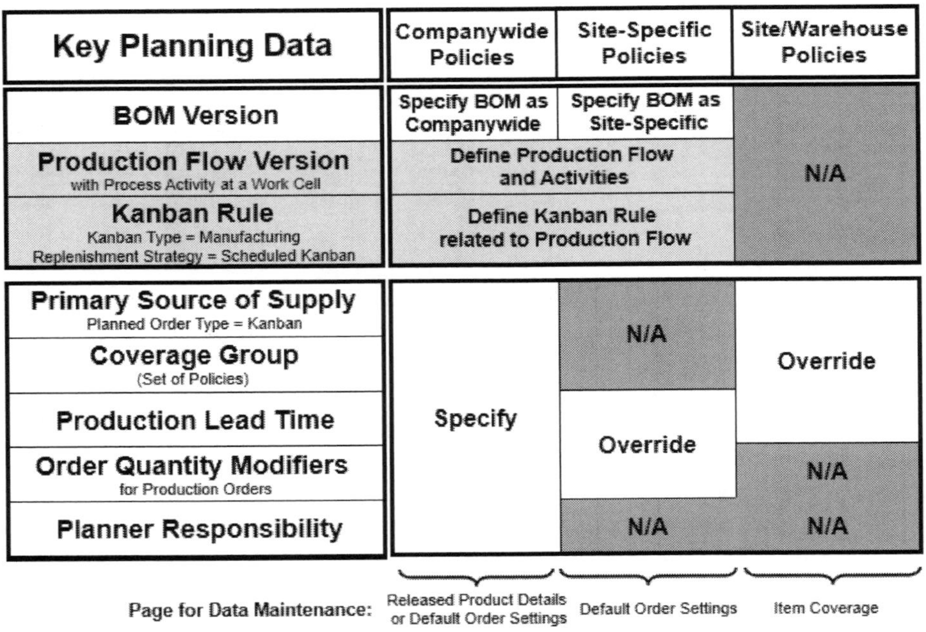

◆ *Production Flow with a Process Activity.* A production flow for a manufactured item replaces the concept of routing information. It consists of one or more process activities. A process activity identifies the relevant work cell and processing time, and a work cell is assigned to a site. Different versions of a production flow can have different effectivity dates.

◆ *Kanban Rule.* A kanban rule identifies the applicable production flow and process activity for a manufactured item. It also indicates a kanban type of manufacturing and the replenishment strategy of a scheduled kanban. It also identifies a minimum and maximum quantity that only apply when manually creating a scheduled kanban. Different kanban rules for an item can have different effectivity dates.

◆ *Primary Source of Supply.* A planned order type of Kanban indicates the primary source of supply so that master planning calculations will generate planned kanbans. An item's planned order type (aka default order type) can be specified as a companywide policy, and optionally overridden for a given site/warehouse. For example, a manufactured item may be replenished via scheduled kanbans at one warehouse, but replenished via production orders at a different warehouse.

◆ *Production Lead Time.* An item's fixed production lead time (expressed in days) can be specified as a companywide value, and optionally overridden as a site-specific or site/warehouse policy. It is typically expressed in working days, but it can reflect calendar days. Master planning logic will use this fixed lead time to calculate the required dates for the components of a scheduled kanban.

◆ *Order Quantity Modifiers for Production.* The order quantity modifiers consist of a minimum, maximum and multiple, and they impact the suggested quantity for planned kanbans generated by master planning calculations. However, when manually creating a scheduled kanban, the minimum and maximum quantity reflect values within the kanban rule for the item.

Firming a Planned Kanban Planned kanbans are displayed on the Planned Orders page, and you firm a planned kanban to create a scheduled kanban. The example screen shown in Figure 20.2 illustrates the Planned Orders page, and the first line of the example data displays a planned kanban for the item "X8-Product2-SchKB". The figure includes an example of the resulting kanban after firming a planned kanban. The resulting kanban has a handling unit status of Not assigned (and a job status of Not planned). Subsequent steps update the status by coordinating the scheduled kanban via the kanban boards.

Figure 20.2 Example Screen of Planned Orders with a Planned Kanban

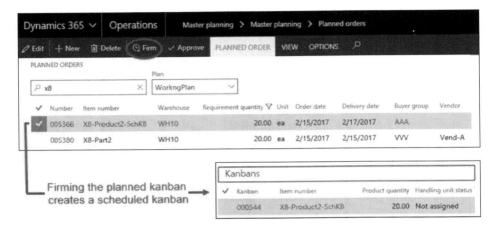

You can optionally approve a planned kanban – just like approving a planned production order -- to lock the scheduled date and quantity, and prevent deletion by master planning calculations or the delete plan task.

Manually Create a Scheduled Kanban A scheduled kanban can be manually created by starting from the Kanban Rules page for the item. Key fields within the dialogue for Create Scheduled Kanbans include the number of new kanbans, the quantity per kanban, the due date/time, and the relevant BOM version for the item.

20.2 Master Planning for Purchased Components

Master planning calculations still apply to purchased components in lean manufacturing scenarios, and the current software capabilities do not yet support purchasing kanbans. Previous chapters described the planning data for purchased items (Section 6.3) and the coordination of purchases via planned purchase orders (Section 4.9). The example screen shown in Figure 20.2 illustrated the Planned Orders page, and the second line of the example data displayed a planned purchase order for the item "X8-Part2". This purchased item represents a component of the manufactured item with scheduled kanbans, and the required delivery date reflects a 2-day production lead time for the parent item.

20.3 Master Planning and the Calculations for the Number of Fixed Kanbans

The suggested number of fixed kanbans for a manufactured item can be calculated based on projected demands or historical demands or a combination of both. More specifically, you define a named set of kanban quantity calculation policies and assign the named set to the kanban rule for each item with fixed kanbans. Based on this data, you can perform the Calculate Kanban Quantity task to generate the suggested number of fixed kanbans and optionally update the kanban rule information. The update creates a new kanban rule with a starting validity date, and assigns an ending validity date to the previous kanban rule.

As one of the kanban quantity calculation policies, you select which set of master plan data (or forecast plan data) will be used as the basis for the calculations. Other policies indicate the relevant date range for considering demands -- expressed as the number of days ahead and behind the calculation date. Optional policies include safety stock considerations (and a related service level percentage) and a safety factor to inflate demands by a specified percentage. A simple example of the resulting formula to calculate the number of fixed kanbans consists of "average daily demand * lead time / product quantity per handling unit". The applicable lead time is defined within the item's kanban rule.

20.4 Impacts on the Conceptual Models for Traditional Manufacturing

The lean manufacturing capabilities involve several significant changes to the conceptual models for traditional manufacturing presented in this book. For example, the use of a production flow and its activities replace the use of routings and routing operations. Impacts on the conceptual models for traditional manufacturing are summarized below. The traditional approaches still apply in a mixed mode scenario.

Impacts on Resources and Routings With lean manufacturing, the constructs for resources, routings and routing operations are replaced by the constructs for work cells, production flows and activities. While you still employ a resource group to identify a work cell, almost all other functionality does not apply. For example, the functionality associated with resource capabilities and employee competencies does not apply, nor do you use master operations, master routings, and route versions.

Impacts on BOM Information Lean manufacturing has several impacts on BOM information. First, the significance of an operation sequence number for a BOM line no longer applies because routings have been eliminated. This slightly impacts the previously described options concerning the warehouse source of components when using the resource consumption policy (Section 10.4). When using kanbans, the warehouse source will reflect the input warehouse/bin assigned to the work cell performing a process activity.   Second, a make-to-order component should no longer be identified by a BOM line type of pegged supply, since this approach has been replaced by the component's kanban rule for a line event kanban.

Impact on Process Manufacturing The lean manufacturing capabilities only apply to manufactured items using the BOM approach to product structure; they do not apply when using the formula approach.

Impacts on Subcontracted Production   The approach to subcontracted production (described in Section 12.7) can be replaced by activities within a production flow. For example, transfer activities can be used to move supplied components to a subcontractor (and move finished quantities to another location), and a process activity specifies the work cell representing the subcontractor. This approach provides inventory visibility for supplied components and the finished quantities.

Impacts on Quality Management Quality orders do not apply to kanbans in the lean manufacturing approach.

Impacts on Product Costing The use of kanban orders requires a standard costing approach for all related items.   The standard cost calculations for a manufactured item are based on its BOM version and the relevant production flow (rather than a route version), where the relevant production flow is determined by the kanban rule assigned to the item. The kanban rule identifies the relevant process activity within the production flow, and this activity defines the hourly rates and time requirements for the work cell.

20.5 Additional Case Studies

Case 20.1: Using Scheduled Kanbans and Fixed Kanbans   A manufacturer changed its approach to producing a family of make-to-stock products as part of a lean initiative. Each product consisted of a two-level bill of material.   In addition to changes in factory layout, the changes in viewpoint included the use of a production flow and kanban rules. The production flow consisted of two work cells and the related activities for subassembly and final assembly. The production flow also included activities to withdraw material from the stockroom and move it to the lineside supermarkets for subassembly and final assembly. The top part of Figure 20.3 illustrates this production flow viewpoint.

Figure 20.3 Production Flow and Kanban Rules for Coordinating Production using Scheduled Kanbans and Fixed Kanbans

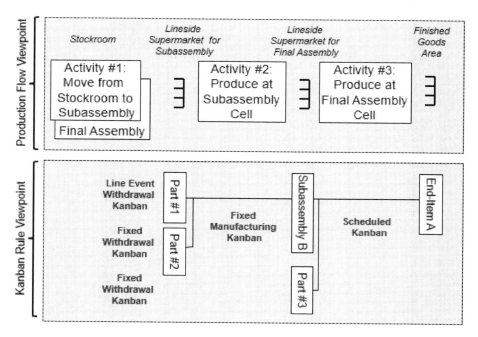

The bottom part of Figure 20.X illustrates the kanban rule viewpoint. The kanban rules determined how to generate kanban orders for items within the product structure -- displayed sideways for showing the correlation between the BOM and the production flow. Scheduled kanbans were used for the end-items, and fixed manufacturing kanbans applied to the subassemblies. Purchased components were moved from the stockroom based on fixed withdrawal kanbans and line event withdrawal kanbans. The deliveries of purchased components to the stockroom (not shown in the figure) were coordinated by planned purchase orders generated by the master planning calculations.

Case 20.2: Partial Implementation of Kanban Orders within the Product Structure A manufacturer was in the early stages of maturity in lean manufacturing, and employed several variations of kanban orders and production orders at different sites for different products. One variation reflected kanban orders for the top of the product structure (such as a final assembly work cell for finished goods), with production of lower level components coordinated by production orders. The second variation was just the reverse, with kanban orders coordinating production of lower level components. Other variations included the use of kanban orders for all items within one entire product structure, and production orders for another product structure.

20.6 Executive Summary

This chapter focused on several aspects of lean manufacturing scenarios supported by master planning calculations. This included scheduled kanbans for a manufactured item, where master planning generates planned kanbans that can be firmed to create the scheduled kanbans. It included planned purchase orders generated by master planning. And it included the calculation of fixed kanban quantities based on the demands within a set of master plan data. Case studies illustrated the use of scheduled kanbans and fixed kanbans, and the partial implementation of kanban orders within the product structure.

Chapter 21

Summary

This book focused on the master planning capabilities within Microsoft Dynamics 365 for Operations, and how they help orchestrate success in supply chain management for manufacturing businesses. The contents also apply to the master planning capabilities within the previous version of Dynamics AX 2012 R3.

The targeted reader consists of SCM professionals that need to learn the master planning capabilities for running day-to-day operations. In many cases, they represent those responsible for maintaining the S&OP game plans within a company, where the role has traditionally been called a master scheduler. In other cases, they represent members of the project team responsible for system implementation. In some cases, they may need to learn master planning because of a change in positions or job responsibilities. In addition, many people with some experience may want to confirm and extend their knowledge via selective learning of master planning topics.

21.1 Accomplishing Your Learning Objectives

The introductory chapter provided several suggestions for the targeted reader, where the suggestions were expressed as different learning objectives. The broad range of master planning capabilities were segmented into three groups -- consisting of core topics, additional considerations, and variations of scenarios – that were also reflected in the organization of book chapters. This segmentation provided the basis for several learning objectives shown in Figure 21.1.

Your learning objectives may have focused on just the core topics for master planning. They may have included the additional considerations and/or the applicable variations in scenarios, such as a multicompany supply chain, process manufacturing, project manufacturing or lean manufacturing. Alternatively, they may have covered selected topics by role, such as selective learning for the master scheduler, production planner, purchasing agent or DRP coordinator.

Figure 21.1 Learning Objectives for Master Planning Capabilities

Learning Objective	Estimated Pages Applicable	Total
Learn Core Topics for Master Planning	90	124
Learn Additional Considerations for Master Planning	50	86
Incremental Learning for Different Scenarios		
- Master Planning in Multicompany Scenarios		8
- Master Planning in Process Manufacturing Scenarios		32
- Master Planning in Project Manufacturing Scenarios		8
- Master Planning in Lean Manufacturing Scenarios		8
Total =	140	266
Selective Learning of Master Planning Topics		
- Topics for the Master Scheduler role	90	
- Topics for the Production Planner role	50	
- Topics for the Purchasing Agent role	25	
- Topics for the DRP Coordinator role	20	

The key issue within this summary chapter focuses on whether you accomplished your learning objectives. A related concern involves the amount of learning. A page count analysis provides a rough metric for quantifying the amount of learning, as illustrated in the right side of Figure 1.1. The total number of book pages provide one metric, and the applicable pages for a given company or role provide a second metric.

21.2 Concluding Remarks

When learning any ERP software package, it is important to understand its underlying conceptual models and how it supports key business processes and their variations. This is especially important for running a manufacturing business from top by using S&OP games plans and master planning to orchestrate success within the supply chain.

Appendix A
Scope of Book Topics
and Prior Research

The book focuses on master planning in manufacturing, and this focus guided the prior research and the scope of book topics.

Prior Research Several steps of prior research were undertaken to understand the master planning requirements in manufacturing, and the software functionality to support those requirements. With respect to Dynamics 365 for Operations (as well as previous AX versions), these steps included participation in training classes, webinars, and conference sessions; reviews of the existing training materials, e-learning lessons, user documentation and sales demo materials; reviews of blogs and articles; discussions with users, development personnel, and field consultants; and hands-on testing for hundreds of use cases that reflected common requirements in manufacturing. With few exceptions, only those capabilities personally tested and proven were included in the book contents.[1] The same approach was also undertaken for my previous books about Dynamics AX. The discussions with experienced field consultants helped identify the dominant business practices at current users. On-going opportunities to consult with current users have supplemented this understanding.

The prior research about master planning in manufacturing included my consulting and teaching experiences across the past three decades. These included responses to numerous RFPs (requests for proposal) for an ERP system, face-to-face consulting engagements with several hundred firms, and teaching executive seminars, APICS certification classes, MBA courses, and user group sessions. My understanding is continually being supplemented by staying abreast of the current

---

[1] The prior research and hands-on testing for Dynamics 365 for Operations reflect the software capabilities through the 1611 version. They also reflect the hands-on testing of AX 2012 R3 through the CU10 release.

literature and discussions with various thought leaders about using ERP systems in discrete manufacturing.

Scope of Book Topics The book topics focus on the use of master planning capabilities in the broader context of supply chain management, and the selection of book topics was shaped by several factors. First, the selection of core topics represented the critical mass for understanding the use of master planning. The selection of additional considerations – ranging from items and bills of material to quality – identified only those aspects directly related to master planning. The explanation of different scenarios covered just the incremental differences.

The book topics did not include the many technical and administrative aspects of master planning. Other important topics of system development and usage were also excluded, such as business intelligence, security, and customization capabilities.

Contributions to the Body of Knowledge The body of knowledge related to Microsoft Dynamics 365 for Operations (and the previous versions of Dynamics AX) consists of several levels and components. The foundation level consists of the software, documentation and training materials provided by Microsoft. Additional contributions to the body of knowledge build on this foundation. In terms of the book's contributions, I have attempted to summarize the relevant information with an integrative viewpoint of how the whole system fits together to support master planning and supply chain management in manufacturing businesses. The book explains the embedded conceptual models and business processes for running these businesses.

Appendix B
Comparing AX 2012 R3 and Dynamics 365 for Operations

This appendix summarizes a comparison of Dynamics AX 2012 R3 and Dynamics 365 for Operations, and focuses on the master planning topics covered within the book. The comparison indicates that the master planning capabilities are almost identical in both software versions, even though the technology foundation and some of the terminology have changed. The few exceptions include some new functionality listed below. The list includes some general differences between the two versions, such as a change in the user experience. Additional changes in software functionality – such as changes for retail, projects and costing – fell outside the book's scope and are not included here.

Analyze Delivery Alternatives for a Sales Order Line As a new capability within Dynamics 365 for Operations, you can analyze the delivery alternatives for meeting a customer's requested delivery date and quantity. This includes product availability at different ship-from warehouses, and the available vendors when selling a purchased item as a direct delivery or special order. When the vendor represents a sister company, the delivery promises can reflect the item's availability at the vendor. The analysis also includes availability of different product variants (such as size or color) when applicable, and the applicable modes of delivery.

You can evaluate these options for a sales line using the Delivery Alternatives information, and select the desired option for updating the promised dates, ship-from warehouse (or vendor), and mode of delivery on the sales line. You can also choose to ship a smaller quantity than ordered (based on availability) and ship the remainder on a later date, which results in a delivery schedule for the sales line. These capabilities were described as one of the sales order considerations (Section 8.7).

Manage Consigned Inventory A new type of replenishment order provides visibility of incoming vendor-owned inventory, and the vendor-owned inventory can be reserved and moved prior to reporting an ownership change. There is no impact on inventory value until the ownership change, and the need for payment occurs after the change. The capabilities were described as one of the purchase order considerations (Section 13.6).

Calculate Demand Forecasts based on Historical Usage A different approach for calculating demand forecasts was introduced using the Microsoft Azure Machine Learning cloud service. The service performs best match model selection and offers key performance indicators for calculating forecast accuracy.

Support BOMs with the Same Item Number for the Parent and Component (but with different variants) The new capability removes the previous limitation about circularity. The same item number can now identify a parent item and its component, but they have different values for a variant code. In a process manufacturing scenario, for example, the parent might represent a finished product while the component represents the semi-finished product.

Changes in Terminology A significant number of changes in SCM-related terminology were introduced in Dynamics 365 for Operations, such as changes in the names of fields and forms. As one example, the term "futures message" has been changed to "calculated delays message" – which more accurately indicates its purpose. A comprehensive list of these changes was not yet available at the time of book publication. However, these changes did not affect functionality. This book employs the terminology in Dynamics 365 for Operations.

Changes in User Experience The standard menu structure and user-defined favorites provide commonly used approaches for navigation in both versions. However, there are significant changes in the menu structure and in the approach to maintain favorites. When using Dynamics 365 for Operations, for example, the menu structure is flatter and the topics within the Product Information Management menu now include a broader set of relevant information. Based on my experience, those users familiar with the previous menu structure will initially struggle to determine "where is it?" However, an additional approach to navigation -- termed "search for a page" -- enables you to specify the desired topic, review a list of applicable pages, and then navigate to a selected page.

Workspaces represent one variation in the user experience as further described in the next point. The links within workspaces support navigation to commonly used tasks and pages.

Some aspects of the displayed information have changed, such as a "yes/no switch" (rather than a checkbox) and a message bar and message box (rather than an infolog about warnings and errors). Several changes in terminology were also introduced, as described in a subsequent point.

Workspaces Workspaces represent one variation in the user experience when using the Dynamics 365 for Operations. Workspaces provide an aggregation of tasks related to a specific role or business process. Almost half of the 30+ predefined workspaces apply to SCM-related topics. One specifically provides a Master Planning workspace, and many others address master planning considerations such as items, bills of material, resources, sales orders, purchase orders, production orders and configuration technologies. It is anticipated that additional workspaces and related functionality will become available as the software evolves.

Changes in Technology Technology considerations generally fall outside the book's scope, but some of the changes can be briefly summarized.

The workspace functionality replaces several capabilities in previous AX versions, such as role-centered pages and the enterprise portal. The role-centered pages were built on the deprecated Enterprise Portal capabilities which have been replaced by the new web client platform. This new web client improves usability across multiple platforms and devices.

The Data Import/Export framework replaces the Application Integration Framework (AIF) capabilities in previous AX versions.

Other technology changes include improved integration with Microsoft Office; enhanced use of business intelligence (BI) reports and visualizations; improvements in the "Help" system; and improvements in electronic documents via the Generic Electronic Reporting tool.

Other Minor Changes Minor changes were introduced for displaying and using information on the Gantt Chart and the Action Graph.

Deprecated Functionality The "product builder" capabilities were replaced by the constraint-based configuration technology.

List of Figures

List of Cases

About the Author

Scott Hamilton has specialized in SCM/ERP information systems for three decades and consulted globally with several hundred manufacturing/distribution companies. His publications include multiple books about SCM using Dynamics AX as well as two textbooks about SCM/ERP, and his books have been translated into Russian and Chinese. His regular column "The AX Solution Architect" is published in MSDynamicsWorld.com. Scott has been a frequent speaker at Microsoft and AXUG events around the world, and a multi-year winner of the rarely-given Microsoft MVP award for AX. He earned a doctorate in information systems specializing in manufacturing and taught SCM/ERP as an MBA professor at several leading universities in North America, Europe and the Pacific Rim. He lives in Minnesota, a place where people still build ice castles.

Made in the USA
Lexington, KY
20 July 2018